3rd Edition
English Bus H[
Coaches

EURO TOURER

WA Shearings

We take care of everything

MX05 AKF

British Bus Publishing

Body codes used in the Bus Handbook series.

Type:
A	Articulated vehicle
B	Bus, either single-deck or double-deck
BC	Interurban - high-back seated bus
C	Coach
M	Minibus with design capacity of 16 seats or less
N	Low-floor bus (Niederflur), either single-deck or double-deck
O	Open-top bus (CO = convertible - PO = partial open-top)

Seating capacity is then shown. For double-decks the upper deck quantity is followed by the lower deck.

Please note that seating capacities shown are generally those provided by the operator. It is common practice, however, for some vehicles to operate at different capacities when on certain duties.

Door position:
C	Centre entrance/exit
D	Dual doorway.
F	Front entrance/exit
R	Rear entrance/exit (no distinction between doored and open)
T	Three or more access points

Equipment:
T	Toilet	TV	Training vehicle.
M	Mail compartment	RV	Used as tow bus or engineers' vehicle.

Allocation:
s	Ancillary vehicle
t	Training bus
u	out of service or strategic reserve; refurbishment or seasonal requirement
w	Vehicle is withdrawn and awaiting disposal.

e.g. - B32/28F is a double-deck bus with thirty-two seats upstairs, twenty-eight down and a front entrance/exit., N43D is a low-floor bus with two or more doorways.

Re-registrations:

Where a vehicle has gained new index marks the details are listed at the end of each fleet showing the current mark, followed in sequence by those previously carried starting with the original mark.

Annual books are produced for the major groups.
The Stagecoach Bus Handbook
The First Bus Handbook
The Arriva Bus Handbook
The Go-Ahead Bus Handbook
The National Express Coach Handbook (bi-annual)

Regional books in the series.
The Scottish Bus Handbook
The Welsh Bus Handbook
The Ireland & Islands Bus Handbook
English Bus Handbook: Smaller Groups
English Bus Handbook: Notable Independents
English Bus Handbook: Coaches

Associated series.
The Hong Kong Bus Handbook
The Malta Bus Handbook
The Leyland Lynx Handbook
The Postbus Handbook
The Mailvan Handbook
The Toy & Model Bus Handbook - Volume 1 - Early Diecasts
The Fire Brigade Handbook (fleet list of each local authority fire brigade)
The Police Range Rover Handbook

Some earlier editions of these books are still available. Please contact the publisher on 01952 255669.

Contents

English Bus Handbook: Coaches

English Bus Handbook: Coaches

This third edition of the *English Bus Handbook: Coaches* is part of a series that details the fleets of certain bus and express coach operators throughout Britain. A list of current editions is shown on page 2. This Coaches book comprises those operators that predominantly cater for the private contract and touring markets. There are two other parts to the English Bus Handbook set; one covering the medium-sized groups and a third volume that covers the main independent operators. Information and suggestions that will help us to develop these titles would be welcome.

Quality photographs for inclusion in the series are welcome, for which a fee is payable. Unfortunately the publishers cannot accept responsibility for any loss and they require that you show your name on each picture or slide. High-resolution digital images of six megapixels or higher are also welcome on CD or DVD.

To keep the fleet information up to date we recommend the magazine, Buses, published monthly by Key Publications, or for more detailed information, the PSV Circle monthly news sheets. The writer and publisher would be glad to hear from readers should any information be available which corrects or enhances that given in this publication.

The writer and publisher would be glad to hear from readers should any information be available which corrects or enhances that given in this publication.

Series Editor: Bill Potter.
Principal Editors for *English Bus Handbook: Coaches* **are Stuart Martin and Bill Potter.**

Acknowledgments:
We are grateful to the operating companies, Tom Johnson, Colin Lloyd, Peter Marley and David Thomas for their assistance in the compilation of this book.
The cover photograph is courtesy of Eavesway; the frontispiece is by Steve Rice while the rear covers are by Dave Heath and Steve Rice.

ISBN 9781904875 68 0   © Published by British Bus Publishing Ltd, August 2012

British Bus Publishing Ltd, 16 St Margaret's Drive, Telford, TF1 3PH

Telephone: 01952 255669

web; www.britishbuspublishing.co.uk
e-mail: sales@britishbuspublishing.co.uk

ABBOTT'S of LEEMING

DC & CG Abbott; Blueline Express Ltd, Aumans House, Leeming, DL7 9RZ

Buses

	LUI7869	Mercedes-Benz 811D	Dormobile	B29F	1991	Crystals, Dartford, 2002
w	DCZ1286	Mercedes-Benz 811D	Reeve Burgess Beaver	B31F	1991	Sovereign, 2000
w	DCZ1287	Mercedes-Benz 811D	Reeve Burgess Beaver	B31F	1991	Sovereign, 2000
w	DCZ1288	Mercedes-Benz 811D	Reeve Burgess Beaver	B31F	1991	Sovereign, 2000
w	P137CVN	Ford Transit	Ford	M14	1997	van, 1998
w	P169SGT	LDV Convoy	LDV	M16	1997	van, 1998
	P170SGT	LDV Convoy	LDV	M16	1997	van, 1998
	R174VBM	Mercedes-Benz Vario O810	Plaxton Beaver 2	B27F	1997	Tellings-Golden Miller, 2008
w	S929RNP	LDV Convoy	LDV	M16	1998	Prince Henry, Evesham, 2003
	S151NKE	LDV Convoy	LDV	M16	1998	
	S130NRB	Mercedes-Benz Vario O814	Plaxton Beaver 2	B31F	1998	Burton's, Haverhill, 2009
	S131NRB	Mercedes-Benz Vario O814	Plaxton Beaver 2	B33F	1998	Burton's, Haverhill, 2009
	W286NAE	Fiat Ducato	Autotrim	M14	2000	
	X93EEF	Mercedes-Benz Vito 110 cdi	Mercedes-Benz	M8	2001	
	BL03MVT	LDV Convoy	LDV	M16	2003	
	BL03MWA	LDV Convoy	LDV	M16	2003	
	CU53EYF	Ford Transit	Jaycas	M16	2003	
	CU53EYG	Ford Transit	Jaycas	M16	2003	
	XL03AOL	Optare Solo M920	Optare	N33F	2003	
	XL53AOL	Optare Solo M920	Optare	N31F	2003	
	ND54WKE	Mercedes-Benz Vito 109 cdi	Mercedes-Benz	M7	2004	
	WL06AOL	Optare Solo M950	Optare	N33F	2007	
	XL06AOL	Optare Solo M950	Optare	N33F	2007	
	YJ59NMO	Optare Solo M950 SL	Optare	N28F	2010	
	YJ59NMU	Optare Solo M950 SL	Optare	N28F	2010	

Coaches

	352BWB	Bedford SB8	Plaxton Embassy 1	C41F	1962	Kirkby, Harthill, 1969
	YIL1842	Van Hool T815	Van Hool Alizée	C49FT	1982	Dales, Brampton, 2004
	PBZ3658	Leyland Tiger TRCTL11/3R	Plaxton Paramount 3200 E	C53F	1983	Burgin, Darnall, 2002
	778XYA	Volvo B10M-61	Van Hool Alizée	C46FT	1983	Dales, Brampton, 2005
	774FUO	Volvo B10M-61	Plaxton Paramount 3500	C53FT	1984	
	HNZ1349	DAF MB200	Plaxton Paramount 3200 II E	C53F	1985	Little, Ilkeston, 2005
	NUI1575	Leyland Tiger TRCTL11/2RH	Plaxton Paramount 3200 II	C49F	1985	First Midland Bluebird, 2003
	PBZ3656	Leyland Tiger TRCTL11/3RH	Plaxton Paramount 3200 II E	C53F	1985	Arriva North East, 2001
w	MIL9746	Volvo B10M-61	Duple Caribbean 2	C53F	1985	Dales, Brampton, 2004

Carrying C19ACT plates is one of the Scania coaches that are fitted with Van Hool T8 bodywork. It is seen while operating a service for First.
Steve Rice

UIL7825	Leyland Tiger TRCTL11/3RH	Duple Caribbean 2	C49FT	1986	Heyfordian, Bicester, 2003
WIL3610	Leyland Tiger TRCLXC/2RH	Plaxton Paramount 3200 II E	C53F	1986	First Midland Bluebird, 2003
PBZ8301	Leyland Tiger TRCLXC/2RH	Plaxton Paramount 3200 II E	C53F	1986	First Midland Bluebird, 2003
GIL4267	Volvo B10M-61	Caetano Algarve	C51FT	1986	Simpson, Whitby, 2007
MAZ6771	Leyland Tiger TRCTL11/2RZ	Duple 320	C53FT	1987	First Cymru, 2002
SAZ4077	Leyland Tiger TRCTL11/3RH	Duple 340	C53FT	1987	Barry's, Weymouth, 2003
SJI5861	Leyland Tiger TRCTL11/3RH	Duple 340	C49FT	1987	Heyfordian, Bicester, 2003
UIL7826	Leyland Tiger TRCTL11/3RH	Duple 340	C49FT	1987	First Edinburgh, 2003
UIL7829	Leyland Tiger TRCTL11/3RH	Duple 340	C53F	1987	First Bluebird, 2003
XDZ9422	Scania K112 CRB	Van Hool T8 Alizée	C53F	1987	
NUI1585	Volvo B10M-61	Plaxton Paramount 3500 III	C49FT	1987	Phillips, Pitsea, 2003
F135URP	Volvo B10M-61	Plaxton Paramount 3500 III	C53F	1988	Dodsworth, Boroughbridge, 2009
XDZ9423	Scania K112 CRB	Van Hool T8 Alizée	C49FT	1988	
BLZ8546	Scania K112 CRB	Van Hool T8 Alizée	C49FT	1988	
BLZ8547	Scania K112 CRB	Van Hool T8 Alizée	C49FT	1988	
E97LWP	DAF SB2305	Duple 320	C57F	1988	Hackett, Stretton, 1993
F26ARN	DAF SB2305	Duple 340	C59F	1989	Jackson, Blackpool, 1994
WIL3608	Leyland Tiger TRCTL11/3ARZ	Duple 340	C53F	1989	First Cymru, 2003
DIG8657	Scania K93 CRB	Duple 320	S70F	1990	K-Line, Kirkburton, 1993
JIL2947	Scania K113 TRB	Plaxton Paramount 4000 III	C55/18CT	1990	Rennie's, Dunfermline, 2005
J685THN	DAF SB2305	Duple 320	C57F	1991	
J686THN	DAF SB2305	Duple 320	C57F	1991	
KIW7241	Scania K93 CRB	Plaxton Paramount 3200	C53F	1992	Woods, Standish, 2011
N5AOL	Volvo B10M-62	Plaxton Première 320	C57F	1996	Hodson, Gisburn, 2002
N6AOL	Volvo B10M-62	Plaxton Première 320	C57F	1996	Wickson, Walsall Wood, 2002
P7AOL	DAF SB3000	Plaxton Première 350	S70F	1997	North Kent Express, 2003
P70AOL	DAF SB3000	Ikarus Blue Danube 350	S70F	1997	Holmeswood Coaches, 2006
P700AOL	DAF SB3000	Ikarus Blue Danube 350	C55F	1997	Holmeswood Coaches, 2006
P20GRT	Scania L94 IB4	Irizar Intercentury 12.32	C51FT	1997	Stephenson, Rockford, 2009
P26RFG	Scania L94 IB4	Irizar Intercentury 12.32	C55F	1997	Stephenson, Rockford, 2009
R917YBA	Volvo B10M-62	Plaxton Excalibur	C50F	1998	Shearings, Wigan, 2005
R922YBA	Volvo B10M-62	Plaxton Excalibur	C53F	1998	Shearings, Wigan, 2005
R923YBA	Volvo B10M-62	Plaxton Excalibur	C50F	1998	Shearings, Wigan, 2005
S2AOL	Scania L94 IB4	Irizar Intercentury 12.32	C57F	1999	Dunn-Line, Nottingham, 2003
T2AOL	Scania L94 IB4	Irizar Intercentury 12.32	C57F	1999	Dunn-Line, Nottingham, 2003
T3AOL	Scania L94 IB4	Irizar Intercentury 12.32	C57F	1999	Dunn-Line, Nottingham, 2003
W1AOL	Volvo B10M-62	Van Hool T9 Alizée	C46FT	2000	WA Shearings, Wigan, 2007
W2AOL	Volvo B10M-62	Van Hool T9 Alizée	C46FT	2001	WA Shearings, Wigan, 2007
W3AOL	Volvo B10M-62	Van Hool T9 Alizée	C46FT	2001	WA Shearings, Wigan, 2007
GO02AOL	Scania K114 IB4	Van Hool T9 Alizée	C49FT	2002	
MY02AOL	Scania K114 IB4	Irizar Century 12.35	C49FT	2002	
OK02AOL	Scania K114 IB4	Irizar Century 12.35	C49FT	2002	
OK53AOL	Scania K124 EB6	Irizar PB	C49FT	2003	

Sunsundegui Sideral 350 XL08AOL is shown on tour. Like many Spanish-built coaches the Sideral was a striking design when introduced in 2007.
John Birtwistle

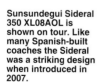

English Bus Handbook: Coaches

UK53AOL	Mercedes-Benz Vario 0814	TransBus Cheetah	C33F	2003	
OK54AOL	Scania K124 EB6	Irizar PB	C53F	2004	
NX54CHR	Scania K124 EB6	Irizar PB	C53F	2004	
CL05AOL	Volvo B12B	Sunsundegui Sideral 350	C49FT	2005	
DL05AOL	Volvo B12B 13.7m	Sunsundegui Sideral 350	C57FT	2005	
AE55NYN	Mercedes-Benz Vario 0814	Eurocoach	C29F	2005	Stansted Hotel Sprinter, 2006
OK06AOL	Volvo B12B 13.7m	Sunsundegui Sideral 350	C57FT	2006	
XK06AOL	Volvo B12B 13.7m	Sunsundegui Sideral 350	C57FT	2006	
FJ06BTF	Volvo B12B 13.7m	Sunsundegui Sideral 350	C57FT	2006	
FJ06BTE	Volvo B12B	Sunsundegui Sideral 350	C49FT	2006	McLeans, Witney, 2010
BX07NLL	Mercedes-Benz Tourino 0510	Mercedes-Benz	C35F	2007	Lewis, Coventry, 2008
XL08AOL	Volvo B12B 13.7m	Sunsundegui Sideral 350	C53F	2008	
XX58AOL	Scania K380 EB4	Irizar	C49FT	2009	
YP09NPK	Scania K340 EB4	Scania OmniExpress	C51FT	2009	Clarkes, London, 2010
MX59XJT	Volvo B12B 13.7m	VDL Jonckheere SHV	C59FT	2010	Weardale, Stanhope, 2012
YN11FTT	Mercedes-Benz Vario 0816	Plaxton Cheetah	C33F	2011	
YN11FWP	Volvo B9R	Plaxton Panther	C57FT	2011	
CL61AOL	Volvo B9R	Sunsundegui Sideral 330	C42FT	2011	
DL61AOL	Volvo B9R	Sunsundegui Sideral 330	C42FT	2011	
XK12AOL	Scania K400 EB6	Irizar i6	C53FT	2012	

Previous registrations:

774FUO	A717JDC	P70AOL	P163RWR
778XYA	PGC523Y	P700AOL	P165RWR
BLZ8546	E905NVN	PBZ3656	B284KPF
BLZ8547	E906NVN	PBZ3658	ERF74Y, USU638
DIG8657	G997HKW	PBZ8301	D54VSO, PSU625
GIL4267	C703KDS	S2AOL	S374SET
HNZ1349	B625JRC	S95AUP	S2STX
JIL2947	G28HKY	SAZ4077	D321RNS, MSU464, D772YAU
KIW7241	J279NNC	SJI5861	D272FAS, SJI1998
LUI7869	H427KPA	T2AOL	T36CNN
MAZ6771	D615HBX, 8098DD	T3AOL	T34CNN
MIL9746	B702GJR, LIL8557	UIL7825	C72KLG, 2110UK
MX59XJT	GO59WMS	UIL7826	D142HMS, SSU857
N5AOL	N56MDW, VVU271	UIL7829	D347ESC, A17SMT
N6AOL	1513RU, N685YUJ, WT8355	WIL3608	F114UBX, 5519DD
NUI1575	B342RLS, KSU392	WIL3610	D51VSO, PSU622
NUI1585	WSV479, E958KDP	XDZ9422	E532LAJ
NX54CHR	XK54AOL	XDZ9423	E268NAJ
P7AOL	P166RWR	YIL1842	NOX750X, RXO828

Depots: Sussex Street, Bedale; Stockwell Road, Knaresborough and The Garage, Leeming.

Abbott's operates nine Volvo coaches fitted with Sunsundegui Sideral bodywork. Illustrating this styling is CL05AOL. *Mark Doggett*

ALFA

Alfa Coaches Ltd, Euxton Lane, Euxton, Chorley, PR7 6AF

21	PN03OVM	Dennis R410	Plaxton Paragon	C49FT	2003
22	PN03OVP	Dennis R410	Plaxton Paragon	C49FT	2003
23	PN03PFV	Dennis R410	Plaxton Paragon	C49FT	2003
24	PN03PFX	Dennis R410	Plaxton Paragon	C49FT	2003
25	PN03POA	Dennis R410	Plaxton Paragon	C49FT	2003
26	PN04NMY	TransBus R410	TransBus Paragon	C53F	2004
27	PN04NMX	TransBus R410	TransBus Paragon	C53F	2004
28	PN04NMV	TransBus R410	TransBus Paragon	C53F	2004
29	PN04NMU	TransBus R410	TransBus Paragon	C53F	2004
30	PN04NMM	TransBus R410	TransBus Paragon	C53F	2004
32	PN05AFE	Alexander Dennis R410	Plaxton Paragon	C49FT	2005
34	PN05AEZ	Alexander Dennis R410	Plaxton Paragon	C53F	2005
35	PN05AMV	Alexander Dennis R410	Plaxton Paragon	C53F	2005
36	PN06KJV	Volvo B12B	Plaxton Paragon	C53F	2006
37	PN06KJX	Volvo B12B	Plaxton Paragon	C53F	2006
38	PN06KJY	Volvo B12B	Plaxton Paragon	C53F	2006
39	PN06KJZ	Volvo B12B	Plaxton Paragon	C49FT	2006
40	PN06KKA	Volvo B12B	Plaxton Paragon	C49FT	2006
41	PN07LLE	Volvo B12B	Plaxton Paragon	C49FT	2007
42	PN07LLF	Volvo B12B	Plaxton Paragon	C49FT	2007
43	PN07LLG	Volvo B12B	Plaxton Paragon	C49FT	2007
44	PN07LLJ	Volvo B12B	Plaxton Paragon	C49FT	2007
45	PN07LLK	Volvo B12B	Plaxton Paragon	C49FT	2007
46	PN08KXH	Volvo B12B	Plaxton Paragon	C49FT	2008
47	PN08KXJ	Volvo B12B	Plaxton Paragon	C49FT	2008
48	PN08KXK	Volvo B12B	Plaxton Paragon	C49FT	2008
49	PN08KXL	Volvo B12B	Plaxton Paragon	C49FT	2008

Alfa's earlier coach deliveries were Dennis R series vehicles with Plaxton Paragon bodywork, although some were built while Plaxton was part of TransBus. From the 2004 delivery, PN04NMV is seen. *John Birtwistle*

Alfa operates holiday tours from its base in Chorley with most centred on hotels owned by sister company Leisureplex. Plaxton-bodied Dennis coaches have recently given way to Volvo and Mercedes products. PN05AEZ, one of the Dennis R410s, is shown. *Mark Doggett*

50	PN08KXM	Volvo B12B	Plaxton Paragon	C49FT	2008
51	PN08KXO	Volvo B12B	Plaxton Paragon	C49FT	2008
52	PN09HMJ	Volvo B12B	Plaxton Paragon	C49FT	2009
53	PN09HMH	Volvo B12B	Plaxton Paragon	C49FT	2009
54	PO59FHX	Volvo B12B	Plaxton Paragon	C49FT	2009
55	PO59FHY	Volvo B12B	Plaxton Paragon	C49FT	2009
56	YN10EOC	Volvo B12B	Plaxton Paragon	C49FT	2010
57	YN10EOF	Volvo B12B	Plaxton Paragon	C49FT	2010
58	YN10EOG	Volvo B12B	Plaxton Paragon	C49FT	2010
59	YN10EOK	Volvo B12B	Plaxton Paragon	C49FT	2010
60	BN11UFJ	Mercedes-Benz Tourismo 0350	Mercedes-Benz	C49FT	2011
61	BN11UFK	Mercedes-Benz Tourismo 0350	Mercedes-Benz	C49FT	2011
62	BN11UFL	Mercedes-Benz Tourismo 0350	Mercedes-Benz	C49FT	2011
63	BN11UFM	Mercedes-Benz Tourismo 0350	Mercedes-Benz	C49FT	2011
64	BN11UFP	Mercedes-Benz Tourismo 0350	Mercedes-Benz	C49FT	2011
65	BN12CLU	Mercedes-Benz Tourismo 0350	Mercedes-Benz	C49FT	2012
66	BN12CLV	Mercedes-Benz Tourismo 0350	Mercedes-Benz	C49FT	2012
67	BN12CLX	Mercedes-Benz Tourismo 0350	Mercedes-Benz	C49FT	2012
68	BN12CLY	Mercedes-Benz Tourismo 0350	Mercedes-Benz	C49FT	2012
69	BN12CLZ	Mercedes-Benz Tourismo 0350	Mercedes-Benz	C49FT	2012

Depots: Old Airfield, Thornaby and Millennium Park, Ridscar, Preston
Web: www.alfatravel.co.uk

AMBASSADOR

Ambassador - Semmence

Ambassador-Travel (Anglia) Ltd, James Watt Close, Great Yarmouth, NR31 0NX

H Semmence & Company Ltd, 34 Norwich Road, Wymondham, NR18 0NS

101	S	M35KAX	Volvo B10M-62	Plaxton Première 350	C49FT	1995	
102	S	P411MDT	Volvo B10M-62	Plaxton Première 350	C46FT	1997	
107	S	P412MDT	Volvo B10M-62	Plaxton Première 350	C46FT	1997	
103	S	S482ETV	Volvo B10M-62	Plaxton Première 350	C49FT	1998	Bus Eireann, 2004
104	S	790CVD	Volvo B10M-62	Caetano Algarve II	C49FT	1999	
105	S	K68BKG	Volvo B10M-62	Plaxton Première 350	C53F	1994	Bebb, Llantwit Fardre, 2004
106	S	S550ETV	Volvo B10M-62	Plaxton Première 350	C49FT	1998	Bus Eireann, 2004
107	w	G107HNG	Volvo B10M-60	Plaxton Paramount 3500 III	C53F	1989	
108	w	G108HNG	Volvo B10M-60	Plaxton Paramount 3500 III	C55F	1989	
109	w	GLZ1270	Volvo B10M-60	Plaxton Paramount 3500 III	C53F	1987	Paul James, Hugglescote, 2005
110	A	G261UAS	Volvo B10M-60	Plaxton Paramount 3500 III	C53F	1989	Southgate, Finchley, 2006
111	A	G262UAS	Volvo B10M-60	Plaxton Paramount 3500 III	C53F	1989	Southgate, Finchley, 2006
112	w	G512MNG	Volvo B10M-60	Plaxton Paramount 3500 III	C51F	1990	
135	A	TJI5402	Volvo B10M-60	Plaxton Première 350	C49FT	1992	Park's of Hamilton, 1993
138	A	PIJ3379	Volvo B10M-62	Plaxton Première 350	C49F	1994	
139	A	FNZ7761	Volvo B10M-62	Plaxton Première 350	C49F	1995	
141	A	M743KJU	Volvo B10M-62	Plaxton Première 350	C49FT	1995	
142	A	FNZ7762	Volvo B10M-62	Plaxton Première 350	C49F	1995	
143	A	FNZ7763	Volvo B10M-62	Plaxton Première 350	C49F	1995	
144	A	FNZ7764	Volvo B10M-62	Plaxton Première 350	C49FT	1995	
147	A	FNZ7716	Volvo B10M-62	Plaxton Première 350	C49F	1997	
150	A	FNZ1014	Volvo B10M-62	Plaxton Première 350	C53F	1998	
151	A	240FRH	Volvo B10M-62	Plaxton Première 350	C49FT	1998	
152	A	FNZ1015	Volvo B10M-62	Plaxton Première 350	C49F	1999	
154	A	TIL3338	Volvo B10M-62	Plaxton Première 350	C49FT	2000	
172	A	FNZ1012	Volvo B10M-62	Caetano Enigma	C49FT	1999	
173	A	FNZ1013	Volvo B10M-62	Caetano Enigma	C49FT	1999	
180	A	FD54DGU	Volvo B12B	VDL Jonckheere Mistral 50	C49FT	2005	
181	A	FD54DGV	Volvo B12B	VDL Jonckheere Mistral 50	C49FT	2005	
182	A	FD54DHX	Volvo B12B	VDL Jonckheere Mistral 50	C49FT	2005	
183	A	FD54DHY	Volvo B12B	VDL Jonckheere Mistral 50	C49FT	2005	
195	A	P803BLJ	Volvo B10M-62	Plaxton Expressliner 2	C49FT	1997	Excelsior, Bournemouth, 2001
196	A	KIG1856	Volvo B12M	Plaxton Paragon Expressliner	C49FT	2002	
197	A	KIG1857	Volvo B12M	Plaxton Paragon Expressliner	C49FT	2002	
198	A	CN53NWB	Volvo B12M	TransBus Paragon	C49FT	2003	Veolia Cymru, 2007
201	w	F621SAY	Dennis Javelin 12m	Plaxton Paramount 3200 III	C53F	1991	Lloyd, Shouldham, 2005
202	w	H177EJU	Dennis Javelin 12m	Duple 320	C53F	1991	Lloyd, Shouldham, 2005
203	S	PBZ9153	Dennis Javelin 12m	Duple 320	C57F	1989	Reg's, Hertford, 2005
204	u	TAZ4518	Dennis Javelin 12m	Duple 320	C57F	1990	Voel, Dyserth, 1998
205	w	G852VAY	Dennis Javelin 12m	Duple 320	C57F	1989	Top Marks Travel, Crayford, 1995
206	A	FJ09DXA	Scania K340 EB4	Caetano Levanté	C49FT	2009	
207	A	FJ09DXB	Scania K340 EB4	Caetano Levanté	C49FT	2009	
208	A	FJ09DXC	Scania K340 EB4	Caetano Levanté	C49FT	2009	
209	A	FJ09DXE	Scania K340 EB4	Caetano Levanté	C49FT	2009	
206	S	K777GSM	Dennis Javelin 12m	Plaxton Première 320	C57F	1993	R&D Burrows, Ogmore Vale, 2002
207	S	H157DJU	Dennis Javelin 12m	Plaxton Première 320	C57F	1990	KB Coaches, Boultington, 1997
208	S	G169ODH	Dennis Javelin 12m	Plaxton Paramount 3200 III	C53F	1992	Shire Coaches, Park Street, 2001
209	u	RJI5723	Dennis Javelin 12m	Plaxton Paramount 3200 III	C53F	1988	Baker, Weston-super-Mare, 1994
210	u	RJI5721	Dennis Javelin 12m	Plaxton Paramount 3200 III	C57F	1988	Baker, Weston-super-Mare, 1994
211	S	K261FUV	Dennis Javelin 12m	Plaxton Première 320	C53F	1993	Reliance Coaches, Benfleet, 2001
212	S	J14WSB	Dennis Javelin 12m	Plaxton Paramount 3200 III	C53F	1992	Western Buses, 1998
214	S	K262FUV	Dennis Javelin 12m	Plaxton Première 320	C53F	1993	Reliance Coaches, Benfleet, 2001
215	u	TAZ4517	Dennis Javelin 12m	Duple 320	C57F	1990	Voel, Dyserth, 1998
220	A	FNZ7714	Scania K124 IB4	Irizar Century 12.35	C49FT	1999	
221	A	FNZ7715	Scania K124 IB4	Irizar Century 12.35	C49FT	1999	
250	A	FJ06BPZ	Volvo B12B	Sunsundegui Sideral 350	C49FT	2006	
251	A	FJ06BRF	Volvo B12B	Sunsundegui Sideral 350	C49FT	2006	
252	A	FJ08FYA	Volvo B12B	Sunsundegui Sideral 350	C49FT	2008	
253	A	FJ08FYB	Volvo B12B	Sunsundegui Sideral 350	C49FT	2008	

Two Volvo B12Bs with **Sunsundegui Sideral 350** bodywork were added to the fleet during 2008. One of these, 253, FJ08FYB, is seen in Sunrise contract livery. *Mark Doggett*

301	S	L445FHD	Scania K113 CRB	Plaxton Première 350	C53F	1995	Fowlers, Holbeach Drove, 2001
302	S	TIL9217	Scania K113 CRB	Van Hool Alizée HE	C53F	1996	
303	S	N824DKU	Scania K113 CRB	Van Hool Alizée HE	C53F	1996	
304	S	N822DKU	Scania K113 CRB	Van Hool Alizée HE	C49FT	1996	
305	S	TIL9216	Scania K113 CRB	Van Hool Alizée HE	C53F	1996	
312	w	G49HDW	Dennis Javelin 12m	Duple 320	C57F	1990	Wilson, Carnwath, 1997
601	A	MX54KYA	Optare Solo M850	Optare	N28F	2004	
602	A	MX54KYB	Optare Solo M850	Optare	N28F	2004	
603	A	MX54KYC	Optare Solo M850	Optare	N28F	2004	
604	A	MX54WME	Optare Solo M850	Optare	N28F	2004	
611	A	S350SET	Scania K94UB	Wright Solar	N41F	1993	Bus Eireann, 2008
701	S	SN56ENP	Volkswagen LT46	VDL Kusters	N17F	2006	
702	S	SN56ENR	Volkswagen LT46	VDL Kusters	N17F	2006	
703	S	SN56EOA	Volkswagen LT46	VDL Kusters	N17F	2006	
-	S	SN08EHL	Volkswagen Crafter	Volkswagen	M13	2008	*Operated for Norfolk CC*
-	S	SN58CCU	Volkswagen Crafter	Volkswagen	M13	2008	*Operated for Norfolk CC*
-	S	SN58CCV	Volkswagen Crafter	Volkswagen	M13	2008	*Operated for Norfolk CC*
-	w	K409BAX	Mercedes-Benz 811D	Plaxton Beaver	BC33F	1993	First Cymru, 2004
-	S	E892MKU	Mercedes-Benz Sprinter 410		M14	2000	Cushing, Acle, 2007
	S	SF04HXU	Mercedes-Benz Vario O814	TransBus Beaver	BC33F	2004	
-	S	S376TMB	Mercedes-Benz Vario O814	Plaxton Beaver 2	B31F	1998	Go West, King's Lynn, 2008
-	S	S707JJH	Mercedes-Benz Vario O810	Plaxton Beaver 2	B31F	1998	Travel London, 2008
751	w	K938ORC	Mercedes-Benz Vario 811D	Plaxton Beaver	B31F	1994	
752	A	N375EAK	Mercedes-Benz Vario O814	Plaxton Beaver 2	BC33F	1996	Neal's, Isleham, 2005
753	w	SF53KUV	Mercedes-Benz Vario O814	TransBus Beaver	B33F	2003	
920	A	PJT267R	Leyland National 11351A/2R	East Lancs Greenway (1994)	B49F	1976	Blackburn, 2003

Operating in an all-white scheme is Plaxton Première 350 TIL3338. Based on the central, underfloor-engined Volvo B10M it represents the most common coach supplied to the UK market around the turn of the century. *Mark Doggett*

Plaxton Panther YN60FML represents the Amport & District fleet. It is one of a pair based on the Volvo B9R which was added to the fleet in 2008. *Mark Doggett*

Previous registrations:

240FRH	R85DVF	KIG1856	FN52HRG
790CVD	S789ORY	KIG1857	FN52HRM
F621SAY	F621SAY, 790CVD	L445FHD	L445FHD, L50WHF
FNZ1012	T370AJF	P803BLJ	P803BLJ, XEL941
FNZ1013	T360AJF	PBZ9153	F684CYC
FNZ1014	R425YWJ	PIJ3379	L977UAH
FNZ1015	S585KJF	RJI5721	F421PSE
FNZ7714	T720JHE	RJI5723	E761HJF
FNZ7715	T721JHE	S350SET	98D76402
FNZ7716	P413MDT, 240FRH	S482ETV	98D54643
FNZ7761	M741KJU	S550ETV	98D54639
FNZ7762	M330KRY	TAZ4517	G415YAY, 776VC
FNZ7763	M331KRY	TAZ4518	G425YAY, 1760VC
FNZ7764	M144KRY	TIL3338	V437EAL
G261UAS	G261UAS, 930GJF	TIL9216	P105GHE
G262UAS	G262UAS, 449GLW	TIL9217	N823DKU
GLZ1270	E607KSP, JD3164, 248D334	TJI5402	J432HDS
K68BKG	K68BKG, TIL9216		

Depots: Gapton Hall Industrial Estate, Great Yarmouth; Abbey Farm Industrial Estate, Horsford, Norwich;
Vulcan Road North, Norwich and Norwich Road, Wymondham
Allocation codes: A Ambassador; S Semmence

AMPORT & DISTRICT

Amport & District Coaches Ltd, Eastfield House, Amesbury Road, Thruxton, SP11 8ED

YN05HVR	Volvo B12B	Plaxton Panther	C49FT	2005	
YN06NYT	Scania K114 EB4	Berkhof Axial 50	C53FT	2006	
YN08JBE	Scania K380 EB4	Berkhof Axial 50	C57F	2008	
YN08MOV	Scania K380 EB4	Berkhof Axial 50	C57F	2008	
KX08OMO	Volvo B12B	Plaxton Panther	C49FT	2008	Weavaway, Newbury, 2011
YN58NCY	Volvo B12B	Plaxton Panther	C53F	2009	
YN60FML	Volvo B9R	Plaxton Panther	C57F	2011	
YN60FMP	Volvo B9R	Plaxton Panther	C57F	2011	
BX11GUU	Volvo B12B	VDL Jonckheere	C53F	2011	

ANDERSON

Anderson Travel Ltd, 178a Tower Bridge Road, Bermondsey, SE1 3LS

London Mini Coaches Ltd, 23 Airlinks Industrial Estate, Spitfire Way, Hounslow, TW5 9NR

LM	YX56AFZ	Mercedes-Benz Sprinter 616cdi	Sitcar Onyx	M16	2000
LM	YX05DHZ	Mercedes-Benz Sprinter 616cdi	Ferqui/Optare Soroco Plus	C16F	2005
AN	YJ06GKZ	VDL Bova Futura FHD12.340XE	VDL Bova	C49FT	2006
AN	WA07BHD	VDL Bova Futura FHD12.340XE	VDL Bova	C53F	2007
AN	WA07BHE	VDL Bova Futura FHD12.340XE	VDL Bova	C53F	2007
AN	YN07NUP	Volvo B12B	Plaxton Panther	C53F	2007
LM	YN07OZX	Volvo B7R	Plaxton Profile	C53F	2007
LM	WA07BGY	Mercedes-Benz Vario O816	Sitcar Beluga 2	C26F	2007
LM	WA08GPX	Mercedes-Benz Vario O816	Sitcar Beluga 2	C29F	2008
LM	WA08GPY	Mercedes-Benz Atego 1022L	Sitcar Marlin	C29F	2008
LM	WA08GPZ	Mercedes-Benz Atego 1022L	Sitcar Marlin	C29F	2008
LM	BN08HNM	Mercedes-Benz Tourismo	Mercedes-Benz	C45F	2008
LM	BN08HNO	Mercedes-Benz Tourismo	Mercedes-Benz	C49FT	2008
LM	BN08HNT	Mercedes-Benz Tourismo	Mercedes-Benz	C45F	2008
LM	BN08HNU	Mercedes-Benz Tourismo	Mercedes-Benz	C45F	2008
AN	WA08GPK	VDL Bova Futura FHD12.260	VDL Bova	C45F	2008
AN	WA08GPJ	VDL Bova Futura FHD12.260	VDL Bova	C45F	2008
AN	WA08GPF	VDL Bova Futura FHD12.260	VDL Bova	C45F	2008
AN	WA08GPE	VDL Bova Futura FHD12.260	VDL Bova	C45F	2008
LM	BX58VNO	Mercedes-Benz Sprinter 515cdi	Excel	C16F	2008
AN	YN09AOW	Volvo B9R	Plaxton Panther	C57F	2009
AN	YN09AOX	Volvo B9R	Plaxton Panther	C57F	2009
AN	YN09APF	Volvo B9R	Plaxton Elite	C57F	2009
LM	WA09DZS	Mercedes-Benz Vario O816	Sitcar Beluga 2	C25F	2009
LM	WA09DZT	Mercedes-Benz Vario O816	Sitcar Beluga 2	C25F	2009
LM	WA09DZV	Mercedes-Benz Vario O816	Sitcar Beluga 2	C25F	2009
LM	WA09DZW	Mercedes-Benz Vario O816	Sitcar Beluga 2	C25F	2009
AN	YN10AAV	Mercedes-Benz Vario O816	Plaxton Cheetah 2	C25F	2010
AN	YN10ABU	Mercedes-Benz Vario O816	Plaxton Cheetah 2	C25F	2010
AN	YN10ACJ	Mercedes-Benz Vario O816	Plaxton Cheetah 2	C25F	2010
AN	YN10ADO	Mercedes-Benz Vario O816	Plaxton Cheetah 2	C25F	2010
AN	YN10BWZ	Volkswagen Crafter	Excel	M16	2010
LM	PO60DBV	Mercedes-Benz Sprinter 515cdi	Unvi Riada	C16F	2010
LM	PO60MMX	Mercedes-Benz Sprinter 515cdi	Unvi Riada	C16F	2010
AN	YN60BZK	Volvo B9R	Plaxton Panther	C32FT	2010
AN	YN60EOL	Volvo B7R	Plaxton Profile	C57F	2011
AN	YN11EOL	Volvo B7R	Plaxton Profile	C57F	2011
LM	WA11AEJ	Mercedes-Benz Vario O816	Sitcar Beluga 2	C25F	2011
LM	WA11AEK	Mercedes-Benz Vario O816	Sitcar Beluga 2	C25F	2011
LM	WA11AEL	Mercedes-Benz Vario O816	Sitcar Beluga 2	C25F	2011
LM	WA11AEM	Mercedes-Benz Vario O816	Sitcar Beluga 2	C25F	2011
AN	WA11HXP	Van Hool TD925 Astramega	Van Hool	C59/18DT	2011
AN	YN61EOU	Volvo B7R	Plaxton Profile	C57F	2011
AN	YN61EOW	Volvo B7R	Plaxton Profile	C57F	2011

Web: www.andersontravel.co.uk; www.lmcoaches.co.uk

ANDREWS of TIDESWELL

Andrews of Tideswell Ltd, Anchor Garage, Tideswell, SK17 8RB

Reg	Chassis	Body	Layout	Year	History
PIL6648	Volvo B10M-60	Van Hool T8 Alizée	C65FT	1993	Hayton, Burnage, 2001
EUA366	Volvo B10M-60	Van Hool T8 Alizée	C48FT	1993	Wallace Arnold, Leeds, 1998
7529UK	DAF SB3000	Van Hool T8 Alizée	C51FT	1994	Fraser Eagle, Padiham, 2009
EAZ2598	Volvo B10M-62	Plaxton Première 320	S70F	1995	Ulsterbus, 2007
NIB6064	Volvo B10M-62	Van Hool T8 Alizée	C49FT	1995	Shearings, Wigan, 2002
J4AOT	Volvo B10M-62	Van Hool T8 Alizée	C49FT	1995	Shearings, Wigan, 2002
PUA917	Volvo B10M-62	Van Hool T8 Alizée	C53F	1996	Shearings, Wigan, 2003
PAZ3878	Mercedes-Benz 308D	Crystals	M8	1997	Alternative, Oxford, 2003
PAZ3882	Mercedes-Benz 308D	Crystals	M8	1997	Alternative, Oxford, 2003
TIW2554	Mercedes-Benz 412D	Crest	M16	1997	
VIL6771	Neoplan Skyliner N122/3	Neoplan	C57/22CT	1998	Buzzlines, Hythe, 2003
T4FEG	Neoplan Starliner N516 SHD	Neoplan	C44FT	2001	Malik, Walsall, 2010
J2AOT	Volvo B10M-62	Plaxton Première 320	C49FT	2001	TM Travel, Sheffield, 2008
P11JWH	Mercedes-Benz Vario 0814	Plaxton Cheetah	C29F	2001	
YT06CEK	Ford Transit	Ford	M8	2006	
8732PG	Neoplan Euroliner N316/3 SHD	Neoplan	C61FT	2006	
J1AOT	Neoplan Skyliner N122/3	Neoplan	C59/20FT	2007	Park's of Hamilton, 2009
J3AOT	Mercedes-Benz Vario 0816	Plaxton Cheetah 2	C29F	2007	
345BLA	Volvo B12B	Plaxton Panther	C53FT	2007	
SF07YTU	Volvo B12B 15m	Plaxton Panther	C65FT	2007	Park's of Hamilton, 2011
YN58CHC	Volvo B12B	Plaxton Panther	C53FT	2008	
YN09AOT	Volvo B12B	Plaxton Panther	C53FT	2009	
YN10ADZ	Volvo B12B	Plaxton Panther	C57F	2010	
YN11AXX	Volvo B9R	Plaxton Panther	C57F	2011	
YN11AXD	Mercedes-Benz Vario 0813	Plaxton Cheetah 2	C33F	2011	

Previous registrations:

345BLA	YN57BWV	P11JWH	74MMC, C8PSV
7529UK	L520EHD	PIL6648	K804HUM, 7820WA
8732PG	M682KVU, 345BLA	PUA917	N703UVR
EUA366	7243WA, K803HUM	SF07YTU	LSK878
J1AOT	SF56UAE, 290WE	T4FEG	Y151HWE
J2AOT	HF51CGG	TIW2554	R86BUB
J3AOT	YN07ONZ	VIL6771	S101SET
NIB6064	M685KVU		

Following its UK launch in 2008, the B9R is now becoming the principal coach from Volvo and is successor to the B12M and B12B. Delivered in 2011, YN11AXX carries Plaxton Panther bodywork. *Mark Doggett*

ANTHONY'S TRAVEL

A, A & RA Bamber, 8 Cormorant Drive, Runcorn, WA7 4UD

K555ANT	Setra S250	Setra Special	C34FT	1999	Coach Stop, Leigh-on-Sea, 2002
G20ANT	Scania K124 IB4	Irizar Century 12.37	C32FT	2001	Go-Goodwins, Eccles, 2005
P30ANT	Neoplan Euroliner N316 SHD	Neoplan	C44FT	2002	Parry's, Cheslyn Hay, 2005
AB02ANT	Mercedes-Benz Sprinter 413	Olympus	M16	2002	
RB53ANT	Mercedes-Benz Sprinter 413	Olympus	M12	2003	
JB05ANT	Neoplan Euroliner N316 SHD	Neoplan	C44FT	2005	
CB06ANT	Neoplan Euroliner N316 SHD	Neoplan	C49FT	2006	
A288ANT	LDV Convoy	Olympus	M16	2006	
D19ANT	LDV Convoy	Concept	M16	2006	
MB07ANT	Neoplan Tourliner N2216 SHD	Neoplan	C49FT	2007	
OB07ANT	Mercedes-Benz Tourismo	Mercedes-Benz	C32FT	2007	
ANT856T	Mercedes-Benz Tourino O510	Mercedes-Benz	C30FT	2008	
K22ANT	Optare Solo M880 SL	Optare	N28F	2008	
W10ANT	Iveco Daily 45C15	Excel Excalibur	M16	2009	
DB09ANT	Neoplan Tourliner N2216 SHD	Neoplan	C49FT	2009	
GB59ANT	Neoplan Tourliner N2216 SHD	Neoplan	C49FT	2010	
P50ANT	Neoplan Tourliner N2216 SHD	Neoplan	C49FT	2011	Neoman demonstrator, 2011

Previous registrations:

ANT856T	from new	P30ANT	YR02UNN
G20ANT	GO51WES, C1ECB	P50ANT	MJ60KZD
K555ANT	S369FTL		

Pictured at Cheltenham Race Course is K55ANT of Anthony's Travel. This Setra S250 is now the oldest coach in the fleet. *Colin Martin*

ATKINSONS'

H Atkinson & Son (Ingleby) Ltd, Ingleby Arncliffe, Northallerton, DL6 3LN

R160GNW	DAF SB3000	Van Hool T9 Alizée	C49FT	1998	Dalesman, Bridlington, 2012
Y605JSH	Scania K124 IB4	Van Hool T9 Alizée	C49FT	2000	
NK51ORN	Scania K124 IB4	Van Hool T9 Alizée	C49FT	2000	Durham Travel, 2012
C4MTA	Iveco EuroMidi CC80. E18MP	Indcar Maxim	C27F	2001	
BX54EDC	Setra S315 GT-HD	Setra	C49FT	2004	
HA08ATK	MAN 18.400	Beulas Aura	C55FT	2008	
HA09ATK	Irisbus EuroRider 397E.12.43A	Beulas Cygnus	C55FT	2009	
AK09ATK	Van Hool T916 Astron	Van Hool	C55FT	2009	
HA60ATK	MAN 18.400	Beulas Aura	C55FT	2010	
AK61ATK	Temsa Safari HD	Temsa	C53FT	2011	
H19ATK	Temsa Safari HD	Temsa	C53FT	2011	
H16ATK	Neoplan Tourliner N2216/3 SHD	Neoplan	C55FT	2012	

Previous registrations:

C4MTA	Y543OVN		H19ATK	AT61ATK
H16ATK	From new			

Web: www.atkinsoncoaches.co.uk

Carrying Atkinsons' livery at the 2011 industry trade show is a Temsa Safari HD. This family-based company was established by the late Harry Atkinson in 1922 and in 1998 control passed to his grandsons, Martin and David. *Bill Potter*

AUSDEN CLARK

Ausden Clark Ltd, Dysart Way, Leicester, LE1 2JY

C110UBC	Scania N112 DRB	East Lancs	B46/33F	1986	Mayne's, Warrington, 2004
NIB6179	Scania N112 DRB	East Lancs	B47/33F	1988	PC Coaches, Lincoln, 2008
H211LOM	Scania N113 DRB	Alexander RH	B45/31F	1990	Travel West Midlands, 2003
G726RYJ	Scania N113 DRB	East Lancs	B47/33F	1990	Brighton & Hove, 2004
DRZ5272	Scania N113 DRB	East Lancs	B47/33F	1990	Telling-Golden Miller, 2010
G728RYJ	Scania N113 DRB	East Lancs	B47/33F	1990	Telling-Golden Miller, 2010
G74UNU	Scania K113 TRB	Berkhof Excellence 3000	C57/16CT	1990	Porteous, Hull, 2006
BIG9827	Scania K113 TRB	Van Hool Astrobel	C57/17CT	1990	Bostock's, Congleton, 2001
YJI7372	Scania K113 TRB	Van Hool T8 Alizée	C55F	1991	
J819HMC	Scania N113 DRB	Alexander RH	B47/31F	1991	Metroline, Harrow, 2003
J820HMC	Scania N113 DRB	Alexander RH	B47/31F	1991	Metroline, Harrow, 2003
6791RU	Scania K93 CRB	Plaxton Paramount 3200 III	C53F	1991	Leons, Stafford, 2003
YAZ4111	Scania K93 CRB	Van Hool T8 Alizée	C55F	1992	Luckett's, Fareham, 2002
IIL8585	Scania K113 CRB	Van Hool T8 Alizée	C51FT	1992	Harding's, Redditch, 2000
PLZ6542	Scania K93 CRB	Van Hool T8 Alizée	C55FT	1992	Craske, Sutton, 2007
LIL2174	Scania K112 CRB	Van Hool T8 Alizée	C55FT	1992	Appleby, 2001
BIG9833	Scania K113 TRA	Van Hool Astrobel	C57/17CT	1993	Dove, Pallion, 2010
BIG9829	Scania K113 TRB	Berkhof Excellence 3000	C55/18CT	1993	Hunter, Felling, 2008
BIG9831	Scania K113 TRA	Berkhof Excellence 3000	C57/23DT	1994	Thomas, Rhondda, 2001
BIG9832	Scania K113 TRA	Berkhof Excellence 3000	C57/21DT	1994	The King's Ferry, Gillingham, 2006
FNZ1049	Scania K113 CRB	Van Hool Alizée HE	S70F	1994	Taylor, Barrow, 2008
GAZ4501	Scania K113 TRB	Van Hool Alizée HE	C46FT	1994	Brown, South Kirkby, 2004
LUI1508	Scania K113 CRB	Van Hool Alizée HE	C57F	1994	Kirkham, Oswaldtwistle, 2007
MUI7799	Scania K113 CRB	Van Hool Alizée HE	C53F	1994	Peake's, Pontypool, 2007
MUI7939	Scania K113 CRB	Berkhof Excellence 2000	C51F	1994	Majestic, Shareshill, 2005
PNZ4424	Scania K93 CRB	Van Hool T8 Alizée	C57F	1995	Maynes of Buckie, 2010
BIG9834	Scania K113 TRA	Berkhof Axial 100	C57/20DT	1996	Thomas Rhondda, 2003
REZ5237	Scania K113 CRB	Van Hool Alizée HE	C51FT	1997	Aston's, Worcester, 2003
PLZ6542	Scania K113 CRB	Van Hool Alizée HE	C49FT	1997	Hardings, Redditch, 2008
YEZ5553	Scania K113 CRB	Van Hool Alizée HE	C49FT	1997	Hardings, Redditch, 2008
ASV895	Scania K113 CRB	Van Hool Alizée HE	C53F	1997	The King's Ferry, Gillingham, 2008
GAZ4503	Scania K113 CRB	Van Hool Alizée HE	C49FT	1997	Paragon, Stramshall, 2004
GIL3122	Scania K113 CRB	Van Hool Alizée HE	C53F	1997	The King's Ferry, Gillingham, 2007
UDZ3004	Scania K113 CRB	Van Hool Alizée HE	C53F	1997	The King's Ferry, Gillingham, 2007
WEZ5969	Scania K113 CRB	Van Hool Alizée HE	C53F	1997	The King's Ferry, Gillingham, 2008
WCZ9954	Scania K113 CRB	Van Hool Alizée HE	C51FT	1997	Teal, Cranswick, 2006
WCZ9955	Scania K113 CRB	Van Hool Alizée HE	C53F	1998	Leons, Stafford, 2003
KAZ4523	Scania K113 CRB	East Lancs	B47/33F	1983	PC Coaches, Lincoln, 2008
KAZ4524	Scania K113 CRB	Van Hool Alizée HE	C49FT	1998	Paragon, Stramshall, 2003
FSU386	Scania K113 CRB	Berkhof Axial 70	C30FT	1998	Bamber, Runcorn, 2008
S20ACL	Scania K124 IB6	Irizar Century 12.37	C32FT	1998	Coach Options, Middleton, 2006
TIL8252	Mercedes-Benz Vario O814	Autobus Nouvelle 2	C29F	1998	St Margaret's Minibuses, 2005
TIL8251	Mercedes-Benz Vario O814	Autobus Nouvelle 2	C29F	1999	Leons Stafford, 2003
TIL3714	Mercedes-Benz Vario O814	Plaxton Cheetah	C33F	1999	
CRZ6379	Scania K124 IB4	Van Hool T9 Alizée	C53F	1999	Hunter, Daventry, 2011
CRZ6380	Scania K94 IB4	Van Hool T9 Alizée	C53F	1999	Three Cs, Ipswich, 2011
CNZ3828	Scania L94 IB4	Van Hool T9 Alizée	C49FT	1999	Chambers, Moneymore, 2002
CNZ8300	Scania L94 IB4	Van Hool T9 Alizée	C49FT	1999	Ward, Alresford, 2008
BIG9830	Scania K124 IB4	Berkhof Axial 100	C45/17CT	1999	The King's Ferry, Gillingham, 2009
CNZ1541	Scania K124 IB4	Van Hool T9 Alizée	C49FT	2000	Turners, Wickham St Paul, 2010
CRZ6378	Scania K124 IB4	Van Hool T9 Alizée	C48FT	2000	Bachs, Hamilton, 2011
ONZ1167	Scania K94 IB	Irizar Intercentury 12.32	C57F	2001	Romsey Coaches, 2005
ONZ1168	Scania L94 IB4	Irizar Century 12.37	C57F	2001	Romsey Coaches, 2005
XIL5932	Mercedes-Benz Sprinter 413cdi	Excel	M16	2001	Whitehead, Hoddesdon, 2006
NUI2424	MAN 13.220	Berkhof Axial 35	C39FT	2001	Newbury Mini, Thatcham, 2010
CRZ6381	Scania K124 IB4	Van Hool T9 Alizée	C49FT	2001	Moxon, Oldcotes, 2011
CRZ6382	Scania K124 IB4	Van Hool T9 Alizée	C49FT	2001	Eve, Dunbar, 2011
CRZ6376	Scania K124 IB4	Van Hool T9 Alizée	C49FT	2001	Edinburgh Coach Lines, 2011
CRZ6377	Scania K124 IB4	Van Hool T9 Alizée	C49FT	2001	Blakes, East Anstey, 2011
CNZ2983	Scania L94 IB4	Van Hool T9 Alizée	C49FT	2001	Telford, Newcastleton, 2007
CNZ4060	Scania L94 IB4	Van Hool T9 Alizée	C53F	2002	Byley Coaches, Middlewich, 2010
XJI3831	Mercedes-Benz Sprinter 413cdi	Optare/Ferqui	C16F	2003	Holmes, Newport, 2007
FX53FRK	Mercedes-Benz Vario O814	Autobus Nouvelle 2	C33F	2003	Smith, Market Harborough, 2007
BIG5977	Scania K114 EB6	Berkhof Axial 100	C61/14CT	2004	Siesta, Middlesbrough, 2010

YN04AJY	Scania K94 IB4	Irizar S-kool	S70F	2004	
YN04AKY	Scania K94 IB4	Irizar S-kool	S70F	2004	
YN05GXY	Scania K94 IB4	Irizar S-kool	S70F	2005	
YN05HFS	Scania K94 IB4	Irizar S-kool	S70F	2005	
BIG9829	Scania L114 EB4	Irizar Century	C49FT	2005	Chambers, Moneymore, 2012
TIL9653	Mercedes-Benz Vario 0814	Plaxton Cheetah	C33F	2005	Smith, Market Harborough, 2008
SN05MFY	Mercedes-Benz Atego 1223L	UNVI/Esker Touring	C35F	2005	
YN05BJS	MAN 10.220	Noge Catalan Star 320	C35F	2005	Garfield, Bedlington, 2011
BIG8835	Scania K113 TRA	Berkhof Axial 100	C47/17FT	2005	Dreamline, Blackburn, 2009
DRZ5272	Scania K114 EB6	Berkhof Axial 100	C51/23DT	2005	Reid, Clough Mills, 2011
FJ56FFZ	Scania K114 EB4	Berkhof Axial 50	C49FT	2006	
BIG9883	Scania K114 EB6	Berkhof Axial 100	C63/20FT	2007	
YN57GBV	Scania K340 EB6	Berkhof Axial 65	C65FT	2008	
YT61FDU	Scania K340 EB6	Berkhof Axial 100	C63/20FT	2012	

Previous registrations:

6791RU	R200LCT	GAZ4503	P975HNT, P98GHE, PAG366A, PAR460N
ASV895	P802MKL, A14TKF	GIL3122	P805MKL, A19TKF
BIG5977	YN04AGZ	IIL8585	J2HCR, J838JNP
BIG8835	M9SCC	KAZ4523	E719EFG
BIG9827	H10WLE, H2HWD, H163PGF, TIL8252	KAZ4524	R100LCT, R127WNT, R7TMT, PAG366A
BIG9828	YN05HDG, V55CCH, DRZ5272	LIL2174	E562FFW, UTL798
BIG9829	K330YDW, OAZ9330, K5HWD, K590ABV	LUI1508	M253TAK
BIG9830	T11SCC, H9TKF	MUI7799	L403LHE
BIG9831	WGT1, M329RKG	MUI7939	M4HWD, M652BBV
BIG9832	L338DTG, 8686DN, L8KFC	NIB8179	E708EFG
BIG9833	K21GVC, 3COV, A7HLC, K151NDU, XJI3831	NUI2424	Y876KDP
BIG9834	YSU985, P3WGT	ONZ1167	S370SET
BIG9883	YN56NNM	ONZ1168	X424WVO
C110UBC	C110UBC, KAZ4524	PLZ6542	P4HCR, P89FWP
CNZ2983	YN51MKK	PNZ4424	M500GSM
CNZ3828	V88CCH	REZ5237	P133GHE, 24PAE
CNZ4060	VX51RDU	S20ACL	S11BFC
CNZ8300	T732JHE	TIL3714	V100ACL
CRZ6376	01D50257, PSU613, Y474KSF	TIL8251	S200LCT
CRZ6377	Y200LCT, WIB137	TIL8252	R741ECT
CRZ6378	W4FEN, 330GGX	TIL9653	YN54ZHK
CRZ6379	S783RNP, 3698E, VIL9998	UDZ3004	P661LKO, A16TKF
CRZ6380	T401OWA, L8KFC	WCZ9954	R1JBT, R92CHE
CRZ6381	Y602JSH, JIL7889, B15DWA	WCZ9955	R300LCT
CRZ6382	Y604JSH, Y10EVE, B18DWA	WEZ5969	P803MKL, A15TKF
FNZ1049	L567FND, A19EYC	XJI3831	FY52GNP
FSU386	R84RBY, HSK643, C1ECB, R615GNB, R40ANT	YAZ4111	J218XKY, A14LLT
G74UNU	G545PRH, ASV895, BIG9828	YEZ5553	P6HCR, P723EAB
G722RYJ	G722RYJ, TIL9653	YJI7372	J219XKY, A15LLT
GAZ4501	M246TAK		

Depots: Syston Road, Cossington; Dysart Way, Leicester and Great Bowden Road, Market Harborough

Seen near Marble Arch is SN05MFY from the Ausden Clark fleet. This Mercedes-Benz Atego carries an UNVI Touring body with a capacity of thirty-five, supplied in the UK by Esker.
Colin Lloyd

BAKERS DOLPHIN

Bakers Coaches Ltd, 48 Locking Road, Weston-super-Mare, BS23 3DN

2	JNZ4302	Volvo B10M-62	Van Hool T9 Alizée	C46FT	1998	
3	JNZ4393	Volvo B10M-62	Van Hool T9 Alizée	C46FT	1998	
4	JNZ4304	Volvo B10M-62	Van Hool T9 Alizée	C48FT	2001	
5	JNZ4395	Volvo B10M-62	Van Hool T9 Alizée	C48FT	1999	
6	JNZ4326	Volvo B10M-62	Van Hool T9 Alizée	C46FT	1999	
7	340MYA	Volvo B10M-60	Van Hool Alizée	S70F	1990	Shearings, Wigan, 1993
8	BV58MKG	Mercedes-Benz Tourismo	Mercedes-Benz	C49FT	2009	Swans, Chadderton, 2011
9	BV58MKJ	Mercedes-Benz Tourismo	Mercedes-Benz	C49FT	2009	Swans, Chadderton, 2011
10	JNZ2310	Volvo B10M-62	Van Hool T9 Alizée	C48FT	2001	
15	UJI3791	Volvo B10M-61	Van Hool Alizée	C53F	1988	Bow Belle of Devon, 1997
17	WJI6880	Volvo B10M-60	Van Hool Alizée	C53F	1992	Metroline (Brents), Watford, 1996
18	NIL4981	Volvo B10M-61	Van Hool Alizée	C53F	1988	Edwards Bros, Tiers Cross, 1997
19	UKZ6724	Dennis Javelin 12m	Plaxton Première 320	S70F	1996	Epsom Coaches, 2003
23	NIL4982	Volvo B10M-61	Van Hool Alizée	C53F	1988	Clarkes of London, 1997
24	NIL5381	Volvo B10M-61	Van Hool Alizée	C53F	1988	Clarkes of London, 1997
25	NIL5382	Volvo B10M-61	Van Hool Alizée	C53F	1988	Clarkes of London, 1997
26	YXI2730	Volvo B10M-61	Van Hool Alizée	C53F	1989	Shearings, Wigan, 1996
29	WJI6879	Volvo B10M-60	Van Hool Alizée	C53F	1989	Clarkes of London, 1998
31	NIL4983	Volvo B10M-61	Plaxton Paramount 3200 II	C53F	1986	Shearings, Wigan, 1993
32	BJ08KNK	Mercedes-Benz Tourismo	Mercedes-Benz	C49FT	2008	Swans, Chadderton, 2010
33	BJ08KNL	Mercedes-Benz Tourismo	Mercedes-Benz	C49FT	2008	Swans, Chadderton, 2010
35	EIG4335	Volvo B10M-62	Plaxton Expressliner 2	C53F	1999	Park's of Hamilton, 2003
36	EIG4336	Volvo B10M-62	Plaxton Expressliner 2	S70F	1999	Park's of Hamilton, 2003
37	XIL8422	Volvo B10M-62	Plaxton Excalibur	C53FT	1999	Excelsior, Bournemouth, 2004
38	XIL8423	Volvo B10M-62	Plaxton Excalibur	C53FT	1999	Excelsior, Bournemouth, 2004
39	7740KO	Volvo B10M-62	Plaxton Première 320	S70F	1999	Excelsior, Bournemouth, 2004
40	XIL8425	Volvo B10M-62	Plaxton Première 320	C53FT	1999	Excelsior, Bournemouth, 2004
41	WJI3491	Leyland Tiger TRCTL11/3LZM	Plaxton Derwent	BC52F	1987	MoD (82KF26), 1998
43	WJI3493	Leyland Tiger TRCTL11/3LZM	Plaxton Derwent	BC52F	1987	MoD (82KF19), 1998
45	XJI6331	Leyland Tiger TRCTL11/3LZM	Plaxton Derwent	BC54F	1987	Beeline, Warminster, 1999
46	WJI3496	Leyland Tiger TRCTL11/3LZM	Plaxton Derwent	BC52F	1987	MoD (82KF23), 1998
48	XJI6330	Leyland Tiger TRCTL11/3LZM	Plaxton Derwent	BC52F	1987	MoD (87KF48), 1998
52	XJI5459	Leyland Tiger TRCTL11/3LZM	Plaxton Derwent	S68F	1987	MoD (87KF36), 1998
53	XJI5458	Leyland Tiger TRCTL11/3LZM	Plaxton Derwent	S68F	1987	MoD (82KF37), 1998
54	XJI6332	Leyland Tiger TRCTL11/3LZM	Plaxton Derwent	S68F	1987	Turner, Bristol, 1999
55	XJI6333	Leyland Tiger TRCTL11/3LZM	Plaxton Derwent	S68F	1987	MoD (87KF42), 1998
57	XJI5457	Leyland Tiger TRCTL11/3LZM	Plaxton Derwent	S68F	1987	MoD (87KF48), 1998
60	WJI3497	Leyland Tiger TRCTL11/3LZM	Plaxton Derwent	S68F	1987	MoD (82KF30), 1998
62	ET10BDT	Scania K360EB4	Irizar Inter-Century	C49FT	2010	
63	FT10BDT	Scania K360EB4	Irizar Inter-Century	C49FT	2010	
64	GT10BDT	Scania K360EB4	Irizar Inter-Century	C49FT	2010	
66	791WHT	Volvo B12T	Van Hool Astrobel	C51/16CT	1998	
72	MX09MJE	Optare Solo M880	Optare	N28F	2009	
73	194WHT	Optare Solo M850	Optare	N26F	1999	Go North East, 2008
74	UKZ2874	Volkswagen Caravelle	Volkswagen	M8	2000	
78	UKZ2873	Mercedes-Benz Vito 111 cdi	Mercedes-Benz	M8	2004	
81	WF10ZRU	Mercedes-Benz Vito 111 cdi	Mercedes-Benz	M8	2010	
82	WF10ZRV	Mercedes-Benz Vito 111 cdi	Mercedes-Benz	M8	2010	
83	WF10ZRX	Mercedes-Benz Vito 111 cdi	Mercedes-Benz	M8	2010	
84	WF10ZRY	Mercedes-Benz Vito 111 cdi	Mercedes-Benz	M8	2010	
91	UPV487	Optare Solo M920	Optare	N31F	1999	National Express, 2009
92	XLH570	Optare Solo M850	Optare	N26F	1999	Ace Travel, Aintree, 2009
93	AJ58PZB	MAN 14.240	MCV Evolution	N43F	2008	Perryman, Berwick, 2012
94	AJ58PZC	MAN 14.240	MCV Evolution	N43F	2008	Perryman, Berwick, 2012
95	AJ58PZD	MAN 14.240	MCV Evolution	N43F	2008	Perryman, Berwick, 2012
96	AJ58PZE	MAN 14.240	MCV Evolution	N43F	2008	Perryman, Berwick, 2012
97	MX12DYS	Wrightbus Streetlite WF	Wrightbus	N33F	2012	
98	MX12DYT	Wrightbus Streetlite WF	Wrightbus	N33F	2012	
104	958VKM	Volvo B7R	Plaxton Prima	C57F	1999	
105	315MWL	Volvo B10M-62	Van Hool Alizée HE	C53F	1996	
110	IHZ3110	Volvo B10M-62	Plaxton Première 350	C53F	1999	Excelsior, Bournemouth, 2004
112	HD08GLD	Scania K470 EB6	Irizar PB	C36FT	2008	
113	BD08GLD	Scania K470 EB6	Irizar PB	C36FT	2008	
114	UKZ2875	Iveco EuroRider 395E.9.27	Beulas El Mundo	C48FT	2002	Diamond, Morriston, 2005

115	UKZ2915	Iveco EuroRider 395E.9.27	Beulas El Mundo	C44FT	2002	Diamond, Morriston, 2005
116	UKZ2916	Iveco EuroRider 395E.9.27	Beulas El Mundo	C44FT	2002	Diamond, Morriston, 2005
117	UKZ2917	Volvo B10M-62	Van Hool T9 Alizée	C46FT	2001	WA Shearings, Wigan, 2007
118	UKZ2923	Volvo B10M-62	Van Hool T9 Alizée	C46FT	2001	WA Shearings, Wigan, 2007
119	UKZ2926	Volvo B10M-62	Van Hool T9 Alizée	C46FT	2001	WA Shearings, Wigan, 2007
121	UKZ2932	Mercedes-Benz Touro OC500	Mercedes-Benz	C49FT	2004	Veolia - Dunn Line, 2007
122	UKZ5476	Mercedes-Benz Touro OC500	Mercedes-Benz	C49FT	2004	Veolia - Dunn Line, 2007
123	UKZ5478	Mercedes-Benz Touro OC500	Mercedes-Benz	C49FT	2004	Veolia - Dunn Line, 2007

Previous registrations:

194WHT	T462BCN	UKZ2917	W216JBN
315MWL	N203DYB	UKZ2923	W217JBN
340MYA	G868RNC, 340MYA, RJI5716	UKZ2926	W219JBN
958VKM	T920UEU, DEZ8804	UKZ2932	YX04GSZ
791WHT	R632VYB, EIG4966	UKZ5476	YX04JFZ
7740KO	A14EXC, T443VHO, XIL8424	UKZ5478	YX04HKK
EIG4335	T708UOS. LSK473	UKZ5491	-
EIG4336	T721UOS, LSK824	UKZ6724	N405HPC, A6HRR, N308OGJ
IHZ3110	T398VHO, A10EXC	UKZ6725	-
JNZ4301	P725JYA	WJI3491	82KF28
JNZ4302	R372XYD	WJI3493	82KF19
JNZ4304	Y227NYA	WJI3496	82KF23
JNZ4326	T762JYB	WJI3497	82KF30
JNZ4393	?	WJI6879	F552TMH, A3WLS
JNZ4395	T761JYB	WJI6880	J461HDS, KSK501, J690LGE
NIL4981	E622UNE, WSV528, E956CBU, 3432RE, E86ODE		
NIL4982	E220JJF	XIL8422	A6EXC, T442VHO
NIL4983	C345DND	XIL8423	A3EXC, T451VHO
NIL4984	-		
NIL4985	-	XIL8425	A17EXC, T445VHO
NIL4986	C355DND	XJI5457	87KF48, D287XRB
NIL5381	E222LBC	XJI5458	82KF27
NIL5382	E223LBC	XJI5459	87KF36
UJI3791	E634BFJ	XJI6330	87KF47
UPV487	T414OUB	XJI6331	03KJ22, G514XWS
UKZ2845	-	XJI6332	82KF28, D76JHY
UKZ2873	YT04KSK	XJI6333	87KF42
UKZ2874	V946UBD	XLH570	T461BCN
UKZ2875	FN02FBY	YX04HKK	UKZ5478
UKZ2915	FN02VCF	YXI2730	F730ENE
UKZ2916	FN02VCK	YXI2732	-

Depots: Locking Road, Weston-super-Mare; Cattle Market, Bath Road, Bridgwater; Outstation: Nailsea
Web: www.bakersdolphin.com

Bakers Dolphin is one of the largest coach travel and holiday firms in South West England and operates bus services in addition to its coaching activities. Representing the fleet is 115, UKZ2915, an Iveco EuroRider with Beulas El Mundo bodywork seen near Hyde Park in London. *Dave Heath*

BANSTEAD COACHES

Banstead Coaches Ltd, 1 Shrubland Road, Banstead, SM7 2ES

D72HRU	Bedford Venturer YNV	Plaxton Paramount 3200 III	C53F	1987	
R2BAN	Dennis Javelin 12m	Plaxton Première 320	C53F	1998	
T50BAN	Dennis Javelin 12m	Plaxton Première 320	C53F	1999	
E6BAN	Toyota Coaster BB50R	Caetano Optimo IV	C21F	1999	Sunbury, Shepperton, 2009
W7BAN	Dennis Javelin GX 12m	Berkhof Axial 50	C53F	2000	
P4BAN	DAF SB3000	Van Hool Alizée	C53F	2001	Westbus, Hounslow, 2012
N30BAN	DAF SB3000	Van Hool Alizée	C53F	2001	Westbus, Hounslow, 2012
Y6BAN	Dennis R	Berkhof Axial 50	C53F	2001	
MY02BAN	Dennis R	Plaxton Panther	C53F	2002	
MY52BAN	Dennis R	Plaxton Panther	C53F	2002	
GO04BAN	Mercedes-Benz Touro OC500	Mercedes-Benz	C53F	2004	
CH05BAN	Mercedes-Benz Touro OC500	Mercedes-Benz	C53F	2005	
OO06BAN	Mercedes-Benz Touro OC500	Mercedes-Benz	C53F	2006	
AH07BAN	Volvo B12B 12.2m	Plaxton Panther	C53F	2007	
BC07BAN	Toyota Coaster BB50R	Caetano Optimo V	C26F	2007	BM Coaches, Hayes, 2009
MH08BAN	Mercedes-Benz Tourismo	Mercedes-Benz	C53F	2008	
DH09BAN	Volvo B9R 12.3m	Plaxton Panther	C53F	2009	
MH10BAN	MAN 18.280	Beulas Stergo Spica	C53F	2011	

Previous registrations:

BC07BAN	FN07BYY		N30BAN	Y562HUA
E6BAN	S612KUT		P4BAN	Y561HUA

Web: www.bansteadcoaches.co.uk

Banstead Coaches operates mostly new coaches, all with BAN index marks, from its Surrey base. Three Mercedes-Benz Touro coaches are operated including OO06BAN, seen at the UK Coach Rally. The Touro was specifically designed for the British market as there was no right-hand-drive version of the Travego. *John Marsh*

BARFORDIAN

Barfordian Coaches Ltd, The Coach Depot, 500 Goldington Road, Bedford, MK41 0DX

Reg	Chassis	Body	Seating	Year	History
DBJ969Y	Bedford YNT	Duple Dominant	B63F	1983	Chambers, Bures, 1990
SIW1931	Bova Futura FHD12.290	Bova	C51FT	1989	
SIW1932	Bova Futura FHD12.290	Bova	S70F	1989	
230WYA	Dennis Javelin 11m	Plaxton Paramount 3200	C53F	1991	Souls, Olney, 2011
L50ULS	Volvo B10M-60	Plaxton Première 320	C50F	1994	Souls, Olney, 2011
TFX663	Neoplan Skyliner N122/3	Neoplan	C57/20CT	1995	Souls, Olney, 2011
IAZ3915	Toyota Coaster HZB50R	Caetano Optimo IV	C21F	1996	Eddie Brown, Helperby, 2000
K50ULS	Volvo B10M-60	Plaxton Première 320	C53F	1996	Souls, Olney, 2011
M50ULS	Volvo B10M-62	Plaxton Première 320	C49FT	1996	Souls, Olney, 2011
SIW1936	Volvo B10M-62	Jonckeere Mistral 50	C51FT	1996	Souls, Olney, 2011
N222ASH	Mercedes-Benz 811	Mellor	BC24F	1996	Craske, Sutton, 2006
224ASV	Bova Futura FHD12.340	Bova	C53FT	1997	Coopers, Bedlington, 2003
489SYB	Bova Futura FHD12.370	Bova	C49FT	2001	
YN51XMH	Neoplan Skyliner N122/3	Neoplan	C57/20CT	2001	Souls, Olney, 2011
YR02UOB	Neoplan Skyliner N122/3	Neoplan	C57/20CT	2002	
B3WFB	Mercedes-Benz Sprinter 413 cdi	Koch	C16F	2003	Nightingales, Ellough, 2010
RX53AWF	Renault Master	Renault	B12F	2003	Nightingales, Ellough, 2010
SN03TKF	VDL Bova Futura FHD14.430	VDL Bova	C57FT	2003	Austin, Earlston, 2006
675PBM	VDL Bova Futura FHD12.340	VDL Bova	C49FT	2004	
YN53CSY	Mercedes-Benz Sprinter 614	Onyx	C24F	2004	Hutchinson, Easingwold, 2005
YN05HVB	Mercedes-Benz Vario O814	Plaxton Cheetah	C29F	2005	
YJ05FXR	VDL Bova Futura FHD15.430	VDL Bova	C67FT	2005	
YJ55EYY	VDL Bova Futura FHD13.340	VDL Bova	C53FT	2005	

Previous registrations:

224ASV	P334DBB	RX53AWF	RX53AWF, A15WFB
230WYA	H660AST	SIW1931	F692ONR
489SYB	YK51KPR	SIW1932	G98VFP
675PBM	YJ53CFM	SIW1936	N538SJF
IAZ3915	N939RBC	SN03TKF	SN03TKF, USU543, Y369UOM
K50ULS	N93FWJ	TFX663	N580AWJ, 7195BY
L50ULS	L936NWW, TAZ4995	YN51XMH	YN51XMH, 50DBD
M50ULS	FTG5, N389DRW		

Web: www.barfordiancoaches.co.uk

Pictured in Barfordian livery is Bova Futura 675PBM which still carried index mark YJ53CFM when seen.
Mark Doggett

BARNES

Barnes Coaches Ltd, Unit E, Woodside Road, South Marston Park, Swindon, SN3 4AQ

XIB3421	Volvo B10M-62	Van Hool T9 Alizée	C49FT	1999	
WIB1444	Volvo B10M-62	Van Hool T9 Alizée	C49FT	2002	
WJ02VRO	Volvo B10M-62	Van Hool T9 Alizée	C49FT	2002	
WJ52MTO	Volvo B12M	Van Hool T9 Alizée	C49FT	2002	
WA03HPZ	Volvo B12M	Van Hool T9 Alizée	C53F	2003	
WA04EWL	Volvo B12M	Van Hool T9 Alizée	C49FT	2004	
OU05AVY	Volvo B9TL	East Lancs Vyking	BC63/39F	2005	Weavaway, Newbury, 2011
WA05DFF	Volvo B12M	Van Hool T9 Alizée	C49FT	2005	
CN55ZXR	Ford Transit Tourneo	Ford	M8	2005	
EN06ZXR	Ford Transit Tourneo	Ford	M8	2006	
WA06CDK	Volvo B12M	Van Hool T9 Alizée	C49FT	2006	
WA06JGO	Volvo B12B	Van Hool T9 Alizée	C49FT	2006	
FG56WBE	Ford Transit	Ford	M14	2006	
WA07BGX	Volvo B12B	Van Hool T9 Alizée	C49FT	2007	
WA07BHL	VDL Bova Futura FHD12.430	VDL Bova	C53F	2007	
WA57JZW	Volvo B12B	Van Hool T917 Alicron	C49FT	2008	
WA08GRU	VDL Bova Futura FHD12.365	VDL Bova	C53FT	2008	
WA08JVO	VDL Bova Futura FHD12.340	VDL Bova	C53FT	2008	
WA58JNN	Volvo B12B 14m	Van Hool T917 Acron	C61FT	2009	
WA09AZN	Volvo B12B 14m	Van Hool T917 Acron	C61FT	2009	
WA09KZO	Volvo B12B 12m	Van Hool T9 Alizée	C37FT	2009	
WA09AZL	VDL Bova Futura FHD13.360	VDL Bova	C53FT	2009	
YR59YND	Ford Transit Tourneo	Ford	M8	2009	
CP10WHJ	Ford Transit Tourneo	Ford	M8	2010	
WA10CFU	VDL Bova Futura FHD127.365	VDL Bova	C53FT	2010	
WA10CFZ	VDL Bova Futura FHD127.365	VDL Bova	C53FT	2010	
PN10FOA	Volvo B9TL	Optare Olympus	N61/39F	2010	Birmingham International, 2011
WA10CFX	Volvo B12B 14m	Van Hool T917 Acron	C61FT	2010	
WA10CFY	Volvo B12B 12m	Van Hool T9 Alizée	C49FT	2010	
WA60DZO	VDL Bova Futura FHD127.365	VDL Bova	C53FT	2010	
WA11HXO	Volvo B13R 14m	Van Hool T9 Alizée	C61FT	2011	
YJ12CGG	VDL SB4000	Van Hool T9 Alizée	C53FT	2012	
WA12AWN	VDL Bova Futura FHD12.365	VDL Bova	C53FT	2012	
WA12AWO	VDL Bova Futura FHD12.365	VDL Bova	C53FT	2012	

Previous registrations:

WIB1444	WJ02KDO	XIB3421	T522PYD

Depot: Woodside Road, South Marston Park, Swindon
Web: www.barnescoaches.co.uk

Pictured while heading for the Cheltenham racecourse is Barnes' WA11HXO, a tri-axle variant of the Volvo B13R with Van Hool T9 Alizée bodywork.
Steve Rice

BATTERSBY - SILVER GREY

Harrisons Coaches (Morecambe) Ltd, The Coach Station, Middlegate, Morecambe, LA3 3PE

10	K10BSG	Dennis Javelin 12m	Wadham Stringer Vanguard III	S70F	1992	Stonehouse Coaches, 2006
20	K20BSG	Dennis Javelin 12m	Wadham Stringer Vanguard III	S70F	1992	MoD, 2006
30	K30BSG	Dennis Javelin 12m	Wadham Stringer Vanguard III	S70F	1992	MoD, 2006
40	K40BSG	Dennis Javelin 12m	Wadham Stringer Vanguard III	S70F	1992	South Gloucester, 2006
301	3182NF	Mercedes-Benz Vario O814	Plaxton Cheetah	C24F	2005	
302	5096WF	Mercedes-Benz Vario O814	Plaxton Cheetah	C33F	1999	
304	PF51KHC	Mercedes-Benz Vario O814	Plaxton Beaver 2	BC33F	2001	
307	7845UG	Mercedes-Benz Vario O814	Plaxton Cheetah	C33F	2001	
308	PO53KZZ	Mercedes-Benz Vario O814	Plaxton Beaver 2	BC33F	2003	
312	KF52TZN	Mercedes-Benz Vario O814	Plaxton Beaver 2	BC33F	2002	Nottingham CC
450	BX56VUB	Mercedes-Benz Tourino O510	Mercedes-Benz	C34F	2006	Evobus demonstrator, 2009
910	5108VX	Dennis Javelin 12m	Plaxton Première 320	C57F	1998	Ryan, Longridge, 2010
933	8850WU	Volvo B12B	Plaxton Panther	C53F	2005	
935	4360WF	Volvo B12B	Plaxton Panther	C53F	2005	
938	7017UN	Volvo B12B 12.8m	Plaxton Panther	C49FT	2006	
939	4148VX	Volvo B12M 12.8m	Plaxton Panther	C53Ft	2006	Park's of Hamilton, 2008
940	YN07OPL	Volvo B12M 12.8m	Plaxton Panther	C50FT	2007	Logan, Dunloy, 2009
941	YN07OPE	Volvo B12M 12.8m	Plaxton Panther	C50FT	2007	Logan, Dunloy, 2009
942	YN10JYG	Volvo B12B 12.8m	Plaxton Panther	C49FT	2010	
943	YN11AYH	Volvo B9R 12.8m	Plaxton Panther II	C40FT	2011	
944	YN10FZT	Volvo B9R 12.8m	Plaxton Elite	C49FT	2010	Logan, Dunloy, 2012
945	YN10FZV	Volvo B9R 12.8m	Plaxton Elite	C49FT	2010	Logan, Dunloy, 2012
946	YN07KHH	Volvo B7R	Plaxton Profile	C57F	2007	Cresswells, Moira, 2012
951	1359UP	Volvo B12B 14.2m	Jonckheere Mistral 70	C57FT	2006	Lochs & Glens, Aberfoyle, 2009
952	7622UK	Volvo B12B 14.2m	Jonckheere Mistral 70	C57FT	2006	Lochs & Glens, Aberfoyle, 2009
953	YN10JYH	Volvo B12B 14.2m	Van Hool T917 Acron	C48FT	2010	
954	YN09HRJ	Volvo B12B 14.2m	Plaxton Elite	C52FT	2009	Logan, Dunloy, 2011

Previous registrations:

1359UP	FJ06BSV	7622UK	FJ06BSY
3182NF	YN05HVE	7845UG	Y808UDT
3267HX	-	8850WU	YN54WWE
4148VX	LSK495, SF06WEA	K10BSG	47KL52, L882ASU
4360WF	YN05HVC	K20BSG	75KK26, L369KTO
5096WF	V302DRN	K30BSG	MIW5189, K160PUJ
5108VX	R275UDE	K40BSG	75KK33, K326PHT
7017UN	YN06MXD		

Web: www.battersbys.co.ukO

Based in the seaside town of Morecambe, Battersby Silver Grey has remained a family firm for over sixty years. One of a pair of coaches which joined the fleet in 2009 is YN07OPL, a Plaxton Panther-bodied Volvo B12M.
Mark Doggett

BELLE COACHES

B R Shreeve & Sons Ltd, Hadenham Road, Lowestoft, NR33 7NF

03	DAZ4304	Volvo B10M-60	Plaxton Paramount 3200 III	C53F	1989	Kimes, Folkingham, 1996
04	LIL9713	Setra S315 GT-HD	Setra	C49FT	2000	Redwing, Camberwell, 2003
05	NJI9241	Volvo B10M-62	Van Hool Alizée	C53F	1997	Kerry, Killarney, 2003
06	NJI9244	Volvo B10M-62	Van Hool Alizée	C53F	1997	Kerry, Killarney, 2003
07	LIL9457	Setra S250	Setra Special	C53F	1997	Anderson, Bermondsey, 2003
09	AE05MZN	Mercedes-Benz Vario O814	Eurocoach	C33F	2005	
11	LIL9452	Setra S315 GT-HD	Setra	C49FT	2001	Ardcavan, Castlebridge, 2006
12	LIL9455	Scania K113 CRB	Van Hool Alizée HE	C53F	1995	Silver Knight, Malmesbury, 1997
14	NJI9245	Setra S315 GT-HD	Setra	C49FT	2001	Welsh, Upton, 2006
15	SIL9043	Setra S250	Setra Special	C53F	1997	Streamline, Maidstone, 2003
19	OJI4755	Scania K113 CRB	Van Hool Alizée HE	C49FT	1998	Leons, Stafford, 2004
22	NJI9243	Scania K113 CRB	Van Hool Alizée HE	C53F	1995	Fargo Coachlines, Rayne, 1999
23	LIL9454	Setra S250	Setra Special	C53F	1997	Sleaford Taxi, 2003
24	LIL9717	Setra S315 GT-HD	Setra	C53F	2001	Cropley, Boston, 2007
25	LIL9456	Setra S315 GT-HD	Setra	C49FT	2004	Ross, Featherstone, 2009
29	K2JTB	Kässbohrer Setra S215 HD	Kässbohrer Setra	C53F	1992	Clarke, Burbage, 2004
31	SIL9044	Volvo B10M-62	Van Hool T9 Alizée	C53F	1999	Kerry, Killarney, 2005
33	LIL9715	Setra S315 GT-HD	Setra	C49FT	2002	Greeves, Netherton, 2005
37	MIL3503	Setra S315 GT-HD	Setra	C53F	2000	Redwing, Herne Hill, 2004
38	SJI9076	Scania K112 CRS	Plaxton Paramount 3200 II	C53F	1987	Snell, Newton Abbot, 1998
39	OJI4754	Setra S315 GT-HD	Setra	C49FT	2000	Redwing, Camberwell, 2004
40	OJI4758	Setra S315 GT-HD	Setra	C49FT	2003	Hellyer's, Fareham, 2006
42	LIL9714	Scania K113 CRB	Van Hool Alizée HE	C53F	1995	Galvin, Dunmanway, 2001
43	OJI4756	Setra S315 GT-HD	Setra	C53F	2001	Stainton, Kendal, 2008
44	BX08VBK	Toyota Coaster BB50R	Caetano Optimo V	C26F	2008	
46	LIL9718	Setra S315 GT-HD	Setra	C49FT	2004	Leons, Stafford, 2008

The name "Setra" is derived from the German word "selbsttragend" which means self-supporting and thus indicated one of the early integral vehicles, being a move away from the then traditional body on chassis. Setra then became part of the company name, Kässbohrer-Setra. Setra is now part of the Daimler-Benz Group. Illustrating the S315 GT-HD styling is AR03JKX, seen here in Chichester before its recent registration change.
Dave Heath

47	LIL9716	Scania K113 CRB	Van Hool T9 Alizée	C53F	1995	Woodcock, Felbridge, 2002
48	LIL9458	Scania K113 CRB	Van Hool T9 Alizée	C53F	1995	Woodcock, Felbridge, 2002
50	OJI4627	Kässbohrer Setra S215 HR	Kässbohrer Setra Rational	C53F	1988	Dereham Coachways, 2003
	BX05UVO	Setra S315 GT-HD	Setra	C53F	2005	City Circle, Bonnyrigg, 2008
	AO05TGJ	Volkswagen Transporter	Volkswagen	M7	2005	
	AO08MVH	Volkswagen Transporter	Volkswagen	M7	2008	
	AV08YHY	Ford Transit	Ford	M16	2008	
	AV08YHZ	Ford Transit	Ford	M16	2008	
	BC09BEL	Mercedes-Benz Tourismo	Mercedes-Benz	C49FT	2009	
	BC10BEL	Mercedes-Benz Tourismo	Mercedes-Benz	C49FT	2010	
	LD10BEL	Mercedes-Benz Tourismo	Mercedes-Benz	C49FT	2010	
	BE10LLE	Mercedes-Benz Vario O816	Plaxton Cheetah	C29F	2010	
	BC11BEL	Scania OmniExpress K340 EB4	Scania	C53FT	2011	
	BE11BEL	Scania OmniExpress K340 EB4	Scania	C53FT	2011	
	BC12BEL	Scania OmniExpress K340 EB4	Scania	C53FT	2012	

Previous registrations:

DAZ4304	F45TMU	MIL3503	W254UGX
LIL8481	-	NJI9241	97KY809, P737UAH
LIL9452	03WX3471, AR03JKX	NJI9242	-
LIL9453	-	NJI9243	M310VET
LIL9454	P466YFE	NJI9244	97KY810, P736UAH
LIL9455	M312VET	NJI9245	Y752DDA
LIL9456	BU04EZJ	OJI4627	5877MW, E346MLC, VIA137, E346MLC
LIL9457	P467XFE	OJI4754	W296UGX
LIL9458	M20ULY	OJI4755	R400LCT, R367VNT
LIL9713	W215UGX	OJI4756	01KY2807, Y961VOP
LIL9714	95C4802, M542GRT	OJI4758	UF03HOF
LIL9715	Y997JAY	SIL9043	P601XFE
LIL9716	M10ULY	SJI9076	D969ROD
LIL9717	BV51BNY		
LIL9718	AT04LCT		

Depots: Nine Acres, Aldringham, Leiston and Hadenham Road, Lowestoft.
Web: www.bellecoaches.co.uk

Another view of a S315 GT-HD, this time OJI4754. Otto Kässbohrer was born in 1904 and after his apprenticeship worked in his father's car factory and in 1928 bought the Ulm facility. He died in 1973 but his K symbol continues. As this book goes to press we hear that the 500 series will be launched during 2012. *Mark Doggett*

BERKELEY

Berkeley Coach & Travel Ltd, Ham Lane, Paulton, Bristol, BS39 7PL

LIB6445	Volvo B10M-60	Duple 340	C57F	1989	Skills, Nottingham, 1996
UIL5952	Volvo B9M	Plaxton Paramount 3200 III	C43F	1992	Brijan, Bishop's Waltham, 2005
L2POW	Volvo B10M-60	Van Hool Alizée	C53F	1994	
R2POW	Volvo B10M-62	Plaxton Excalibur	C57F	1998	
R4POW	Volvo B10M-62	Plaxton Excalibur	C49FT	1998	
T4POW	Volvo B10M-62	Plaxton Excalibur	C53F	1999	
W107RTC	Volvo B10M-62	Plaxton Panther	C43FT	2000	
Y289RSO	Volvo B10MT	Van Hool Alizée	C49FT	2001	Toolan, Glenrothes, 2007
WR02RVX	Volvo B10M-62	Plaxton Panther	C43FT	2002	
EO54XNA	Ford Transit	Ford	M8	2004	PS Travel, Nailsea, 2010
WX05YTT	Volvo B12B	Plaxton Panther	C49FT	2005	
SN05FLP	Volvo B12B	Van Hool T9 Alizée	C49FT	2005	Brown, Broxburn, 2008
SK07FVA	Volvo B12B	Van Hool T9 Alizée	C49FT	2007	Brown, Broxburn, 2009
WA57CYW	Volvo B12B	Van Hool T916 Acron	C53FT	2008	
WA59EAP	Volvo B12B	Van Hool T916 Acron	C34FT	2009	Hookways, Meeth, 2011
UU53BOY	Mercedes-Benz Sprinter 413 cdi	Ferqui Soroco	C19F	2010	
FX60YEF	Mercedes-Benz Sprinter 515 cdi	Ferqui Soroco	C16F	2010	
YN11FUB	Volvo B9R	Plaxton Panther	C57F	2011	

Previous registrations:

LIB6445	F28LTO	WA59EAP	WA59EAP, C111EFS
UIL5952	J332LLK, NFX502		

Web: www.berkeleycoachandtravel.co.uk

Representing Berkeley Coach & Travel is WA57CYW, a Volvo B12B with Van Hool T916 Acron bodywork. While Van Hool's body on chassis is normally the Alizée, from 2007 some of the bodies on rear-engined Volvo B12B chassis were designated Acron. *Mark Doggett*

BERRYS

Berry's Coaches (Taunton) Ltd, Cornishway West, New Wellington Road, Taunton, TA1 5NA

C219FMF	Volvo B9M	Plaxton Paramount 3200 II	C41F	1986	Richmond, Barley, 2002
PIB4019	Volvo B10M-61	Van Hool Alizée	C53FT	1987	
E131KGM	Volvo B9M	Plaxton Paramount 3200 III	C41F	1987	Gerry, Plymouth, 2001
SIB8398	Volvo B10M-61	Van Hool Alizée	C55F	1988	Avalon Cs, Glastonbury, 1995
E63XYC	Volvo B10M-61	Van Hool Alizée	C53F	1988	
F476WFX	Volvo B10M-60	Plaxton Paramount 3200 III	C53F	1989	Excelsior, Bournemouth, 1989
SIB9309	Volvo B10M-60	Van Hool Alizée	C49FT	1989	
G46RGG	Volvo B9M	Plaxton Paramount 3200 III	C41F	1990	Holmeswood Coaches, 2003
J819EYC	Volvo B10M-60	Jonckheere Deauville	C51FT	1992	
L238OYC	Volvo B10M-60	Van Hool Alizée HE	C53F	1993	
N10TGM	Volvo B10M-62	Van Hool Alizée HE	C40FT	1996	Tellings-Golden Miller, 2006
N758CYA	Volvo B10M-62	Van Hool Alizée HE	C49FT	1996	
N199DYB	Volvo B10M-62	Van Hool Alizée HE	C53F	1996	
P24FTA	Volvo B10M-62	Van Hool Alizée HE	C53F	1997	Thomas, Upton, 2008
P814GBA	Volvo B10M-60	Van Hool Alizée	C53F	1997	Berkeley, Paulton, 2011
P821GBA	Volvo B10M-60	Van Hool Alizée	C53F	1997	Berkeley, Paulton, 2011
PIB3360	Volvo B10M-62	Jonckheere Mistral	C26FT	1998	Four Seasons, Duns, 2009
W161RYB	Volvo B10M-62	Van Hool T9 Alizée	C49FT	2000	
WA04MHF	Volvo B12M	Van Hool T9 Alizée	C49FT	2004	
WA05JWU	Volvo B12M	Van Hool T9 Alizée	C49FT	2005	
WU55OAB	Mercedes-Benz Vito 111cdi	Mercedes-Benz	M8	2005	
FJ07VLV	Volvo B12B	Volvo 9700	C57FT	2007	McKenna, Lisburn, 2009
WA07KYC	Volvo B12B	Van Hool T917 Acron	C53FT	2007	
WA07BGV	Volvo B12B	Van Hool T925 Astrobel	C59/12CT	2007	
WA08APF	Volvo B12B	Van Hool T925 Astrobel	C59/12CT	2008	
WA08AOZ	Volvo B12B	Van Hool T917 Alicron	C53FT	2008	
WA09AYY	Volvo B12B	Van Hool T917 Acron	C53FT	2009	
FN09AOJ	Volvo B12B	Volvo 9700	C53FT	2009	Cropley, Boston, 2010
WA59EAW	Volvo B12B	Van Hool T925 Astrobel	C59/12CT	2009	
FJ60EKC	Volvo B12B	Volvo 9700	C53FT	2010	
BX61DXC	Volvo B13R	Volvo 9700	C53FT	2011	Volvo demonstrator, 2012
WA61GPO	Volvo B12B	Van Hool T925 Astrobel	C63/14DT	2011	
WA61GRX	Volvo B12B	Van Hool T925 Astrobel	C63/14DT	2012	

Previous registrations:

C219FMF	C219FMF, 851FYD	PIB3360	S62UBO, K3FST
E63XYC	E63XYC, PIB3360	PIB4019	D547OYD
E131KGM	WSV478	SIB8398	E272XYA
G46RGG	G46RGG, SIA327	SIB9309	F121GYB
P24FTA	97KY1021		

Web: www.berrycoaches.co.uk

Berrys Coaches comprises an all-Volvo-based fleet with Van Hool bodywork a main feature. New in 2009, WA09AYY carries the longer T917 Acron body on a B12B chassis.
Dave Heath

BIBBY'S OF INGLETON

Bibby's of Ingleton Ltd, New Road, Ingleton, LA6 3NU

R175GNW	DAF SB3000	Ikarus Blue Danube 350	C53F	1997	North Kent Express, 2003
BIB5491	DAF SB3000	Ikarus Blue Danube 350	C55F	1997	North Kent Express, 2003
BIB4844	DAF SB3000	Ikarus Blue Danube 350	C55F	1997	Alfa, Chorley, 2005
BIB3994	DAF SB3000	Ikarus Blue Danube 350	C53F	1998	Alfa, Chorley, 2007
BIB7670	DAF SB3000	Ikarus Blue Danube 350	C55F	1998	
BIB728	DAF SB3000	Van Hool T9 Alizée	C49FT	1998	Burrell, Newsham, 2003
T439KPP	LDV 400	LDV	M16	1999	
BIB1186	DAF SB3000	Van Hool T9 Alizée	C53F	1999	National Express, 2009
BIB6413	DAF SB3000	Van Hool T9 Alizée	C48FT	1999	Pullman, Crofty, 2011
W214CDN	DAF SB3000	Ikarus Blue Danube 350	C53F	2000	Alfa, Preston, 2012
BIB7667	DAF SB3000	Ikarus Blue Danube 350	C53F	2001	US Dept of Defense, 2005
BIB4843	DAF SB3000	Van Hool T9 Alizée	C49FT	2001	
MS03MER	Mercedes-Benz Sprinter 413 cdi	Crest	M16	2003	
BIB5740	DAF SB4000	Van Hool T9 Alizée	C48FT	2004	
BIB5428	DAF SB4000	Van Hool T9 Alizée	C49FT	2004	
BIB9840	DAF SB4000	Van Hool T9 Alizée	C48FT	2004	
BIB9842	DAF SB4000	Van Hool T9 Alizée	C49FT	2004	
BIB7871	DAF SB4000	Van Hool T9 Alizée	C49FT	2005	Wickson, Walsall, 2011
BIB8443	DAF SB4000	Van Hool T9 Alizée	C49FT	2005	
PB55LFC	Mercedes-Benz Vario O814	Esker Riada 815	C24F	2006	
YN06CFV	Mercedes-Benz Sprinter 413 cdi	Esker Riada 815	C16F	2006	
YN56NDC	Mercedes-Benz Vario O814	KVC	C24F	2006	Reay's, Wigton, 2009
YN07DUA	Mercedes-Benz Vario O814	Plaxton Cheetah	C33F	2007	Fourway, Guisley, 2010
u PB07DAF	VDL Bus SB4000	Van Hool T9 Alizée	C48FT	2007	
WR57LWY	Ford Transit Tourneo	Ford	M9	2007	
BIB4231	VDL Bus SB4000	Van Hool T9 Alizée	C48FT	2008	
PO58LLV	LDV Maxus	LDV	M8	2008	
YJ08ECT	Temsa Safari HD	Temsa	C49FT	2008	Arrive Bus & Coach, 2012
YN58FXP	Mercedes-Benz Vario O816	Plaxton Cheetah	C33F	2008	Reays, Wigton, 2011
YJ09CWY	VDL Bus SB4000	Van Hool T9 Alizée	C48FT	2009	
PB10DAF	VDL Bus SB4000	Van Hool T9 Alizée	C48FT	2010	
YJ60GBY	Temsa Safari HD	Temsa	C53F	2010	
AY60YBN	Ford Transit	Ford	M8	2011	
MB61FWB	VDL Bus SB4000	Van Hool T9 Alizée	C48FT	2012	

Special event vehicle:

ACC629	Bedford OB	Duple Vista	C29F	1950	Penmaenmawr Motor Co.

Previous registrations:

ACC629	ACC629, J3617, ACC629, TRN618A	BIB5491	R172GNW
BIB728	R93GNW, 98KK1024	BIB5740	PB04DAF
BIB1186	T211AUA	BIB6413	V705VWT
BIB3934	-	BIB7667	YJ51EKL
BIB3994	R120GNW	BIB7670	R67GNW
BIB4231	YJ57BBV	BIB7871	YJ05PVU
BIB4843	X884NWX	BIB8443	YJ05PVV, PB05DAF
BIB4844	P213RUM	BIB9840	PB04DAF
BIB4850	currently on a Volvo ancilliary vehicle	BIB9842	YJ04BND
BIB5428	YJ04BNE	R175GNW	R175GNW, BIB5740
		YN56NDC	YN56NDC, 487FHW

BIRMINGHAM INTERNATIONAL

Birmingham International Coaches Ltd, 10 Fortnum Close, Tile Cross, Birmingham, B33 0JT

B3BHX	Bova Futura FHD12.370	Bova	C49FT	2000	
B5BHX	Bova Futura FHD12.370	Bova	C49FT	2001	
B4BHX	VDL Bova Futura FHD12.340	VDL Bova	C49FT	2004	
B2BHX	VDL Bova Futura FHD12.290	VDL Bova	C49FT	2005	
YJ05XWO	VDL Bova Futura FHD13.340	VDL Bova	C53FT	2005	Ellison, St Helens, 2006
YJ06GKV	VDL Magiq XHD122.340	VDL Bova	C49FT	2006	
YJ57EYT	VDL Magiq MHD131.460	VDL Bova	C53FT	2007	Ellison, St Helens, 2009
YJ08NSF	VDL Magiq MHD122.410	VDL Bova	C48FT	2008	
YJ09FHM	VDL Bova Futura FHD127.365	VDL Bova	C49FT	2009	
FJ60EHW	Volvo B13R	VDL Jonckheere SHV	C32FT	2010	
BX11GVG	Volvo B13R	VDL Jonckheere SHV	C36FT	2011	
YJ11AOK	VDL Futura FHD127.365	VDL Bova	C53FT	2011	
YJ12KFO	VDL Futura FHD127.365	VDL Bova	C53FT	2012	

Previous registrations:

| B2BHX | YJ05XWR | | B4BHX | YK04FWA |
| B3BHX | W601GUG | | B5BHX | Y663HWY |

One of the well-known names of British coaching is Bibby's of Ingleton. Representing this Yorkshire-based operation is VDL SB4000 with appropriate index mark PB10DAF; DAF being the forerunner to the Dutch firm VDL, the initials of family van der Leegte with Pieter establishing a company in Eindhoven in 1953. An initial stake in the DAF business was acquired in 1997. Bodywork on this vehice is a Van Hool T9 Alizée. *Mark Doggett*

BLUEBIRD

Bluebird Coaches (Weymouth) Ltd, 450 Chickerell Road, Weymouth, DT3 4DH

Reg	Chassis	Body	Seating	Year	Notes
YJI8595	Volvo B10M-61	Van Hool Alizée	C53F	1985	Group Travel, Bodmin, 2007
654JHU	Volvo B10M-61	Van Hool Alizée	C53F	1985	Tellings-Golden Miller, 1988
ESK931	Volvo B10M-61	Van Hool Alizée	C53F	1986	Cole, Winford, 2006
M741RCP	DAF SB3000	Van Hool Alizée HE	C55F	1995	North Kent Express, 2001
S276LGA	Mercedes-Benz Vario 0814	Mellor Opus	B31F	1998	Speldhurst, Bedford, 2011
WJ02YYK	Toyota Coaster BB50R	Caetano Optimo IV	C22F	2002	Dawlish Coaches, 2010
779UXU	Neoplan Euroliner N316SHD	Neoplan	C34FT	2003	Bowers, Chapel-en-le-Frith, 2004
UCT838	Bova Futura FHD 10.340	Bova	C36FT	2003	City Circle, Edinburgh, 2007
FJ05APX	Volvo B12M	Plaxton Panther	C53F	2005	Anderson, Bermondsey, 2009
DC05BBC	VDL Bova Futura FHD 12.340	VDL Bova	C53F	2005	
BC06BBC	VDL Bova Futura FHD 12.340	VDL Bova	C36FT	2006	
WA06GSU	VDL Bova Futura FHD 122.340	VDL Bova	C53FT	2006	Weaverway, Newbury, 2009
YJ07DVT	VDL Bova Futura FHD 127.365	VDL Bova	C53FT	2007	Gracedown, Prestwich, 2008
BC07BBC	VDL Bova Magiq MHD13.340	VDL Bova	C48FT	2007	
WA57CYT	VDL Bova Futura FHD 127.365	VDL Bova	C53FT	2007	
WA57CYU	VDL Bova Futura FHD 127.365	VDL Bova	C53FT	2007	
BC08BBC	VDL Bova Magiq MHD13.340	VDL Bova	C53FT	2008	
RO08PZM	Volkswagen Caravelle	Volkswagen	M8	2008	
AC60BBC	VDL Bova Futura FHD 13.380	VDL Bova	C53FT	2010	
BC60BBC	VDL Bova Futura FHD 13.380	VDL Bova	C53FT	2010	
BC11BBC	Volvo B13R	Plaxton Elite	C49FT	2011	

Previous registrations:

654JHU	C335FSU	UCT838	WA03HRG
779UXU	YN03AWY	YJI8595	B319UNB, XFJ379, YCV500
ESK931	C332DND		

Web: www.bluebirdcoaches.com

The top of the range model from Plaxton's is the Elite which was launched in 2008. The design features glass fibre for the roof and side panels while the windscreen continues into the roof. BC11BBC is seen at the UK Coach Rally shortly after delivery. *John Marsh*

BM COACHES

BM Coaches Ltd, Shackles Dock, Silverdale Road Hayes, Middlesex, UB3 3BN.

KP04GKA	Neoplan Skyliner N112/3 13.7m	Neoplan	C61/20DT	2004	Stagecoach, 2011
KP04GKC	Neoplan Skyliner N112/3 13.7m	Neoplan	C61/20DT	2004	Stagecoach, 2011
OU04BZR	Neoplan Skyliner N112/3 13.7m	Neoplan	C61/20DT	2004	Stagecoach, 2011
FJ07VWY	Volvo B12B	Berkhof Axial 50	C53F	2007	
YJ08DLD	Van Hool T915 Acron	Van Hool	C41FT	2008	
BD08DZM	Setra S416 GT-HD	Setra	C53F	2008	
BV08ZWS	Mercedes-Benz Touro O510	Mercedes-Benz	C30FT	2008	Swans, Chadderton, 2012
YJ08ECX	VDL SB4000	VDL Berkhof Axial 50	C57FT	2008	
YJ58FDM	VDL SB4000	VDL Berkhof Axial 50	C57FT	2008	
WA58EOK	VDL SBR4000	VDL Berkhof Synergy	C63/22DT	2008	
YN58AFU	Mercedes-Benz Vario O816	Esker Riada GT	C29F	2008	
YN58AFZ	Mercedes-Benz Vario O816	Esker Riada GT	C29F	2008	
BK58URV	Mercedes-Benz Tourismo O315	Mercedes-Benz	C49FT	2008	
BK58URW	Mercedes-Benz Touro O510	Mercedes-Benz	C32FT	2008	
BK58URZ	Mercedes-Benz Touro O510	Mercedes-Benz	C32FT	2008	
YN09HZA	Mercedes-Benz Sprinter 515cdi	KVC	C16F	2009	
YN09HZB	Mercedes-Benz Sprinter 515cdi	KVC	C16F	2009	
FJ09XGO	Volvo B12B	Volvo 9700	C55FT	2009	
FJ09XGP	Volvo B12B	Volvo 9700	C55FT	2009	
FJ09XGR	Volvo B12B	Volvo 9700	C55FT	2009	
FJ09XGS	Volvo B12B	Volvo 9700	C55FT	2009	
FJ09XGT	Volvo B12B	Volvo 9700	C55FT	2009	
YJ09CUU	Van Hool T916 Astron	Van Hool	C53FT	2009	
YJ09CVV	Van Hool T916 Astron	Van Hool	C53FT	2009	
YJ59BAA	Van Hool T917 Astron	Van Hool	C59FT	2009	
YJ59BBE	Van Hool T916 Astron	Van Hool	C57FT	2009	
YJ59BBF	Van Hool T916 Astron	Van Hool	C57FT	2009	
YJ59BBK	Van Hool T916 Astron	Van Hool	C57FT	2009	
YJ59BBV	Van Hool T917 Astron	Van Hool	C40FT	2009	
YJ59BBX	Van Hool T916 Astron	Van Hool	C57FT	2009	
YJ59BBZ	Van Hool T916 Astron	Van Hool	C57FT	2009	
YN59CXR	Mercedes-Benz Sprinter 515cdi	KVC	C16F	2009	
BV10ZKN	Mercedes-Benz Touro O510	Mercedes-Benz	C34F	2010	Swans, Chadderton, 2012
BV10ZWS	Mercedes-Benz Tourino	Mercedes-Benz	C49FT	2010	Swans, Chadderton, 2012
WA10ENE	Mercedes-Benz Vario O816	Sitcar Beluga 2	C29F	2010	
YJ10DCV	Van Hool T916 Astron	Van Hool	C53FT	2010	
YJ10DCX	Van Hool T916 Astron	Van Hool	C53FT	2010	
YJ10DCY	Van Hool TD927 Astrobel	Van Hool	C53FT	2010	
YJ10DCZ	Van Hool T915 Acron	Van Hool	C53FT	2010	
WA10KNC	Van Hool T915 Acron	Van Hool	C53FT	2010	
WA10KND	Van Hool T915 Astron	Van Hool	C53FT	2010	
YJ60GKK	Van Hool T917 Astronef	Van Hool	C61F	2010	

Previous registration:
OU04BZR   T60UBE

Van Hool T916 Astron coach YJ59BBK is seen at Marble Arch when working in London. The T916 is 13.2m long, while the T917 is 14.04m. *Dave Heath*

BOWENS

Appleby's Coach Travel - Bowens - Jeffs - Nottingham City - Woottens - Yorks

L F Bowen Ltd, 104 Mariner, Lichfield Road Ind Est, Tamworth, B79 7UL

Jeffs Coaches Ltd, Station Road, Helmdon, Brackley, NN13 5QT

Opperman (1990) Ltd, The Coach Yard, Lycrome Road, Lye Green, Chesham, HP5 3LG

	J	TPD118X	Leyland Olympian ONTL11/1R	Roe	B43/29F	1982	
	J	SCK225X	Leyland Olympian ONLXB/1R	Eastern Coach Works	BC42/28F	1982	Burnley & Pendle, 2002
	J	VJO204X	Leyland Olympian ONLXB/1R	Eastern Coach Works	B47/28D	1982	Cityline, Oxford, 2000
W16	W	ABW310X	Leyland Leopard PSU3G/4R	Willowbrook Warrior (1990)	B48F	1982	Cityline, Oxford, 2002
W60	W	WWW883	Leyland Tiger TRCTL11/3R	East Lancs Myllennium (2000)	BC49F	1982	Stagecoach, 2008
W61	W	DFP492Y	Leyland Tiger TRCTL11/3R	East Lancs Myllennium (2000)	BC49F	1983	Stagecoach, 2008
W64	W	CUD222Y	Leyland Olympian ONLXB/1R	Eastern Coach Works	B47/32F	1983	Ford, Althorne, 2010
W57	W	JIL2199	Leyland Tiger TRCTL11/3R	East Lancs Myllennium (2000)	BC49F	1983	Stagecoach, 2008
W58	W	A12WTN	Leyland Tiger TRCTL11/3R	East Lancs Myllennium (2000)	BC49F	1984	Stagecoach, 2008
	J	C649LJR	Leyland Olympian ONLXB/1R	Eastern Coach Works	B45/32F	1985	Go North East, 2005
	J	C660LJR	Leyland Olympian ONLXB/1RV	Eastern Coach Works	B45/32F	1985	Go North East, 2005
84	B	OUI3920	Volvo B10M-61	Plaxton Paramount 3200 II	C53F	1985	Yorks, Cogenhoe, 2004
W59	W	B11WTN	Leyland Tiger TRCTL11/3R	East Lancs Myllennium (2000)	BC49F	1987	First, 2008
	J	OUI3914	Volvo B10M-61	Van Hool Alizée	C53F	1988	
	J	OUI3918	Volvo B10M-61	Plaxton Paramount 3200 III	C53F	1988	
	J	LUI7871	Volvo B10M-61	Plaxton Paramount 3200 III	C53F	1988	
W31	W	E227CFC	Leyland Olympian ONLXB/1RH	Alexander RL	B47/36F	1988	Arriva The Shires, 2003
W56	W	B8WTN	Leyland Tiger TRCTL11/3ARZ	Plaxton Paramount 3500 III	C53F	1989	Holmeswood Coaches, 2008
	J	F480AKC	Mercedes-Benz 609D	North West Coach Sales	C24F	1989	Windrush Valley, Witney, 1990
88	Y	EIG8588	Kässbohrer Setra S215 HD	Kässbohrer Setra Tornado	C49FT	1989	Yorks, Cogenhoe, 2004
	W	G231VWL	Leyland Olympian ON2R50G16Z4	Alexander RL	B47/29F	1990	Arriva The Shires, 2011
	W	G235VWL	Leyland Olympian ON2R50G16Z4	Alexander RL	B47/29F	1990	Arriva The Shires, 2011
	J	G907WAY	Volvo B10M-60	Caetano Algarve	C53F	1990	
	J	G908WAY	Volvo B10M-60	Caetano Algarve	C53F	1990	
	J	G910WAY	Volvo B10M-60	Caetano Algarve	C53F	1990	
	J	G911WAY	Volvo B10M-60	Caetano Algarve	C53F	1990	
	J	G912WAY	Volvo B10M-60	Caetano Algarve	C53F	1990	
90	Y	HSK511	Volvo B10M-61	Van Hool Alizée H	C49FT	1990	Yorks, Cogenhoe, 2004
	J	J520LRY	Dennis Javelin 12m	Caetano Algarve I	C53F	1991	
	J	J521LRY	Dennis Javelin 12m	Caetano Algarve I	C53F	1991	
	J	J471NJU	Toyota Coaster HDB30R	Caetano Optimo II	C18F	1992	
	J	VBW846	Volvo B10M-60	Caetano Algarve II	C35FT	1992	
	J	195JOH	Volvo B10M-60	Caetano Algarve II	C49FT	1992	Wilson's, Carnwath, 1998
	J	647PJO	Volvo B10M-60	Caetano Algarve II	C49FT	1992	
	J	TGY698	Volvo B10M-60	Caetano Algarve II	C49FT	1992	Wilson's, Carnwath, 1998
	J	FSV720	Volvo B10M-60	Caetano Algarve II	C49FT	1992	
	J	279JJO	Volvo B10M-60	Caetano Algarve II	C49FT	1992	
W65	W	UXI1372	Leyland Tiger TR2R56V16Z4	Alexander Q	BC53F	1992	Ulsterbus, 2010
W66	W	UXI1375	Leyland Tiger TR2R56V16Z4	Alexander Q	BC53F	1992	Ulsterbus, 2010
W67	W	UXI1376	Leyland Tiger TR2R56V16Z4	Alexander Q	BC53F	1992	Ulsterbus, 2010
W68	W	UXI1377	Leyland Tiger TR2R56V16Z4	Alexander Q	BC53F	1992	Ulsterbus, 2010
W69	W	WXI4384	Leyland Tiger TR2R56V16Z4	Alexander Q	BC53F	1992	Ulsterbus, 2010
18	Y	YJI6038	Toyota Coaster HDB30R	Caetano Optimo II	C18F	1992	
19	Y	YJI8597	Toyota Coaster HDB30R	Caetano Optimo II	C18F	1992	
	J	K97UFP	Dennis Javelin 12m	Caetano Algarve II	C57F	1993	
	J	K98UFP	Dennis Javelin 12m	Caetano Algarve II	C57F	1993	
92	Y	846FHA	Kässbohrer Setra S215 HD	Kässbohrer Setra	C49FT	1993	
	J	487VYA	Volvo B10M-62	Caetano Algarve II	C53F	1994	
	J	VXT571	Volvo B10M-62	Caetano Algarve II	C53F	1994	
	J	938HNM	Volvo B10M-62	Caetano Algarve II	C53F	1994	
W51	W	BIG2625	Volvo B10M-62	Plaxton Première 320	S70F	1994	Ulsterbus, 2007
	J	L408GDC	Volvo B6 9.9m	Plaxton Pointer	B40F	1994	Go North East, 2005
	B	LUI1522	Scania K113 CRB	Irizar Century 12.35	C49FT	1995	
	J	WPX852	Toyota Coaster HZB50R	Caetano Optimo III	C21F	1995	
	J	M849LFP	Volvo B10M-62	Caetano Algarve II	C53F	1995	
	J	M850LFP	Volvo B10M-62	Caetano Algarve II	C53F	1995	
	J	SIL3924	Volvo B10M-62	Caetano Algarve II	C53F	1996	Baker's, Biddulph, 2004

YP10VZB carries the latest livery style with Appleby's name as it works an Omega tour. It is from a batch of ten Scania OmniExpress coaches supplied to the group in 2010. *Mark Doggett*

	J	802AOJ	Volvo B10M-60	Jonckheere Mistral 50	C52F	1996	Park's of Hamilton, 1999
	J	112AXN	Volvo B10M-60	Jonckheere Mistral 50	C52F	1996	Park's of Hamilton, 1999
	J	3493CD	Volvo B10M-60	Jonckheere Mistral 50	C52F	1996	Park's of Hamilton, 1999
	J	XWG254	Volvo B10M-60	Jonckheere Mistral 50	C52F	1996	Park's of Hamilton, 1999
148	B	PUI6626	Scania K113 CRB	Irizar Century 12.35	C49FT	1997	
149	B	PUI6629	Scania K113 CRB	Irizar Century 12.35	C49FT	1997	
	J	VKX510	Volvo B10M-62	Plaxton Première 350	C53F	1997	Bus Eireann, 2002
	J	NUI4181	Volvo B10M-62	Caetano Algarve II	C49FT	1997	
W36	W	B10WTN	Volvo B10M-62	Plaxton Première 350	C53F	1997	Bysiau Cwm Taf, Whitland, 2005
W37	W	B7WTN	Volvo B10M-62	Plaxton Première 350	C53F	1998	Gordon's, Rotherham, 2005
W38	W	HSV673	Volvo B10M-62	Plaxton Première 350	C57F	1998	Country Lion, Northampton, 2005
	J	NKZ2490	Volvo B10M-62	Caetano Algarve II	C49FT	1998	
	J	YIL7713	Volvo B10M-62	Jonckheere Mistral 50	C53F	1998	Lochs & Glens, Aberfoyle, 2002
	J	LLZ5719	Volvo B10M-62	Jonckheere Mistral 50	C53F	1998	Park's of Hamilton, 2002
	J	NUI7726	Volvo B10M-62	Jonckheere Mistral 50	C49FT	1998	Park's of Hamilton, 2002
	J	FNZ7729	Volvo B10M-62	Jonckheere Mistral 50	C49FT	1998	Park's of Hamilton, 2002
	B	OVS822	Scania K113 TRB	Irizar Century 12.37	C49FT	1998	
	B	NUI1589	Scania K113 TRB	Irizar Century 12.37	C49FT	1998	
	A	NDO609	Scania K124 IB4	Irizar Century 12.35	C49FT	1998	
73	Y	XEA745	MAN 18.310	Noge Catalan 350	C49FT	1998	Yorks, Cogenhoe, 2004
74	Y	405MDV	MAN 18.310	Noge Catalan 350	C49FT	1999	Yorks, Cogenhoe, 2004
75	Y	TVY659	MAN 18.310	Noge Catalan 350	C49FT	1999	Yorks, Cogenhoe, 2004
76	B	593UXJ	MAN 18.310	Noge Catalan 350	C49FT	1999	
77	B	UOL387	MAN 18.310	Noge Catalan 350	C49FT	1999	
93	Y	KPR698	MAN 24.400	Noge Catalan 350	C49FT	1999	Yorks, Cogenhoe, 2004
104	B	VFJ627	Scania K124 IB6	Irizar Century 12.37	C49FT	1999	Applebys, Louth, 2000
61	A	TRX615	Scania K124 IB4	Irizar Century 12.35	C49FT	1999	Applebys, Louth, 2000
	B	ESU628	Scania K124 IB4	Irizar Century 12.35	C49FT	1999	Applebys, Louth, 2000
	B	W799KVL	Scania K124 IB4	Irizar Century 12.35	C49FT	2000	Applebys, Louth, 2000
	B	TSU324	Scania K124 IB4	Irizar Century 12.35	C49FT	2000	Applebys, Louth, 2000
151	B	W822BOM	Toyota Coaster BB50R	Caetano Optimo IV	C22F	2000	Yorks, Cogenhoe, 2004
22	B	V359POB	Toyota Coaster BB50R	Caetano Optimo IV	C22F	2000	
94	Y	W751AAY	MAN 24.400	Marcopolo Explorer 360	C49FT	2000	
752	B	XTJ802	MAN 18.310	Marcopolo Continental 340	C49FT	2000	
753	B	KFF917	MAN 18.310	Marcopolo Continental 340	C49FT	2000	

60	Y	XVY392	Volvo B10M-62	Plaxton Paragon	C48FT	2000	Wallce Arnold, Leeds, 2004
61	Y	UFC221	Volvo B10M-62	Plaxton Paragon	C48FT	2000	Wallce Arnold, Leeds, 2004
62	W	WBN106	Volvo B10M-62	Plaxton Paragon	C48FT	2000	Wallce Arnold, Leeds, 2004
	Y	VHM847	Volvo B10M-62	Plaxton Paragon	C48FT	2000	Wallce Arnold, Leeds, 2004
	J	ESK897	Volvo B10M-62	Plaxton Panther	C26FT	2000	Wallce Arnold, Leeds, 2003
	J	VNP893	Volvo B10M-62	Plaxton Paragon	C48FT	2000	Wallce Arnold, Leeds, 2003
	J	YSV815	Volvo B10M-62	Plaxton Paragon	C48FT	2000	Wallce Arnold, Leeds, 2003
	J	ESU635	Volvo B10M-62	Plaxton Paragon	C48FT	2000	Wallce Arnold, Leeds, 2003
	J	872KMY	Volvo B10M-62	Plaxton Paragon	C48FT	2000	Wallce Arnold, Leeds, 2003
	J	VVV66S	Irisbus EuroMidi CC80E18	Indcar Maxim	C29F	2001	
	J	147VKN	Irisbus EuroRider 391	Beulas Stergo E	C51F	2001	
	J	5615RO	Irisbus EuroRider 391	Beulas Stergo E	C49FT	2001	
70	Y	FSV305	MAN 18.310	Noge Catalan 350	C49FT	2002	
104	B	FN02HGJ	MAN 18.310	Noge Catalan 350	C49FT	2002	
100	B	SYK910	MAN 18.310	Noge Catalan 350	C49FT	2002	
106	B	WPX582	MAN 18.310	Noge Catalan 350	C49FT	2002	
57	Y	FN02HGX	Dennis Javelin GX	Marcopolo Continental 340	C48FT	2002	
58	Y	KPR698	Dennis Javelin GX	Marcopolo Continental 340	C48FT	2002	
	N	FP02YDK	Volvo B12M	Plaxton Panther	C53F	2002	
	N	FP02YDM	Volvo B12M	Plaxton Panther	C53F	2002	
	N	FP02YDN	Volvo B12M	Plaxton Panther	C53F	2002	
	N	YE03VSK	Bova Futura FHD 12.340	Bova	C49FT	2003	
M20	B	KX03OYE	Volkswagen Transporter	Volkswagen	M7	2003	
M10	Y	ET04FSS	Volkswagen Transporter	Volkswagen	M7	2004	
M19	B	ET04FRN	Volkswagen Transporter	Volkswagen	M7	2004	
	B	YJB717	Scania K114 EB4	Irizar Century 12.35	C39FT	2004	
	B	NDO619	Scania K114 EB4	Irizar Century 12.35	C49FT	2004	
101	B	YN05HFM	Scania K124 IB4	Irizar Century 12.35	C49FT	2005	
102	B	622HFJ	Scania K124 IB4	Irizar Century 12.35	C40FT	2005	
103	B	XHO856	Scania K124 IB4	Irizar Century 12.35	C49FT	2005	
	N	YN55KWV	Irisbus EuroRider 397 E.12.35	Beulas Cygnus	C49FT	2006	
	N	YN55KWW	Irisbus EuroRider 397 E.12.35	Beulas Cygnus	C49FT	2006	
	N	YN55KWX	Irisbus EuroRider 397 E.12.35	Beulas Cygnus	C49FT	2006	
49	Y	YN06CHV	Scania K114 EB4	Irizar Century 12.35	C49FT	2006	
	B	YN07LJV	Scania K114 EB4	Irizar Century 12.35	C40FT	2006	
M1	Y	KR06TVF	Volkswagen Transporter	Volkswagen	M7	2006	
M2	Y	KR06TVJ	Volkswagen Transporter	Volkswagen	M7	2006	
M3	Y	KR06TVK	Volkswagen Transporter	Volkswagen	M7	2006	
M4	Y	KR06TVL	Volkswagen Transporter	Volkswagen	M7	2006	
M5	Y	KR06TVM	Volkswagen Transporter	Volkswagen	M7	2006	
M6	Y	KR06TVN	Volkswagen Transporter	Volkswagen	M7	2006	
M7	Y	KR06TVO	Volkswagen Transporter	Volkswagen	M7	2006	
M8	Y	KR06TVP	Volkswagen Transporter	Volkswagen	M7	2006	
M9	Y	KR06TVT	Volkswagen Transporter	Volkswagen	M7	2006	
M11	B	KR06TVU	Volkswagen Transporter	Volkswagen	M7	2006	
M12	B	KR06TVV	Volkswagen Transporter	Volkswagen	M7	2006	
M13	B	KR06TVW	Volkswagen Transporter	Volkswagen	M7	2006	
M14	B	KR06TVX	Volkswagen Transporter	Volkswagen	M7	2006	
M15	B	KR06TVY	Volkswagen Transporter	Volkswagen	M7	2006	
M16	B	KR06TVZ	Volkswagen Transporter	Volkswagen	M7	2006	
M17	B	KR06TWA	Volkswagen Transporter	Volkswagen	M7	2006	
M18	B	KR06TWC	Volkswagen Transporter	Volkswagen	M7	2006	
W44	W	YN06MXW	Volvo B12B	Plaxton Panther	C49FT	2006	
W46	W	W100TEN	Volvo B12B	Plaxton Panther	C49FT	2006	
80	B	YN07DZV	Irisbus EuroRider 397 E.12.35	Beulas Cygnus	C49FT	2007	
81	B	YN07DZU	Irisbus EuroRider 397 E.12.35	Beulas Cygnus	C49FT	2007	
	N	YN07DZW	Irisbus EuroRider 397 E.12.35	Beulas Cygnus	C49FT	2007	
	B	FJ07VWR	Volvo B12B	Jonckheere SHV	C53F	2007	City Circle, Hayes, 2011
	B	WA07BGY	Mercedes-Benz Vario O816	Sitcar Beluga 2	C27F	2007	Anderson, Bermondsey, 2011
	B	EO08KWN	Ford Transit	Ford	M8	2008	
	B	CP08JBY	Ford Transit	Ford	M8	2008	Days' Rental, 2011
50	B	YN08OBW	Scania K124 IB4	Irizar Century 12.35	C49FT	2008	
	J	YN08NWV	Volvo B12B	Plaxton Panther	C53F	2008	
63	B	YN08OWC	Volvo B12B	Plaxton Panther	C49FT	2008	
64	B	YN08OWD	Volvo B12B	Plaxton Panther	C49FT	2008	
200	B	YN08OWF	Volvo B12B	Plaxton Panther	C49FT	2008	
201	B	YN08OWG	Volvo B12B	Plaxton Panther	C49FT	2008	
202	B	YN08OWH	Volvo B12B	Plaxton Panther	C49FT	2008	
	N	YN58CGF	Volvo B12B	Plaxton Panther	C53F	2008	
	J	YN58CGE	Volvo B12B	Plaxton Panther	C48FT	2008	
	B	YT09FLX	Scania OmniExpress K340 EB4	Scania	C44FT	2009	
	Y	YX10FFR	Volvo B12B	Plaxton Panther	C53F	2010	

Bowens' name features on six of the OmniExpress coaches. Here 302, YP10VZF, is seen rounding Marble Arch shortly after delivery. *Colin Lloyd*

65	Y	YX10FFP	Volvo B12B	Plaxton Panther	C53F	2010
66	Y	YX10FFS	Volvo B12B	Plaxton Panther	C53F	2010
67	Y	YX10FFT	Volvo B12B	Plaxton Panther	C53F	2010
68	Y	YX10FFU	Volvo B12B	Plaxton Panther	C53F	2010
	A	YP10VZA	Scania OmniExpress K400 EB4	Scania	C51FT	2010
	A	YP10VZB	Scania OmniExpress K400 EB4	Scania	C51FT	2010
	A	YP10VZC	Scania OmniExpress K400 EB4	Scania	C51FT	2010
	A	YP10VZD	Scania OmniExpress K400 EB4	Scania	C51FT	2010
301	B	YP10VZE	Scania OmniExpress K400 EB4	Scania	C51FT	2010
302	B	YP10VZF	Scania OmniExpress K400 EB4	Scania	C51FT	2010
303	B	YP10VZG	Scania OmniExpress K400 EB4	Scania	C51FT	2010
304	B	YP10VZH	Scania OmniExpress K400 EB4	Scania	C51FT	2010
305	B	YP10VZJ	Scania OmniExpress K400 EB4	Scania	C51FT	2010
306	B	YP10VZK	Scania OmniExpress K400 EB4	Scania	C44FT	2010
	B	BG10WCL	Volkswagen Transporter	Volkswagen	M8	2010
	B	BG10WCM	Volkswagen Transporter	Volkswagen	M8	2010
M21	B	BG10WCN	Volkswagen Transporter	Volkswagen	M8	2010
M26	B	BG10WCO	Volkswagen Transporter	Volkswagen	M8	2010
W70	W	YN60FMV	Volvo B12B	Plaxton Panther	C53FT	2010
W71	W	YN60FMX	Volvo B12B	Plaxton Panther	C53FT	2010
	A	BJ11UDY	Volkswagen Transporter	Volkswagen	M5	2011

Depots: Canters Close, Brandesburton (A); Short Lane, Cogenhoe (Y); Lycrome Road, Chesham (W); Julian Street, Grimsby (A); Old Station Yard, Helmdon (J); George Street, Lincoln (A); Ashby Road Central, Shepshed (N); Keeling Street, North Somercotes (A); Lichfield Industrial Estate, Tamworth (B) and High Street, Witney (J).
Web: www.jeffscoaches.com

Previous registrations:

112AXN	M628FNS	NKZ2490	R490UFP
147VKN	Y807YBC	NUI1589	-
195JOH	J473NJU	NUI4181	P181ANR
279JJO	J477NJU	NUI7726	LSK835, T726UOS
405MDV	T191SUT	OHN173	W799KVL
487VYA	L35CAY	OUI3916	-
593UXJ	T193SUT	OUI3918	E70LVV, UFC221
622HFJ	YN05HFO	OUI3920	-
647PJO	J474NJU	OUI4659	-
802AOJ	M627FNS	OUI4797	-
846FHA	K121OCT	OVS822	P388WVL
872KMY	W636FUM	PUI6626	P148GHE
938HNM	L39CAY	PUI6629	P149GHE
3493CD	M629FNS	RUI5290	G880VNA, WSV528, G791YND, HSK511
5615RO	Y809YBC	SIL3924	N789SJU, 8399RU
A12WTN	A127ESG, VLT93	SIJ405	BAJ637Y, 2090VT, DFP492Y, MIA2192, YOI139, DBZ918, DFP492Y
ABW310X	VUD33X	SYK901	N566AWJ
B7WNT	R186TKU, B12WTN	TGY698	J475NJU
B8WTN	F341XFR, PBV779	TRX615	T814RTL
B10WTN	P288ENT	TSU324	W816XEE
B11WTN	D315SGB, WLT943	TVY659	T192SUT
BIG2625	DAZ1557	UFC221	W615FUM
EIG8588	F992MTW, VHM847	UOL387	T194SUT
ESK896	FN02HGX	VBW846	J472NJU
ESK897	W603FUM, 7820WA	VFJ627	FN02HGJ
ESU628	T849JFU	VKX510	97D45867, R620BAY
ESU635	W635FUM	VHM847	X662NWY,8665WA
FNZ7729	KSK981, 7729UOS	VNP893	W607FUM
FSV305	FN02HGG	VVV66S	T865JBC
FSV720	J476NJU	VXT571	L38CAY
G907WAY	G907WAY, PSV815	W100TEN	YN06MXY
G908WAY	G908WAY, ESU635	WBN106	W606FUM
G910WAY	G910WAY, 147VYN	WPX852	FN02HGM
G911WAY	G911WAY, VNP893	WWW883	VSS5X, WLT921, MSL185X, KIB6527, VLT217, MSL469X
G912WAY	G912WAY, 872KMY	XEA745	R638VNN
HSK511	V359POB	XHO856	FN02HGY
HSV673	R551TKV, A20CLC	XTJ802	W752AAY
KFF917	W753AAY	XVY392	W604FUM
OUI3914	E655UNE, LSK839, E619CDS, ESK897	XWG254	M630FNS
KPR698	FN02HGU	YIL7713	HSK644, T713UOS
JIL2199	THL290Y, YSV318	YJI6038	K713RNR
LLZ5719	HSK650, T719UOS	YJI8597	K714RNR
LUI7871	E607VNW, A20MCW, XEA745	YJB717	YN54APY
NDO609	YN54APZ	YSV815	W633FUM

Showing Jeffs' livery is Plaxton-bodied Volvo B10M-62 ESK897, one of several of the Panther model in the fleet that were new to Wallace Arnold, the Yorkshire operator now part of Shearings. *Mark Doggett*

BUZZLINES

Buzzlines Ltd; Buzzlines Travel Ltd, G1 Lympne Industrial Estate, Hythe, CT21 4LR

Reg	Chassis	Body	Seating	Year	Previous owner
N623RAP	Volvo Olympian	Alexander RH	B47/31F	1996	Dublin Bus, 2009
NBZ2248	Toyota Coaster HZB50R	Caetano Optimo III	C18F	1996	Advantage Travel, Gorebridge, '00
VX53AVF	Mercedes-Benz Sprinter 413 cdi	Advanced	M16	2004	
SB04BUZ	Toyota Coaster BB50R	Caetano Optimo IV	C26F	2004	
AE54HYU	TransBus Dart	Caetano Compass	N28F	2004	NCP, West Drayton, 2010
GX05AVV	ADL Dart 8.8m	ADL Mini Pointer	NC29F	2005	
UK06BUZ	Setra S416 GT-HD	Setra	C49FT	2006	
B12PRE	Setra S415 GT-HD	Setra	C49FT	2008	Prestige, Renfrew, 2010
B20PRE	Setra S415 GT-HD	Setra	C49FT	2008	Prestige, Renfrew, 2010
BU08BZA	Toyota Coaster XHB50R	Caetano Optimo VI	C22F	2008	Pagan, Heston, 2011
BV58MKK	Mercedes-Benz Tourismo OC510	Mercedes-Benz	C51FT	2009	Shaws, Chadderton, 2010
BK09RLZ	Setra S416 GT-HD	Setra	C49FT	2009	D Coaches, Morriston, 2011
BK09WSY	Setra S416 GT-HD	Setra	C49FT	2009	Harrison, King's Lynn, 2011
YT10ASO	Ford Transit	Ford	M8	2010	
BF60OFZ	Setra S416 GT-HD	Setra	C53FT	2010	
YR60AAZ	Ford Transit	Ford	M8	2010	
YR60AGZ	Ford Transit	Ford	M8	2010	
YR60AKU	Ford Transit	Ford	M8	2010	
YR60AUJ	Ford Transit	Ford	M8	2010	
YR60AUM	Ford Transit	Ford	M8	2010	
PE11KGZ	Neoplan Tourliner N2216/3 SHD	Neoplan	C58FT	2011	Mearns, East Kilbride, 2012
WP11BCK	Mercedes-Benz Sprinter 413 cdi	Mercedes-Benz	M16	2011	
WP11LWW	Mercedes-Benz Sprinter 516 cdi	Mercedes-Benz	M16	2011	
WP11LWX	Mercedes-Benz Sprinter 516 cdi	Mercedes-Benz	M16	2011	
YN61AXW	Irizar i6	Irizar	C59FT	2011	
YN61AXX	Irizar i6	Irizar	C53FT	2011	

Previous registrations:

KB04BUZ	AK04LFL	NBZ2248	P773BJF
N623RAP	96D271		

Web: www.buzzlines.co.uk

BU08BZA is a Toyota Coaster with Caetano Optimo VI bodywork. It is seen in Kingston-upon-Thames.
Dave Heath

CASTLEWAYS

Castleways (Winchcombe) Ltd, Castle House, Greet Road, Winchcombe, GL54 5PU

TJF757	Setra S250	Setra Special	C53F	1996	Travellers, Hounslow, 1998
86JBF	Setra S250	Setra Special	C48FT	1997	Travellers, Hounslow, 1999
V200OCC	Setra S315 GT-HD	Setra	C48FT	2000	
W391JOG	Toyota Coaster BB50R	Caetano Optimo IV	C22F	2000	
BX02CME	Mercedes-Benz Citaro O530	Mercedes-Benz	N38F	2002	
YN03NJE	Volvo B7R	Plaxton Profile	S70F	2003	
BX54ECN	Mercedes-Benz Citaro O530	Mercedes-Benz	N42F	2004	
MX06XMM	Ford Transit	Ford	M7	2006	Fiveway, Codsall, 2007
FJ06BNV	Volvo B7R	Sunsundegui Sideral 330	C53F	2006	
MX07BBN	Optare Solo M950	Optare	N31F	2007	Tussauds, Alton, 2010
YJ07DVZ	VDL Bova Futura FHD 10.340	VDL Bova	C38FT	2007	
YJ58FGO	Temsa Safari HD	Temsa	C57F	2008	
YJ59NNR	Optare Versa V1040	Optare	N38F	2009	

Previous registrations:

86JBF	P200TCC		V200OCC	V200DCC
TJF757	N205PUL			

Web: www.castleways.co.uk

Seen though a telephoto lens as it leaves Netterton is FJ06BNV, a Volvo B7R with Sunsundegui Sideral 330 bodywork. *Colin Martin*

CHALFONT

Chalfont Coaches of Harrow Ltd, 200 Featherstone Road, Southall, UB2 5AQ

WA03EYL	Volvo B12M	Van Hool T9 Alizée	C53FT	2003
WA56ENM	Volvo B12M	Van Hool T9 Alizée	C53FT	2006
WA57JZR	VDL Bova Futura FLD120.365	VDL Bova	S70F	2007
WX57DXY	Mercedes-Benz Sprinter 311cdi	Concept	M16	2007
WA57JZT	Volvo B12B	Van Hool T9 Alizée	C53FT	2007
WA57JZU	Volvo B12B	Van Hool T9 Alizée	C57F	2008
WA57JZV	Volvo B12B	Van Hool T9 Alizée	C53FT	2008
WA09AZC	Volvo B12B	Van Hool T917 Alicron	C53FT	2009
WA59EBC	Volvo B12B	Van Hool T917 Alicron	C53FT	2009
WA10ENJ	VDL Bova Futura FLD127.365	VDL Bova	S75F	2010
WA10ENK	Volvo B12B	Van Hool T9 Alizée	C49FT	2010
WA10ENL	Volvo B12B	Van Hool T9 Alizée	C49FT	2010
WA10ENM	Volvo B12B	Van Hool T9 Alizée	C53FT	2010
WA60DZG	Volvo B12B	Van Hool T9 Alizée	C49FT	2010
WA61AKF	Volvo B13B	Van Hool T9 Alizée	C53FT	2011
WA61AKP	Volvo B13B	Van Hool T9 Alizée	C53FT	2011
WA61AKU	Volvo B13B	Van Hool T9 Alizée	C53FT	2011
FJ61EWN	Volvo B9R	Caetano Levanté	C48FT	2011
FJ61EWO	Volvo B9R	Caetano Levanté	C48FT	2011

Web: www.chalfontcoaches.co.uk

In addition to two Caetano Levanté-bodied coaches dedicated to National Express work, the Chalfont fleet comprises mostly of Van Hool-bodied Volvo products. Representing the fleet is WA57JZV, seen near Victoria rail station. *Dave Heath*

R W CHENERY

P G Garnham & J M McGraffin, The Garage, Norwich Road, Dickleburgh, Diss, IP21 4NJ

GEL504Y	Kässbohrer Setra S215 HR	Kässbohrer Setra Rational	C53F	1984	Solent, Ringwood, 2002
TIA5599	Kässbohrer Setra S215 HR	Kässbohrer Setra Rational	C53F	1989	Dunn-Line, Nottingham, 2001
RYG684	Kässbohrer Setra S250	Kässbohrer Setra Special	C48FT	1993	Tellings-Golden Miller, 2002
NBU707	Kässbohrer Setra S250	Kässbohrer Setra Special	C45FT	1995	Tellings-Golden Miller, 2002
SPV555	Setra S250	Setra Special	C53F	1996	Pullmanor, Herne Hill, 2001
UPV337	Setra S250	Setra Special	C48FT	1996	Tellings-Golden Miller, 2002
PPY238	Setra S250	Setra Special	C48FT	1997	Stort Valley, Stansted, 2002
R102HEV	Setra S250	Setra Special	C48FT	1998	Heritage, Sturminster, 2006
5092EL	Setra S250	Setra Special	C53F	1998	Clarkes of London, 2007
2508EL	Setra S250	Setra Special	C53F	1998	Clarkes of London, 2007
NBN922	Setra S250	Setra Special	C48FT	1999	
T777RWC	Setra S315 GT-HD	Setra	C49FT	1999	
BNG444Y	Setra S315 GT-HD	Setra	C48FT	2000	Patterson, Seahouses, 2007
W354EOL	Setra S315 GT-HD	Setra	C48FT	2000	Safeguard, Guildford, 2006
XBL333	Setra S315 GT-HD	Setra	C49FT	2000	Evobus demonstrator, 2000
J888RWC	Setra S315 GT-HD	Setra	C49FT	2002	Clarkes of London, 2010
P888RWC	Setra S315 GT-HD	Setra	C49FT	2002	Clarkes of London, 2010
N999RWC	Volvo B12B	VDL Jonckheere Mistral 50	C49FT	2005	
FJ05AOV	Volvo B12B	VDL Jonckheere Mistral 50	C49FT	2005	
FJ05AOX	Volvo B12B	VDL Jonckheere Mistral 50	C49FT	2005	
AY57EZS	Setra S416 GT-HD	Setra	C46FT	2007	Galloway, Stowmarket, 2012
FJ11MKA	Volvo B9R	Caetano Levanté	C48FT	2011	
FJ11MKC	Volvo B9R	Caetano Levanté	C48FT	2011	

Previous registrations:

2508EL	R128NFE
5092EL	R892MTL
BNG444Y	W282TRX, TTC86, 8325MW
GEL504Y	A70FPH, NIW6503
J888RWC	LV51ZHK
N999RWC	FJ05AOW
NBN922	T390SBJ, 920ACH, T888RWC
NBU707	4019MW, M838GGJ

P888RWC	R102HEV, A5UNF, J555SOM
PPY238	P500TCC
R102HEV	R102HEV, J55SOM, A5UNF
RYG684	4967MW, M831GGJ
SPV555	N207PUL
TIA5599	F179OVL
UPV337	6963MW, N882JLW
XBL333	W408HOB

Web: www.chenerytravel.co.uk

Chenery was one of the first fleets to favour Setra products after its introduction to the British market in 1972. Several pre-1995 examples from when the manufacturer used the Kässbohrer name remain in this fleet. S250 Special SPV555 is shown. *Colin Martin*

CITY CIRCLE

City Circle UK Ltd, The West London Coach Centre, North Hyde Gardens, Hayes, UB3 4QT

10	L	YN10FLA	Mercedes-Benz Vario O816	Plaxton Cheetah 2	C25F	2010
11	E	YN10FLB	Mercedes-Benz Vario O816	Plaxton Cheetah 2	C25F	2010
16	E	YN57AEZ	Neoplan Tourliner N2216 SHD	Neoplan	C49FT	2008
17	L	YJ08DXC	Van Hool T911 Alicron	Van Hool	C36FT	2008
18	E	YJ08DXD	Van Hool T911 Alicron	Van Hool	C36FT	2008
19	L	YJ08DXE	Van Hool T911 Alicron	Van Hool	C36FT	2008
20	E	YJ08DXF	Van Hool T911 Alicron	Van Hool	C36FT	2008
21	E	YN58OKT	Neoplan Tourliner N2216 SHD	Neoplan	C49FT	2009
22	E	YN58OKU	Neoplan Tourliner N2216 SHD	Neoplan	C49FT	2009
23	E	YN58OKV	Neoplan Tourliner N2216 SHD	Neoplan	C49FT	2009
24	E	YN58OKW	Neoplan Tourliner N2216 SHD	Neoplan	C49FT	2009
25	L	MX10DFJ	Neoplan Tourliner N400X SHD	Neoplan	C49FT	2010
26	L	MX10DFK	Neoplan Tourliner N400X SHD	Neoplan	C49FT	2010
31	E	MJ11DHG	Neoplan Tourliner N2216 SHD	Neoplan	C51FT	2011
32	E	MJ11LVP	Neoplan Tourliner N2216 SHD	Neoplan	C51FT	2011
35	L	MJ11WKU	Neoplan Tourliner N2216 SHD	Neoplan	C51FT	2011
36	E	MJ11WKV	Neoplan Tourliner N2216 SHD	Neoplan	C51FT	2011
37	E	MJ11LVR	Neoplan Tourliner N2216 SHD	Neoplan	C51FT	2011
38	E	PJ12ATU	Neoplan Tourliner N2216/3 SHD	Neoplan	C51FT	2012
39	E	PJ12ATV	Neoplan Tourliner N2216/3 SHD	Neoplan	C51FT	2012
40	L	PJ12ATX	Neoplan Tourliner N2216/3 SHD	Neoplan	C51FT	2012
41	L	PJ12ATY	Neoplan Tourliner N2216/3 SHD	Neoplan	C51FT	2012
42	L	PJ12ATZ	Neoplan Tourliner N2216/3 SHD	Neoplan	C51FT	2012
43	L	BN08OOC	Setra S415 HD	Setra	C49FT	2008
44	L	BN08OOD	Setra S415 HD	Setra	C49FT	2008
45	L	BN08OOE	Setra S415 HD	Setra	C49FT	2008
46	L	BN08OOF	Setra S415 HD	Setra	C49FT	2008
47	L	BN08OOG	Setra S415 HD	Setra	C49FT	2008
48	L	BK08XYD	Setra S415 HD	Setra	C49FT	2008
49	L	BK08XYE	Setra S415 HD	Setra	C49FT	2008
50	L	BK08XYF	Setra S415 HD	Setra	C49FT	2008
51	L	BK08XYG	Setra S415 HD	Setra	C49FT	2008
52	L	BK08XYH	Setra S415 HD	Setra	C49FT	2008
53	E	YJ10DJY	VDL Bus SB4000	Van Hool T9 Alizée	C51FT	2010
54	L	BD60XSR	Mercedes-Benz Tourismo O315	Mercedes-Benz	C49FT	2011
55	L	BD60XST	Mercedes-Benz Tourismo O315	Mercedes-Benz	C49FT	2011
56	L	BD60XSU	Mercedes-Benz Tourismo O315	Mercedes-Benz	C49FT	2011
57	L	BD60XSV	Mercedes-Benz Tourismo O315	Mercedes-Benz	C49FT	2011
58	L	BD60XSW	Mercedes-Benz Tourismo O315	Mercedes-Benz	C49FT	2011
59	L	BD60XSX	Mercedes-Benz Tourismo O315	Mercedes-Benz	C49FT	2011
60	L	BD60XSY	Mercedes-Benz Tourismo O315	Mercedes-Benz	C49FT	2011
61	L	BD60XSZ	Mercedes-Benz Tourismo O315	Mercedes-Benz	C49FT	2011
62	L	YN11FVC	Mercedes-Benz Vario O816	Plaxton Cheetah 2	C25F	2011
63	L	YN11FVD	Mercedes-Benz Vario O816	Plaxton Cheetah 2	C25F	2011
64	L	YN11FVE	Mercedes-Benz Vario O816	Plaxton Cheetah 2	C25F	2011
65	L	PE12OXF	Neoplan Tourliner N2216/3 SHD	Neoplan	C51FT	2012
66	L	PE12OXG	Neoplan Tourliner N2216/3 SHD	Neoplan	C51FT	2012
67	L	PE12OXH	Neoplan Tourliner N2216/3 SHD	Neoplan	C51FT	2012
68	L	PE12OXJ	Neoplan Tourliner N2216/3 SHD	Neoplan	C51FT	2012
69	L	PE12OXK	Neoplan Tourliner N2216/3 SHD	Neoplan	C51FT	2012
70	L	PE12OXL	Neoplan Tourliner N2216/3 SHD	Neoplan	C51FT	2012

Web: www.citycircleuk.com; **Depots:** Butterfield Industrial Estate, Bonnyrigg, Edinburgh (E) and North Hyde, Hayes (L).

Please see page 73 for a picture.

CLARKES OF LONDON

E Clarke & Son (Coaches) Ltd, Kangley Bridge Road, Lower Sydenham, SE26 5AT

LW52AKK	Setra S315 GT-HD		Setra	C49FT	2003
LW52AKN	Setra S315 GT-HD		Setra	C49FT	2003
BU03LYS	Setra S415 HD		Setra	C49FT	2003
BX05UVJ	Setra S315 GT-HD		Setra	C49FT	2005
BX05UVK	Setra S315 GT-HD		Setra	C49FT	2005
FJ06URB	Toyota Coaster BB50R		Caetano Optimo V	C18F	2006
FJ06URC	Toyota Coaster BB50R		Caetano Optimo V	C18F	2006
FJ06URD	Toyota Coaster BB50R		Caetano Optimo V	C18F	2006
FJ06URE	Toyota Coaster BB50R		Caetano Optimo V	C18F	2006
YN06NYU	Scania K114 EB4		Irizar Century Style	C53F	2006
YN06NYV	Scania K114 EB4		Irizar Century Style	C53F	2006
YN06NYW	Scania K114 EB4		Irizar Century Style	C53F	2006
YN07LDJ	Scania K310 EB4		Irizar Capacity	C53F	2007
YN07LDK	Scania K310 EB4		Irizar Capacity	C53F	2007
YN07LDL	Scania K310 EB4		Irizar Capacity	C53F	2007
YN07LDO	Scania K310 EB4		Irizar Capacity	C53F	2007
YN07LDU	Scania K310 EB4		Irizar Capacity	C53F	2007
YN08HZA	Scania K340 EB4	12.9m	VDL Berkhof Axial 70	C53FT	2008
YN08HZB	Scania K340 EB4	12.9m	VDL Berkhof Axial 70	C53FT	2008
YN08HZC	Scania K340 EB4	12.9m	VDL Berkhof Axial 70	C53FT	2008
YN08HZD	Scania K340 EB4	12.9m	VDL Berkhof Axial 70	C53FT	2008
YN08HZE	Scania K340 EB4	12.9m	VDL Berkhof Axial 70	C53FT	2008
YN08HZF	Scania K340 EB4	12.9m	VDL Berkhof Axial 70	C53FT	2008
YN08HZG	Scania K340 EB4	12.9m	VDL Berkhof Axial 70	C53FT	2008
BD08DZV	Setra S416 GT-HD		Setra	C34FT	2008
BF58UEV	Setra S416 GT-HD		Setra	C34FT	2009
BN58BKD	Setra S415 HD		Setra	C34FT	2009
BF58BJZ	Setra S415 HD		Setra	C49FT	2009

Recent arrivals with Clarkes of London have been Mercedes-Benz products. This follows a period when Scania chassis were favoured. From the 2008 delivery, Scania YN08HZD illustrates the VDL Berkhof Axial 70 body as it passes along Park Lane in London. *Dave Heath*

One of three Irizar Century Style coaches currently operated by Clarkes of London, YN06NYW is seen near Waterloo Bridge. For several years after their introduction to Britain in 1993, Irizar products were imported exclusively on Scania chassis. *Steve Rice*

BV10ZKA	Mercedes-Benz Tourismo O315	Mercedes-Benz	C49FT	2010
BV10ZKB	Mercedes-Benz Tourismo O315	Mercedes-Benz	C49FT	2010
BV10ZKC	Mercedes-Benz Tourismo O315	Mercedes-Benz	C49FT	2010
BV10ZKD	Mercedes-Benz Tourismo O315	Mercedes-Benz	C49FT	2010
BV10ZKE	Mercedes-Benz Tourismo O315	Mercedes-Benz	C49FT	2010
BV10ZKF	Mercedes-Benz Tourismo O315	Mercedes-Benz	C49FT	2010
BV10ZKG	Mercedes-Benz Tourismo O315	Mercedes-Benz	C49FT	2010
BV10ZKH	Mercedes-Benz Tourismo O315	Mercedes-Benz	C49FT	2010
BV10ZKJ	Mercedes-Benz Tourismo O315	Mercedes-Benz	C49FT	2010
BV10ZKK	Mercedes-Benz Tourismo O315	Mercedes-Benz	C49FT	2010
BV10ZKM	Setra S416 GT-HD	Setra	C34FT	2010
BN11UGA	Mercedes-Benz Tourismo O315	Mercedes-Benz	C51FT	2011
BN11UGB	Mercedes-Benz Tourismo O315	Mercedes-Benz	C51FT	2011
BN11UGC	Mercedes-Benz Tourismo O315	Mercedes-Benz	C51FT	2011
BN11UGD	Mercedes-Benz Tourismo O315	Mercedes-Benz	C51FT	2011
BN11UGE	Mercedes-Benz Tourismo O315	Mercedes-Benz	C51FT	2011
BN11UGF	Mercedes-Benz Tourismo O315	Mercedes-Benz	C51FT	2011
BN11UGG	Mercedes-Benz Tourismo O315	Mercedes-Benz	C51FT	2011
BN11UGH	Mercedes-Benz Tourismo O315	Mercedes-Benz	C51FT	2011
BN11UGJ	Mercedes-Benz Tourismo O315	Mercedes-Benz	C51FT	2011
BN11UGK	Mercedes-Benz Tourismo O315	Mercedes-Benz	C51FT	2011
BN11UGL	Setra S416 GT-HD	Setra	C49FT	2011
BF61HCH	Mercedes-Benz Tourismo O315	Mercedes-Benz	C51FT	2011
BF61HCJ	Mercedes-Benz Tourismo O315	Mercedes-Benz	C51FT	2011
BF61HCK	Mercedes-Benz Tourismo O315	Mercedes-Benz	C51FT	2011
BF61HCL	Mercedes-Benz Tourismo O315	Mercedes-Benz	C51FT	2011
BF61HCN	Mercedes-Benz Tourismo O315	Mercedes-Benz	C51FT	2011
BF61HCO	Mercedes-Benz Tourismo O315	Mercedes-Benz	C51FT	2011
BF61HCP	Mercedes-Benz Tourismo O315	Mercedes-Benz	C51FT	2011
BF61HCX	Mercedes-Benz Tourismo O315	Mercedes-Benz	C51FT	2011
BF61HCY	Mercedes-Benz Tourismo O315	Mercedes-Benz	C51FT	2011

Web: www.clarkescoaches.co.uk

COMPASS ROYSTON

Compass Royston - Procters - Dales & District - Esk Valley
Compass Royston Travel Ltd, Bowesfield Lane, Stockton-on-Tees, TS18 3EG
K J Procter, Leases Farm, Leeming Bar, DL7 9DE
CW Simpson, Fairfield Way, Whitby, YO22 4PU
Procters Coaches (North Yorkshire) Ltd, Tutin Road, Leeming Bar, DL7 9UJ

E	OUI6364	Volvo B10M-61(1981)	Plaxton Paramount 3500	C49FT	1983	Booth & Wright, Wigham, 2002
S	PBZ8343	Volvo B10M-61	Plaxton Supreme V	S72F	1983	
S	HIL9271	Volvo B10M-61	Plaxton Paramount 3200	C53F	1983	Essex Coachways, Bow, 1997
E	YOI7757	Volvo B10M-61	Van Hool Alizée	C53F	1986	SMS, Towcester, 2007
S	JUI6176	Volvo B10M-61	Van Hool Alizée	C54FT	1987	MacLeod, Rogart, 2005
P	OIL3046	DAF SBR3000	Van Hool Astrobel	C16CT	1988	Nicholson, Hesleden, 2006
S	KIB7257	Volvo B10M-61	Plaxton Paramount 3200 III	S72F	1988	Gordon's, Rotherham, 2002
P	LSU954	Volvo B10M-60	Plaxton Paramount 3200 III	C57F	1988	
S	F408DUG	Volvo B10M-60	Plaxton Paramount 3500 III	C48FT	1989	First, 2006
E	F435DUG	Volvo B10M-60	Plaxton Paramount 3200 III	C57F	1989	Stainthorpe, Skelton, 2011
P	MSU462	Volvo B10M-60	Plaxton Paramount 3500 III	C53F	1989	Messenger, Aspatria, 1997
E	F202GAW	Volvo B10M-60	Plaxton Paramount 3500 III	S70F	1989	Clynnog & Trefor, 2008
S	MIW9046	Volvo B10M-60	Plaxton Paramount 3500 III	C53F	1990	Dodsworth, Boroughbridge, 1994
S	LIL9815	Volvo B10M-60	Plaxton Paramount 3500 III	C50F	1990	Wallce Arnold, Leeds, 1994
S	LIL9816	Volvo B10M-60	Plaxton Paramount 3500 III	C52F	1990	Wallce Arnold, Leeds, 1994
S	NIL5905	Volvo B10M-60	Plaxton Paramount 3500 III	C57F	1991	Dixon, Billingham, 2008
E	NUI7645	Volvo B10M-60	Plaxton Paramount 3500 III	C53F	1991	Stainthorpe, Skelton, 2010
E	D20SMS	Volvo B10M-60	Van Hool Alizée H	C53F	1991	SMS, Towcaster, 2007
S	J171CNU	Mercedes-Benz 709D	Plaxton Beaver	B29F	1991	Porteus, Hull, 2006
S	J172CNU	Mercedes-Benz 709D	Plaxton Beaver	B29F	1991	Porteus, Hull, 2006
P	K796GAK	Ford Transit	Advanced	M8	1992	Young, Copmanthorpe, 2000
P	OSU386	Volvo B10M-60	Plaxton Première 320	S70F	1992	Stainton, Kendal, 2006
P	WSU873	Volvo B10M-60	Plaxton Première 320	S70F	1993	Smith's, Ashington, 2005
S	YIL1227	Volvo B10M-60	Van Hool Alizée HE	C46FT	1993	Shearings, Wigan, 2000
S	YIL1229	Volvo B10M-60	Van Hool Alizée HE	C46FT	1993	Shearings, Wigan, 2000
S	YIL1230	Volvo B10M-60	Van Hool Alizée HE	C53F	1993	Shearings, Wigan, 2000
E	L170PDO	Mercedes-Benz 609D	ACI	C23F	1993	Maiden, Scarborough, 2011
S	K355VRU	Volvo B10M-60	Plaxton Première 350	C49FT	1993	Teneke Travel, Newport, 2009
S	L8TCC	Volvo B10M-62	Plaxton Première 350	S70F	1994	Esk Valley, Whitby, 2006
P	L5BNM	Neoplan Skyliner N122/3	Neoplan	C57/16CT	1994	Bromwich, Southam, 2010
E	M21GAT	Volvo B10M-62	Plaxton Excalibur	C49FT	1994	Belle, Hull, 2009
E	M660VJB	Volvo B10M-62	Plaxton Excalibur	C49FT	1994	Horseman, Reading, 2011
E	M661VJB	Volvo B10M-62	Plaxton Excalibur	C49FT	1994	Horseman, Reading, 2011
S	YIL1223	Volvo B10M-62	Van Hool Alizée HE	C53F	1995	Shearings, Wigan, 2003
S	YIL1224	Volvo B10M-62	Van Hool Alizée HE	C49F	1995	Shearings, Wigan, 2003
S	YIL1225	Volvo B10M-62	Van Hool Alizée HE	C46FT	1995	Shearings, Wigan, 2003
S	YIL1226	Volvo B10M-62	Van Hool Alizée HE	C49F	1995	Shearings, Wigan, 2003
S	YIL1227	Volvo B10M-62	Van Hool Alizée HE	C53F	1995	Shearings, Wigan, 2003
S	YIL1229	Volvo B10M-62	Van Hool Alizée HE	C53F	1995	Shearings, Wigan, 2003
S	YIL1230	Volvo B10M-62	Van Hool Alizée HE	C53F	1995	Shearings, Wigan, 2003
P	M964RKJ	Ford Transit	Devon Conversions	B13F	1995	Kent CC, 2001
P	M2BNM	Scania K113 TRB	Van Hool Astrobel	C4/7CT	1995	Harry Shaw, Coventry, 2010
E	M378FMW	Mercedes-Benz 709	Autobus Classique	B25F	1995	Maynes of Buckie, 1999
S	N776WEF	Mercedes-Benz 711D	Autobus Classique	C24F	1995	McArdle, South Bank, 2004
S	M884WAK	Volvo B10M-62	Plaxton Première 350	C51FT	1995	Eastbourne Coach Tours, 2009
S	GSU230	Volvo B10M-62	Plaxton Première 350	C53F	1995	Esk Valley, Whitby, 2006
S	M40CRT	Volvo B10M-62	Plaxton Première 350	C51FT	1995	Cumfybus, Churchtown, 2008
S	N30CRT	Volvo B10M-62	Plaxton Première 350	C53F	1996	Cumfybus, Churchtown, 2008
S	RSU429	Volvo B10M-62	Plaxton Première 320	C49FT	1996	Arriva The Shires, 2005
P	YSU912	Volvo B10M-62	Plaxton Première 320	C49FT	1996	Arriva The Shires, 2005
S	R619BAY	Volvo B10M-62	Plaxton Première 350	C53F	1997	Bus Eireann, 2002
S	HDZ2615	Volvo B10M-62	Plaxton Première 350	C49FT	1997	Esk Valley, Whitby, 2006
S	DSU313	Volvo B10M-62	Plaxton Première 350	C53F	1997	
S	R459BAY	Volvo B10M-62	Plaxton Première 350	C53F	1997	Bus Eireann, 2006
S	P996JBC	Volvo B10M-62	Plaxton Première 350	C53F	1997	Johnson Bros, Hodthorpe, 2008
S	LIW4291	Volvo B10M-62	Plaxton Première 350	C49FT	1997	Riggott, Kinsley, 2006
P	R278RAU	Mercedes-Benz Vario 0810	Plaxton Beaver 2	B31F	1997	Trent, 2006

16

J33CRT is one of several index numbers used by Compass Royston. It is seen here on a Mercedes-Benz Touro. *Mark Doggett*

17	S	R47LNU	Mercedes-Benz Vario O810	Plaxton Beaver 2	B27F	1997	Trent, 2006
18	S	S295UAL	Mercedes-Benz Vario O810	Plaxton Beaver 2	B31F	1998	Trent, 2006
	S	S592RGA	Mercedes-Benz Vario O810	Plaxton Beaver 2	B27F	1999	Bain, Sauchen, 2009
	P	S874OHN	Volvo Olympian	Alexander RH	B47/31D	1999	Dublin Bus, 2010
	P	99D455	Volvo Olympian	Alexander RH	B47/31D	1999	Dublin Bus, 2010
	P	99D458	Volvo Olympian	Alexander RH	B47/31D	1999	Dublin Bus, 2010
	P	S804LRM	Iveco Daily 59-12	Mellor	B13F	1999	
	S	USU345	Volvo B10M-62	Berkhof Axial 50	C49FT	1999	Yellow Buses, Bournemouth, 2001
	P	NSU611	Volvo B7R	Plaxton Prima	S70F	1999	Midland, Auchterarder, 2004
	P	RLZ1176	Scania K94 IB	Irizar Century	C49FT	1999	Handley, Middleham, 2009
	P	T379PAJ	Ford Transit	Ford	M8	1999	
	E	T442KPP	LDV Convoy	LDV	M16	1999	Sixt-Kenning, 2005
	S	M33CRT	Volvo B10M-62	Plaxton Première 350	C48FT	1999	Eddie Brown, Roecliffe, 2006
	E	ESK793	Volvo B10M-62	Jonckheere Mistral 50	C53F	2000	Thomas, Rhondda, 2003
	K	K33CRT	Volvo B10M-62	Jonckheere Mistral 50	C53FT	2000	
	S	N33CRT	Volvo B10M-62	Jonckheere Mistral 50	C49FT	2000	
	P	V287DBR	LDV Convoy	Crest	M12	2000	Coulman, Edinburgh, 2003
15	S	W87NDW	Optare Solo M850	Optare	N27F	2000	Kimberley, Low Prudhoe, 2006
14	S	T14CRT	Optare Solo M920	Optare	N33F	2001	Kimberley, Low Prudhoe, 2006
	P	W995JNF	Mercedes-Benz Vario O814	Plaxton Beaver 2	B20F	2000	TM Travel, Staveley, 2004
	w	X218HCD	Mercedes-Benz Vario O814	Plaxton Beaver 2	BC24F	2001	Lloyd, Machynlleth, 2011
	P	PX51DVJ	Mercedes-Benz Vito 411cdi	Crest	M16	2001	BNFL, Sellafield, 2010
	P	PX51DVL	Mercedes-Benz Vito 411cdi	Crest	M16	2001	BNFL, Sellafield, 2010
	P	Y335HWT	Optare Solo M850	Optare	N27F	2001	Redby, Sunderland, 2008
	S	J33CRT	Volvo B10M-62	Jonckheere Mistral 50	C51FT	2001	
	S	J33CRT	Volvo B10M-62	Berkhof Axial 50	C51FT	2001	Rowbotham, Kerswell Green, '09
	P	Y2POB	Volvo B10M-62	Plaxton Panther	C49FT	2001	
	P	SN51SZZ	Dennis Dart SLF 10m	Plaxton Pointer MPD	N29D	2001	London United, 2010
	E	HY02OPY	LDV Convoy	LDV	M16	2002	Peek, Scalby, 2010
	S	NV51YFJ	Volvo B7R	Jonckheere Modulo	C53F	2002	
	S	NV51YFU	Volvo B7R	Jonckheere Modulo	C53F	2002	
	S	FL02ZXF	Volvo B7R	Jonckheere Modulo	C53F	2002	Skill's, Nottingham, 2004
	S	FL02ZXG	Volvo B7R	Jonckheere Modulo	C53F	2002	Skill's, Nottingham, 2004
10	P	VA02NTK	Dennis Dart SLF 8.8m	Plaxton Pointer MPD	N29F	2002	Selwyn's, Runcorn, 2006

For several years the Plaxton body for the Volvo B7R was the Profile. However, since the introduction of the Elite to the range the Panther body became a further option. YN11FVB is one of four Panther-bodied B7Rs to join the fleet in 2011.It is seen working a Megabus.com service from London. *Dave Heath*

20	P	VU02TPX	Dennis Dart SLF 8.8m	Plaxton Pointer MPD	N29F	2002	Flagfinders, Braintree, 2006
	S	CE52UWV	Optare Solo M850	Optare	N31F	2002	Crichton, Low Fell, 2008
02	w	MW52PYX	Optare Solo M850	Optare	N27F	2002	
03	P	MW52PYY	Optare Solo M850	Optare	N27F	2002	
04	P	MW52PYZ	Optare Solo M920	Optare	N30F	2002	
06	P	MW52PZB	Optare Solo M920	Optare	N30F	2003	
	S	YM52TOU	Optare Solo M850	Optare	N27F	2003	*Operated for Durham CC*
	E	MLZ3922	Mercedes-Benz Vario O814	KVC	C24F	2003	McDermott, Portaferry, 2003
	P	USU365	Volvo B7R	Jonckheere Modulo	C57F	2003	
	P	LXH869	Volvo B12M	Berkhof Axial 50	C51FT	2003	
01	P	NX03ANF	DAF SB120	Wrightbus Cadet 2	N38F	2003	
	S	1624WY	Neoplan Starliner N516 SHD	Neoplan	C36FT	2003	Gorden, Rotherham, 2009
	S	BW03ZNG	Mercedes-Benz Touro OC500	Mercedes-Benz	C41FT	2003	
	P	149CYY	Mercedes-Benz Touro OC500	Mercedes-Benz	C49FT	2003	
	E	OJZ3499	LDV Convoy	LDV	M16	2003	
	S	BU53AXM	Mercedes-Benz Touro OC500	Mercedes-Benz	C49FT	2003	
	P	NV53YVC	Ford Transit	Ford	M14	2004	
	S	NV53YVE	Ford Transit	Ford	M14	2004	
14	P	YJ04DEF	LDV Convoy	LDV	M16	2004	
12	P	YJ04DEK	LDV Convoy	LDV	M16	2004	
	E	YJ04DEM	LDV Convoy	LDV	M16	2004	
	P	YJ04ZVG	LDV Convoy	LDV	M16	2004	
	P	PSU572	Volvo B12M	Plaxton Panther	C51FT	2004	
07	P	MX05EMV	Optare Solo M880 SL	Optare	N23F	2005	
08	P	MX05ENE	ADL Dart 4	ADL Mini Pointer	N29F	2005	
	P	FSU741	Volvo B12M	Berkhof Axial 50	C51FT	2005	
	P	848KMX	Volvo B12M	Berkhof Axial 50	C51FT	2005	
	P	PR05TER	Volvo B12M	Berkhof Axial 100	C65/18CT	2005	
	P	LF05DPV	Ayats A14 9.6m	Ayats Platinum	C13FT	2005	Scottish Labour, 2010
11	P	MX55BXR	Optare Solo M880 SL	Optare	N28F	2005	

12	P	MX55BXS	Optare Solo M880 SL	Optare	N28F	2005	
	S	BX55FYF	Mercedes-Benz Vario 616cdi	Koch	B24F	2005	
06	P	MX55WUY	LDV Convoy	LDV	M16	2005	
11	P	MX55WVA	LDV Convoy	LDV	M16	2005	
04	P	MX55WVC	LDV Convoy	LDV	M16	2005	
07	P	BV55AEJ	LDV Convoy	LDV	M16	2006	
	P	BV55AEL	LDV Convoy	LDV	M16	2006	
	S	GX55LNF	Optare Solo M950	Optare	N27F	2006	Arriva Southern Counties, 2009
03	P	AE55NNH	LDV Convoy	LDV	M16	2006	
05	P	AE55NNU	LDV Convoy	LDV	M16	2006	
10	P	BV55AEC	LDV Convoy	LDV	M16	2006	
30	P	NT06GKA	Optare Solo M880	Optare	N28F	2006	Thompson, South Bank, 2011
	S	K33CRT	Volvo B12B	Jonckheere SHV	C57FT	2006	Lochs & Glens, Aberfoyle, 2010
23	E	MX06ULP	ADL Dart 8.8m	ADL Pointer	N29F	2006	Swan, Chadderton, 2010
	P	SN06BRV	ADL Dart 8.8m	ADL Pointer	N29F	2006	Coakley, Motherwell, 2009
	P	SN06BRX	ADL Dart 8.8m	ADL Pointer	N29F	2006	Coakley, Motherwell, 2009
26	P	AE56OEH	LDV Maxus	LDV	M15	2006	
	S	NX07BOU	Ayats Bravo 1 A3E/BR1	Ayats	C32/12FT	2007	
	P	YX07HPC	Enterprise Plasma EB01	Plaxton Primo	N28F	2007	Flights Hallmark, Hounslow, 2010
	P	FJ07AEA	Volvo B12B	Jonckheere SHV	C57FT	2007	Lochs & Glens, Aberfoyle, 2010
	P	FJ07AEB	Volvo B12B	Jonckheere SHV	C57FT	2007	Lochs & Glens, Aberfoyle, 2010
	P	FJ07AEC	Volvo B12B	Jonckheere SHV	C57FT	2007	Lochs & Glens, Aberfoyle, 2010
	P	TSU646	Volvo B12B	Jonckheere SHV	C57FT	2007	Lochs & Glens, Aberfoyle, 2010
	P	YN07DVA	Volvo B12B	Plaxton Paragon	C49FT	2007	
	P	MX07JOH	Optare Solo M880 SL	Optare	N28F	2007	
15	P	MX07JOJ	Optare Solo M880 SL	Optare	N28F	2007	
	P	MX07JOU	Optare Solo M880 SL	Optare	N28F	2007	
	S	MX07NTO	Optare Solo M710 SE	Optare	N24F	2007	
2	P	MX57CCD	Optare Solo M880 SL	Optare	N26F	2007	
14	P	MX57CCE	Optare Solo M880 SL	Optare	N26F	2007	
17	P	MX57CCF	Optare Solo M880 SL	Optare	N26F	2007	
	D	WA57CZB	VDL Bova Futura FHD127.365	VDL Bova	C53F	2007	Tranzcare, Radcliffe, 2011
	P	YJ08EBP	Van Hool T917 Acron	Van Hool	C53FT	2008	
	P	SN08CNF	Scania K340 EB	Irizar PB	C49FT	2008	Malcolm, Dysart, 2009
	P	YN09AOU	Mercedes-Benz Vario 0816D	Plaxton Cheetah	C33F	2009	
	P	YJ09CYH	Van Hool T917 Aston	Van Hool	C53FT	2009	
	P	NX59BYC	Volvo B7RLE	Wrightbus Eclipse Urban	N42F	2009	
	P	YJ59AYZ	VDL SB200	Wrightbus Pulsar 2	N44F	2010	
26	P	NX10CCA	Iveco Daily 50C15	-	M16	2010	
	P	MX10DXM	ADL Dart 4 8.9m	ADL Enviro 200	N29F	2010	
	P	MX10DXY	ADL Dart 4 8.9m	ADL Enviro 200	N29F	2010	
	P	YJ10JZA	Volvo B12B	Van Hool Alizée	C57FT	2010	
	S	YN10FZK	Volvo B12M	Plaxton Paragon	C57F	2010	
	S	YN10FZL	Volvo B12M	Plaxton Paragon	C57F	2010	
	P	YN10FNV	MAN 18.240	Fast Starter L	N57D	2010	
	S	YN10HHU	Irisbus EuroRider 391E.12.35	Plaxton Panther	C57F	2010	
	P	NX10AAF	Volvo B12B 13.7m	VDL Jonckheere SHV	C59FT	2010	
	P	NX10AAJ	Volvo B12B 13.7m	VDL Jonckheere SHV	C59FT	2010	
	P	FJ60EJV	Volvo B12B 13.7m	VDL Jonckheere SHV	C59FT	2010	
	S	YN11FTY	Irisbus EuroRider 397E.12.33	Plaxton Panther 2	C53F	2011	
	S	YN11FTZ	Irisbus EuroRider 397E.12.33	Plaxton Panther 2	C53F	2011	
	S	YN11FTX	Volvo B9R	Plaxton Paragon	C57F	2011	
	S	YN11FVA	Volvo B9R	Plaxton Panther	C57F	2011	
	S	YN11FVB	Volvo B9R	Plaxton Panther	C57F	2011	
	S	YN11FVF	Volvo B9R	Plaxton Panther	C57F	2011	
	S	YN11FVG	Volvo B9R	Plaxton Panther	C57F	2011	
	P	PE11KHA	Neoplan Tourliner N2216/3 SHD	Neoplan	C61FT	2011	
	P	PE11KHB	Neoplan Tourliner N2216/3 SHD	Neoplan	C61FT	2011	
	P	PE11KHC	Neoplan Tourliner N2216/3 SHD	Neoplan	C61FT	2011	

Previous registrations:

149CYY	BU53ZWT	NIL5905	H69PDW
848KMX	FN05DFU	NSU611	W7JDS, W736PTS
1624WY	YN03AUW, FDJ75, OJB53, B20WGS	NUI7645	H723VWL, 352STG, H889CVC, SEL36, 382CFM
6769FM	Y626FOD	OIL3046	F625OHD
A693SBM	STT608X	OJZ3499	AE53ZPW
BUA751X	XPP293X, JSV328	OSU386	K222GSM, A5FWS
D20SMS	H198DVM, 539WVJ, C5BOY	OUI6364	STT608X, A693SBM, YSU912
DSU313	97D28799, P487JJU	P996JBC	97D28787
ESK793	KSK982, T730UOS, RSU429	PSU572	YN54WDC
F202GAW	F976HGE, NIW3546, F202GAW, TJI3141	PSU572	YN54WDC
F408DUG	F408DUG, PSU609P	PR05TER	FN05DWO
F435DUG	F435DUG, 7845UG, TIL8177	R459BAY	97D45881
FSU741	FN05DFP	R619BAY	97D45893
GSU230	M551WWT, GSU230, ESK793	R871MRD	R871MRD, LSU954
GX55LNF	YN55UFK	RBZ8343	AAJ674Y, GAZ4618
HDZ2615	97D23189, P981JBC	RLZ1176	T905LKE
HIL9271	FUA390Y, 999BWC, UJN215Y	RSU429	P316RGS
J33CRT	Y194AWP	S874OHN	99D465
JUI1676	D335SHS, WSU224, D165EKS	TSU646	FJ07AED
K33CRT	FJ06BSU	USU345	T320AFX
K796GAK	K796GAK, XUP2	USU365	FJ03AAV
KIB7257	E770HJF	WSU873	K564GSA, TSV721
LIL9815	G522LWU	Y335HWT	Y335HWT, R13DBY
LIL9816	G523LWU	YIL1223	M646KVU
LIW4291	97D29954, P432JJU	YIL1224	M647KVU
LSU954	F989HGE, 2178ND, F219PSP	YIL1225	M653KVU
LXH869	FJ03AAN	YIL1226	M654KVU
M21GAT	M21GAT, 8227RH	YIL1227	K471VVR
M33CRT	A12XEL, 551ALW, T797FRU	YIL1229	K474VVR
M40CRT	M721KPD, C7MFY	YIL1230	K489VVR
M209SCK	M209SCK, 7806RU, 440UXG	YOI7757	C333DND
MIW9046	G719NWY	YSU912	F318RGS
MSU462	G512NHH		
N30CRT	N40SLK, C4MFY		
N33CRT	W828LEF		

Web: www.compassroyston.net;
Depots: Lease Road, Leeming Bar (P); Bowesfield Lane, Stockton-on-Tees (S) and Fairfield Road, Whitby (E).

Procters livery is carried by YN07DVA, a Volvo B12B with Plaxton Paragon bodywork. It is seen taking a break in Stratford-upon-Avon. *Mark Doggett*

COUNTRY LION

Country Lion (Northampton) Ltd, John Bull House, Oxwich Close, Northampton, NN4 7BH

VEX301X	Bristol VRT/SL3/6LXB	Eastern Coach Works	B43/31F	1981	Stagecoach Viscount, 1999
TSO30X	Leyland Olympian ONLXB/1R	Eastern Coach Works	B45/32F	1982	Woottens, Chesham, 2002
C3CLN	Leyland Olympian ONCL10/1RZ	Alexander RH	B43/33F	1988	Arriva North East, 2003
B1CLN	Leyland Olympian ONCL10/1RZ	Alexander RH	B45/30F	1989	Arriva North East, 2003
PRP3V	Volvo Citybus B10M-50	East Lancs	B49/39F	1990	Arriva North West & Wales, 2006
YNH19W	Volvo Citybus B10M-50	East Lancs	B49/39F	1990	Arriva North West & Wales, 2006
A15NFC	Volvo Citybus B10M-50	East Lancs	B49/39F	1990	Arriva North West & Wales, 2006
NIL7250	Dennis Condor DDA1809	Duple Metsec/Caetano	B63/31D	1990	New World First Bus, 2005
J859TSC	Leyland Olympian ON2R56C13Z4	Alexander RH	B51/30D	1991	Lothian Buses, 2009
K70CLN	Dennis Javelin 12m	Wadham Stringer Vanguard II	S70F	1996	MoD, 2004
L70CLN	Dennis Javelin 12m	Wadham Stringer Vanguard II	S70F	1995	MoD, 2004
P4CLN	Dennis Dart SLF	Marshall C39	N43F	1997	
P5CLN	Dennis Dart SLF	East Lancashire Spryte	N47F	1997	
M70CLN	Dennis Javelin 12m	Plaxton Première 320	S70F	1994	Frimley Coaches, 2004
A18CLN	Volvo B10M-62	Plaxton Première 350	C53F	1995	Wallce Arnold, Leeds, 2001
M661MVV	Ford Transit	Devon Conversions	C16F	1995	
A8CLN	Scania L94 IB	Irizar Intercentury 12.32	C55F	1998	
A15CLN	Dennis Javelin 12m	Plaxton Première 320	C57F	1999	
S1CLN	Iveco EuroRider 391E.12.35	Beulas Stergo e	C53F	1999	Redwing, Herne Hill, 2004
T1CLN	Iveco EuroRider 391E.12.35	Beulas Stergo e	C53F	1999	Redwing, Herne Hill, 2004
P174HBC	Iveco EuroRider 391E.12.35	Beulas Stergo e	C51FT	2000	
L1ONU	Volvo B10M-62	Plaxton Panther	C49FT	2002	
CN03HOL	Iveco EuroRider 391E.12.35	Beulas Stergo e	C53F	2003	Warren's, Ticehurst, 2007
A14CLC	Iveco EuroRider 397E.12.35	Beulas Stergo e	C53F	2003	Woottens, Lye Green, 2008
CN04HOL	Iveco EuroRider 397E.9.27	Beulas Midi Cygnus	C35F	2004	Cavalier, Hounslow, 2007
A20CLC	Volvo B7R	TransBus Prima 70	S70F	2004	
L10NCC	Mercedes-Benz Vario O814	Plaxton Beaver 2	BC29F	2004	
A10CLC	Iveco EuroRider 397E.12.35	Plaxton Panther	C57F	2005	
A17CLN	Iveco EuroRider 397E.12.35	Plaxton Panther	C57F	2005	

F1CLN, just one of many CLC and CLN plates used by Country Lion, is currently carried on a Plaxton Paragon-bodied Volvo B12M. It is seen passing along Park Lane and carries the Royal Class branding. *Dave Heath*

In addition to the coaching fleet, Country Lion operates double-deck buses on school contracts. J859TSC was new to Lothian Buses and is an Alexander-bodied Leyland Olympian. *Mark Doggett*

Reg	Chassis	Body	Seating	Year	Notes
CN05HOL	Toyota Coaster BB50R	Caetano Optimo IV	C22F	2005	Prestige Tours, Renfrew, 2007
CN06HOL	Setra S415 HD	Setra	C49FT	2006	Meirion, Aberystwyth, 2007
L7JSF	Mercedes-Benz Vario O814	Plaxton Cheetah	C29F	2006	
L10NBB	Mercedes-Benz Vario O814	Plaxton Cheetah	C29F	2006	
A15CLC	ADL Javelin 12m	Plaxton Profile	S70F	2007	
A12CLN	ADL Javelin 12m	Plaxton Profile	S70F	2007	
A9CLN	Volvo B12B	Plaxton Panther	C49FT	2007	
W1CLN	Volvo B12B	Plaxton Panther	C49FT	2007	
G1CLN	Volvo B12M	Plaxton Paragon	C53F	2008	
CN07HOL	Mercedes-Benz Vito 111 cdi	Mercedes-Benz	M8	2008	
BN08ZFO	Mercedes-Benz Tourino O510	Mercedes-Benz	C36F	2008	
JB58AJB	Mercedes-Benz Vario O816	Plaxton Cheetah	C28F	2008	
TAA744	Mercedes-Benz Vario O816	Plaxton Cheetah	C29F	2009	
L1CLN	Volvo B12B 13.5m	Plaxton Elite	C35FT	2009	
E1CLN	Volvo B12B 13.5m	Plaxton Elite	C29FT	2009	
L1OND	Setra S416 GT-HD	Setra	C49FT	2009	
L10NHH	Mercedes-Benz Vario O816	Plaxton Cheetah	C33F	2010	
L10NKK	Mercedes-Benz Vario O816	Plaxton Cheetah	C29F	2010	
F1CLN	Volvo B12M	Plaxton Paragon	C53F	2010	
A16CLC	ADL Javelin 12m	Plaxton Profile	S70F	2010	
YJ60KHH	Optare Solo M880	Optare	N29F	2010	
YJ60KHK	Optare Solo M950	Optare	N33F	2010	
A19CLN	ADL Javelin 12m	Plaxton Profile	C57F	2012	

Previous registrations:

A9CLN	From new	CN06HOL	AF06MMM
A12CLN	From new	L7JSF	YN06OPX
A14CLC	FG03JBU	L10NBB	YN06OPZ
A15CLC	From new	L70CLN	M614USL
A15NFC	G652EKA	M70CLN	L500WCM, NIL7250
A15CLN	From new	M661MVV	A16CLC
A16CLC	M132UWY	NIL7250	EN275(HK), G324FWC
A18CLN	M117UWY	P141HBC	L1OND
B1CLN	B241YTJ	PRP3V	G661DTJ
C3CLN	F308JTY	S1CLN	T281CGU
CN03HOL	GN53AJU	T1CLN	T286CGU
CN04HOL	YN04AYD	W1CLN	From new
CN05HOL	BX05DHY	YNH19W	G650EKA

CRAWLEY LUXURY

J&M Brown Coaches Ltd, 32 Stephenson Way, Crawley, RH10 1TN

D&P Brown, East Lodge, Old Brighton Road, Pease Pottage, RH11 9AJ

G&D Brown, 38 Saxon Road, Worth, Crawley, RH10 7SB

HJB635W	Bedford YMQS	Dupe Dominant II	C31FT	1980	Ron, Lancing, 2002
DJI654	Volvo B10M-56	Plaxton Paramount 3500 II	C47F	1985	Bell, Winterslow, 1994
NIL9886	Volvo B10M-61	Plaxton Paramount 3200 III	S70F	1986	Clegg & Brooking, Stockbridge '12
52CLC	Volvo B10M-61	Plaxton Paramount 3200 III	C57F	1988	
K621ACK	Volvo B10M-55	Alexander PS	S67F	1990	Tellings-Golden Miller, 2011
ASV440	Volvo B10M-60	Plaxton Paramount 3500 III	C57F	1991	The King's Ferry, Gillingham, 2005
K2CLC	Volvo B10M-55	Alexander PS	S62F	1993	Collier, Earith, 2010
K180PAP	Volvo B10M-55	Plaxton Derwent	B55F	1993	Ramplers, Hastings, 2011
N7CLC	Volvo B10M-62	Plaxton Première 350	C53F	1995	Bus Eireann, 1999
N12CLC	Volvo B10M-62	Plaxton Première 350	C53F	1996	Bradford Communities, 2004
RYY544	Volvo B10M-62	Plaxton Première 350	C53F	1996	Bradford Communities, 2004
LUO391	Volvo B10M-62	Plaxton Première 350	C53F	1996	Stephensons of Essex, 2009
P2CAP	Volvo B10M-62	Plaxton Première 350	C57F	1996	National Express, 2007
P3CAP	Volvo B10M-62	Plaxton Première 350	C57F	1996	National Express, 2007
ASV440	Volvo B10M-62	Plaxton Première 350	C53F	1996	National Express, 2007
N60CLC	Volvo B10M-62	Plaxton Première 350	C51FT	1996	Goode's, West Bromwich, 2005
687CLC	Volvo B10M-62	Plaxton Première 350	C55F	1996	Paul Winson, Loughborough, '01
P519SDM	LDV Convoy	LDV	M16	1997	Furlong, Crawley, 2005
171CLC	Volvo B10M-62	Plaxton Première 350	C51FT	1997	Wallce Arnold, Leeds, 2002
D32CLC	Volvo B10M-62	Plaxton Première 350	C32FT	1997	Tellings-Golden Miller, 2011
P14CLC	Volvo B10M-62	Plaxton Première 350	C55F	1997	Heyfordian, Bicester, 2002
P15CLC	Volvo B10M-62	Plaxton Première 350	C55F	1997	Wallce Arnold, Leeds, 2002
1725LJ	Volvo B10M-62	Plaxton Première 350	C49FT	1997	Cropley, Boston, 2009

Seen passing through the Blackheath district of London is 685CLC from the Crawley Luxury coach fleet, a Volvo B10M with Plaxton Panther bodywork. This Sussex operator commenced in 1955 and has now clocked up fifty-seven years of coaching. *Dave Heath*

Typical of the coaches operated by Crawley Luxury is the Plaxton-bodied Volvo. Here Première 350 W30CLC is seen at Marble Arch. *Dave Heath*

UNJ408	Volvo B10M-66	Plaxton Expressliner II	C48FT	1998	National Express, Heathrow, 2008
R20CLC	Volvo B10M-62	Plaxton Première 350	C50FT	1998	Wallce Arnold, Leeds, 2004
T16CLC	Volvo B10M-62	Plaxton Première 350	C48FT	1999	Wallce Arnold, Leeds, 2003
T17CLC	Volvo B10M-62	Plaxton Première 350	C51FT	1999	WA Shearings, Wigan, 2006
T19CLC	Volvo B10M-62	Plaxton Première 350	C55F	1999	Brian Isaac, Morriston, 2006
W682MVV	Mercedes-Benz Vito 208cdi	Traveliner	M11	2000	Davies, Tredegar, 2010
W30CLC	Volvo B10M-62	Plaxton Première 350	C51FT	2000	Brian Isaac, Morriston, 2006
W608FUM	Volvo B10M-62	Plaxton Première 350	C51FT	2000	McLeans, Witney, 2008
W609FUM	Volvo B10M-62	Plaxton Première 350	C51FT	2000	Taw & Torridge, Merton, 2008
W44CLC	Volvo B10M-62	Plaxton Première 350	C51FT	2000	Wallce Arnold, Leeds, 2005
W55CLC	Volvo B10M-62	Plaxton Première 350	C50FT	2000	Wallce Arnold, Leeds, 2005
W66CLC	Volvo B10M-62	Plaxton Première 350	C51FT	2000	Brodyr Williams, U Tumble, 2005
W309WRE	Volvo B10M-62	Plaxton Première 350	C53F	2000	Guideissue, Knypersley, 2010
YDL435	Volvo B10M-62	Plaxton Première 350	C51FT	2000	Bradshaw, St Annes, 2008
W40CLC	Volvo B10M-62	Plaxton Première 350	C50FT	2000	Wallce Arnold, Leeds, 2005
X50CLC	Volvo B10M-62	Plaxton Première 350	C51F	2000	Wallce Arnold, Leeds, 2005
K3CLC	Volvo B10M-62	Plaxton Première 350	C49FT	2000	Flights, Birmingham, 2010
K5CLC	Volvo B10M-62	Plaxton Première 350	C53F	2000	Brighton & Hove, 2009
V22CLC	Volvo B10M-62	Plaxton Première 350	C51FT	2000	Brighton & Hove, 2009
W77CLC	Volvo B10M-62	Plaxton Première 350	C50FT	2000	Swift, Great Yarmouth, 2006
685CLC	Volvo B10M-62	Plaxton Panther	C53F	2000	Clarke's, Tredegar, 2007
784CLC	Volvo B10M-62	Plaxton Paragon	C48FT	2001	Voel, Dyserth, 2006
VC51CLC	Volvo B10M-62	Plaxton Panther	C51FT	2001	Berry's, Taunton, 2009
CL5561	Volvo B10M-62	Plaxton Paragon	C49FT	2001	Voel, Dyserth, 2006
789CLC	Volvo B10M-62	Plaxton Excalibur	C53F	2001	City of Oxford, 2008
CLC145	Volvo B10M-62	Plaxton Excalibur	C53F	2001	City of Oxford, 2008
Y27OXF	Volvo B10M-62	Plaxton Excalibur	C49FT	2001	Humphrey's, Datchet, 2011
978UYD	Volvo B10M-62	Berkhof Axial 50	C51F	2001	Coachmaster, Leicester, 2009
OC51CLC	Volvo B10M-62	Berkhof Axial 50	C51F	2002	East Yorkshire, 2011
WC02CLC	Volvo B10M-62	Plaxton Panther	C51FT	2002	Belle Vue, 2008
YS02YYB	Volvo B10M-62	Plaxton Panther	C51FT	2002	Clynnog & Trefor, 2011
FK02CLC	Volvo B10M-62	Plaxton Paragon	C53F	2002	Amport & District, 2008
AC04CLC	Volvo B12B	Plaxton Panther	C49FT	2004	OFJ Connections, 2010
KC04CLC	Volvo B12B	Plaxton Panther	C49FT	2004	Tellings-Golden Miller, 2010
DC06CLC	Volvo B12B	VDL Berkhof Axial	C51FT	2006	Griffin, Gravesend, 2010
NC06CLC	Volvo B12B	VDL Berkhof Axial	C51FT	2006	Pullmanor, Herne Hill, 2010

Pictured at its base in Crawley, OC51CLC is a one of four Berkhof-bodied Volvos in the fleet. Berkhof became part of the VDL group in 1998. The assembly hall at Valkenswaard in the Netherlands continues production and product development. *Mark Doggett*

Previous registrations:

52CLC	E269KRT	N12CLC	N243HWX
171CLC	P337VWR	N60CLC	N209HWX, B19GOO, YDL435
685CLC	X663NWY, B10MVO	NC06CLC	FJ06ZMU
687CLC	N227HWX	NIL9886	C580KNO
784CLC	Y745HWT, 1760VC	OC51CLC	A16EYC, YX51AXM
789CLC	Y25OXF, Y954WFC	P14CLC	P335VWR
978VYD	-	P15CLC	P349VWR
1725LJ	97D7810, P388JJU, EAZ5347	P272HBC	P10TGM, 3401MW
AC04CLC	YU04XFD	R20CLC	R416FWT
ASV440	P566MLE	RYY544	N246HWX
CL5561	Y743HWT, 8214VC	T17CLC	T508EUB
CLC145	Y26OXF, Y956WFC	T16CLC	T545EUB
CLC983T	-	T19CLC	T542EUB
D32CLC	P10TGM, 3401MW, P272HBC	UNJ408	S323VNM
D176CLC	-	V22CLC	W605OCD
DC06CLC	FJ06ZMU	VC41CLC	YN51WGX
DJI654	B190XJD	W30CLC	W629FUM
FK02CLC	HJ02HXY	W40CLC	W612FUM
HIL7746	MF51MBU	W44CLC	W656FUM
K2CLC	K726DAO	W55CLC	W614FUM
K3CLC	W100FFC, H12FDC, W676YBN	W66CLC	W621FUM
K5CLC	W606OCD	W77CLC	W647FUM
K11CLC	-	W309WRE	1497RU
K180PAP	K102XPA, TIL1185, TDY746	W682MVV	M682MVV, PXI299
KC04CLC	YU04XFC	WC02CLC	YS02YYA
L6CLC	-	X50CLC	X661NWY
LUO391	N45ARC, A17SOE	YDL435	W632FUM
N7CLC	95D41606(EI), N761AHP	YS02YYB	YS02YYB, KSV361

Depots: Stephenson Way, Crawley and Chartwell Road, Lancing.

DAISH'S COACHES

Daish's Coaches Ltd, The Devonshire Hotel, Park Hill Road, Torquay, TQ1 2DY

SUI8191	Volvo B10M-62	Van Hool T9 Alizée	C49FT	1998	Imperial, Southall, 2006
SUI8194	Volvo B10M-62	Plaxton Première 350	C49FT	1998	Go-Ahead West Midlands, '07
SUI8192	Volvo B10M-62	Jonckheere Mistral 50	C50F	1998	Reay's, Wigton, 2006
SUI8195	Volvo B10M-62	Jonckheere Mistral 50	C50F	1998	Reay's, Wigton, 2006
SUI8198	Bova Futura FHD 12.340	Bova	C49FT	1999	Allander, Milngavie, 2005
SUI8190	Volvo B10M-62	Van Hool T9 Alizée	C46FT	2000	WA Shearings, Wigan, 2007
YC02DJX	Volvo B12B	Jonckheere Mistral	C48FT	2002	WA Shearings, Wigan, 2010
SUI8193	Volvo B12B	TransBus Panther	C49FT	2003	Tai, Batley, 2006
SUI8196	Volvo B12B	TransBus Panther	C50FT	2003	Nova Tours, Chesterfield, 2007
SUI8197	Volvo B12B	Caetano Enigma	C48FT	2003	Linkline, Harlesden, 2009
CC02HOL	Volvo B12B	Caetano Enigma	C48FT	2003	Classic, Annfield Plain, 2010
KX04THE	Volvo B12B	TransBus Panther	C49FT	2004	Flights, Birmingham, 2010
SUI8199	Volvo B12B	VDL Jonckheere Mistral 50	C51FT	2004	Skills, Nottingham, 2007
WA04ZNR	Volvo B12B	VDL Jonckheere Mistral 50	C51FT	2004	Moroney, Bray, 2008
YJ05XXB	Volvo B12B	Van Hool T9 Alizée	C49FT	2005	Mills, Barnsley, 2010
WJ55TVP	Volvo B12B	Volvo 9700	C49FT	2006	Callinan, Claregalway, 2008

Previous registrations:

SUI8190	W209JBN		SUI8196	YN03WXT
SUI8191	R903YBA		SUI8197	GB03LLC
SUI8192	R940YNF, TKU717		SUI8198	YC02DJX
SUI8193	YN03WYG		SUI8199	SIL6437. FB53FYX
SUI8194	R9OXF, R257DWL		WA04ZNR	04WW4200
SUI8195	R951YNF, YSV695		WJ55TVP	06G602

Depots: Tower Road, Newquay; High Street, Shanklin and Park Hill Road, Torquay.
Web: www.daishs.com

Representing Daish's fleet is Caetano Enigma-bodied Volvo B12B CC03HOL. For the British market there are two Enigma models, the 12m version which is available on Volvo chassis and a 9.8m version available on the MAN 14.280 chassis. *Steve Rice*

DODSWORTHS

J Dodsworth (Coaches) Ltd, Wetherby Road, Boroughbridge, YO51 9HS

C481HAK	Volvo B10M-61	Plaxton Paramount 3200	C53F	1985	Tower, Cleckheaton, 2010
G425VGG	Volvo B10M-46	Plaxton Paramount 3200	C41F	1990	Handley, Middleham, 2011
T675ASN	Volvo B10M-62	Plaxton Excalibur	C49FT	1999	Moffat & Williamson, Gaudry, '10
T578MAW	LDV Convoy	LDV	M16	1999	Conning Green, Hammerton, 2010
X787HFE	Mercedes-Benz Sprinter 412 cdi	Ferqui Soroco	C16F	2000	Bates, Wolvey, 2009
YD02FDZ	Volkswagen Caravelle	Volkswagen	M8	2002	WA Shearings, Wigan, 2006
GB03JDC	Setra S415 GT-HD	Setra	C48FT	2003	
GB53JDC	Setra S315 GT-HD	Setra	C49FT	2004	Cropley, Boston, 2007
YJ54CHG	VDL SB4000	Van Hool T9 Alizée	C49FT	2005	Bradshaw, St Annes, 2009
YX06AXN	Mercedes-Benz Vario O814	ACI	C28F	2006	
GB56JDC	Setra S415 GT-HD	Setra	C49FT	2007	Scotline, Earlston, 2009
GB07JDC	Setra S415 GT-HD	Setra	C49FT	2007	
GB58JDC	Mercedes-Benz Tourino O510	Mercedes-Benz	C34FT	2008	

Special event vehicles:

VUB396H	Leyland Leopard PSU3A/4R	Plaxton Panorama Elite	C53F	1970	Wallace Arnold
HYR176W	Volvo B58-56	Plaxton Supreme IV	C38C	1981	Glenton, London
RIL3619	Volvo B58-61	Plaxton Supreme IV	C55F	1981	Patterson, Kilbirnie, 1998

Previous registrations:

G425VGG	G48RGG, LSK14, 90KY3017, G965VGD, TJI6264	HYR176W	HYR176W, 6837KR, EUY619W
GB07JDC	BX07NLR	RIL3619	BNP5W, USV810
GB53JDC	8302NF, AG53ZYT, T200GDN	VUB396H	VUB396H, OO1908, TIB8792, VRY562H
GB56JDC	BX56VUN, KSU175		

The Plaxton Excalibur body was less common than the Première 350, being a premium specification coach featuring a more dramatically styled front end. T675ASN is illustrated. *Ryan Douglas*

DURHAM CITY COACHES

Durham City Coaches Ltd, Brandon Lane, Brandon, Durham DH7 8PL

B998YKJ	Volvo B10M-61	Plaxton Paramount 3200 II	C57F	1985	Galloway, Stowmarket, 1996
J959HRG	MAN MT8.136	Optare	C21FL	1992	Durham CC, 2005
A16TVL	Volvo B10M-60	Van Hool Alizée	C53F	1994	Sim, Boot, 2008
TIL8195	Volvo B10M-62	Plaxton Première 320	C49FT	1995	Harrod, Bexwell, 2008
N256THO	Volvo B10M-62	Plaxton Première 320	C49FT	1996	Sim, Boot, 2008
N2DCC	Volvo B10M-60	Jonckheere Deauville 45	C49FT	1996	Hellyers, Fareham, 2001
JSV487	Volvo B10M-62	Plaxton Première 350	C51FT	1997	Classic, Annfield Plain, 2006
R70DCC	Volvo B10M-62	Jonckheere Mistral 50	C55F	1998	Dodsworth, Boroughbridge, 2009
R7DCC	Bova Futura FHD12.340	Bova	C49FT	1999	Reay's, Wigton, 2008
SK02VSY	Mercedes-Benz Vario O814	KVC	C24F	2002	Reay's, Wigton, 2008
SE02RUV	Mercedes-Benz Vario O814	Autobus Nouvelle 2	C29F	2002	Currie, Carluke, 2005
SL02MVR	Mercedes-Benz Vario O815	Sitcar Beluga	C29F	2002	Cooper, Longbeach, 2006
FJ03AAF	Volvo B7R	TransBus Prima	C57F	2003	
YK04FVZ	VDL Bova Futura FHD 13.340	VDL Bova	C53FT	2004	
BX55FWC	Mercedes-Benz Touro OC500	Mercedes-Benz	C49FT	2005	
NC56FXU	Mercedes-Benz Vito 111 cdi	Mercedes-Benz	M8	2007	
MC07DCC	VDL Bova Futura FHD 13.340	VDL Bova	C55FT	2007	
YJ07DVY	VDL Bova Futura FHD 127.365	VDL Bova	C56FT	2007	Shaw, Maxey, 2010
YN08OWM	Mercedes-Benz Vario O816	Plaxton Cheetah	C25F	2008	

Previous registrations:

A16TVL	HSK659, L648AYS
B998YKJ	B988YKJ, MJI4735
JSV487	T2CLA
N2DCC	RJI8713, N228RGA
N256THO	XEL31
R7DCC	S749XVA, A3HFU

R70DCC	R949YNF
SE02RUV	SE02RUV, KC02BUS
SL02MVR	C10DWA
TIL8195	A13EXC, M341MRU, XJO46, M184ENG
YK04FYZ	YK04FYZ, 712GRM

Web: www.durhamcitycoaches.co.uk

Van Hool Astrobel of Ausden Clark is seen during a school excursion. BIG9833 was new to Shaw's of Coventry in 1993. *Mark Doggett*

EAGLE

AJ & JA Ball, Fireclay House, Natham Road, St George, Bristol, BS5 9PJ

6130EL	DAF MB230	Van Hool Alizée	C53F	1990	Regina, Blaenau Ffestiniog, 1995
FIL9370	DAF MB230	Van Hool Alizée	C51F	1990	Robinson's, Great Harwood, 1996
J693GTC	DAF MB230	Van Hool Alizée	C57F	1992	
VWF328	DAF MB230	Van Hool Alizée	C57F	1993	
863EXX	DAF MB230	Van Hool Alizée	C55F	1995	
M805RCP	DAF MB230	Van Hool Alizée	C51FT	1996	
94SHU	DAF SB3000	Van Hool Alizée	C51FT	1996	
931DHT	DAF SB3000	Van Hool T9 Alizée	C49FT	1998	Pullman, Crofty, 2004
8194WF	DAF SB2750	Smit Stratos	C36FT	1998	Sea View, Poole, 2006
T54AUA	Mercedes-Benz Vario O814	Autobus Nouvelle 2	C29F	1999	
613WHT	DAF SB2750	Smit Stratos	C36FT	1999	
W201CDN	DAF SB3000	Van Hool T9 Alizée	C49FT	2000	
Y738BPR	DAF SB3000	Ikarus Blue Danube	S70F	2001	Sea View, Poole, 2006
Y739BPR	DAF SB3000	Ikarus Blue Danube	S70F	2001	Sea View, Poole, 2006
WX51YXN	Irisbus DailyBus 50C13	Indcar	C16F	2002	
YG52CKE	DAF SB4000	Van Hool T9 Alizée	C49FT	2003	
WT54JAC	VDL SB4000	Van Hool T9 Alizée	C57F	2004	Wickson, Walsall Wood, 2012
FJ05AOO	Volvo B12B	VDL Jonckheere Mistral	C57FT	2005	Lochs & Glens, Aberfoyle, 2010
YJ05PWK	VDL Bus SB4000	Van Hool T9 Alizée	C51FT	2005	
YJ06LCN	VDL Bus SB4000	Marcopolo Viaggio 350	C57F	2006	
YJ08EGC	VDL Bus SB4000	Van Hool T9 Alizée	C53F	2008	
YJ10DLF	Temsa Safari HD	Temsa	C53F	2010	Centurion, Haydon Bridge, 2011

Previous registrations:

94SHU	N993FWT		8194WF	T732GPR
613WHT	V801FWT		FIL9370	G233NCW
863EXX	M775RCP		J693GTC	J693GTC, 2411KR
931DHT	S794JTH		VWF328	K518RJX
6130EL	G999KJX			

Eagle coaches was established in 1926 and in its eighty-six years' existance, the company has built a reputation for safety, comfort and friendly efficient service. The fleet comprises mostly of DAF and later VDL products with Van Hool bodywork dominating. Typical is W201CDN which features T9 Alizée bodywork, seen in the coach paddock at Cheltenham races. *Colin Martin*

EAVESWAY

Eavesway Travel Ltd, Bryn Side, Bryn Road, Ashton-in-Makerfield, Wigan, WN4 8BT

Reg	Model	Body	Seating	Year
YJ05PVX	Van Hool T917 Astron 13.8m	Van Hool	C54FT	2005
YJ06LFM	Van Hool T917 Astron 13.8m	Van Hool	C54FT	2006
YJ06LFN	Van Hool T917 Astron 13.8m	Van Hool	C54FT	2006
YJ06LGC	Van Hool T917 Astron 13.8m	Van Hool	C54FT	2006
YJ06LGD	Van Hool T917 Astron 13.8m	Van Hool	C54FT	2006
YJ07JJV	Van Hool T917 Astron 13.8m	Van Hool	C54FT	2007
YJ07JHE	Van Hool T915 Alicron 12.6m	Van Hool	C48FT	2007
YJ07JHF	Van Hool T915 Alicron 12.6m	Van Hool	C48FT	2007
YJ08EAA	Van Hool TD921 Altano	Van Hool	C52/5FT	2008
YJ08EAC	Van Hool TD921 Altano	Van Hool	C52/5FT	2008
YJ08EAE	Van Hool TD921 Altano	Van Hool	C52/5FT	2008
YJ08EAF	Van Hool TD921 Altano	Van Hool	C52/5FT	2008
YJ08EAG	Van Hool TD921 Altano	Van Hool	C52/5FT	2008
YJ08EAK	Van Hool TD921 Altano	Van Hool	C52/5FT	2008
YJ08EAM	Van Hool TD921 Altano	Van Hool	C52/5FT	2008
YJ08EAO	Van Hool TD921 Altano	Van Hool	C52/5FT	2008
YJ08EAP	Van Hool TD921 Altano	Van Hool	C38/5FT	2008
YJ09CWW	Van Hool TD921 Altano	Van Hool	C40/5FT	2009
YJ09CXX	Van Hool TD921 Altano	Van Hool	C52/5FT	2009
YJ09CYY	Van Hool TD921 Altano	Van Hool	C52/5FT	2009
YJ10DFD	Van Hool TD921 Altano	Van Hool	C52/5FT	2010
YJ10DFE	Van Hool TD921 Altano	Van Hool	C52/5FT	2010
YJ10DFF	Van Hool TD921 Altano	Van Hool	C52/5FT	2010
YJ10DFG	Van Hool TD921 Altano	Van Hool	C52/5FT	2010
YJ11GKA	Van Hool TD921 Altano	Van Hool	C52/5FT	2011
YJ11GKC	Van Hool TD921 Altano	Van Hool	C52/5FT	2011
YJ11GKD	Van Hool TD921 Altano	Van Hool	C52/5FT	2011
YJ11GKE	Van Hool TD921 Altano	Van Hool	C40/5FT	2011
YJ12CKA	Van Hool TD921 Altano	Van Hool	C52/5FT	2012
YJ12CKC	Van Hool TD921 Altano	Van Hool	C52/5FT	2012
YJ12CKD	Van Hool TD921 Altano	Van Hool	C52/5FT	2012
YJ12CKE	Van Hool TDX21 Altano	Van Hool	C52/5FT	2012

Web: www.eaveswaytravel.com

The latest addition to Eavesway's modern coach fleet is YJ12CKE, one of the first Van Hool TX coaches for an English fleet; the TX (X being the Roman character for ten) is the successor to the T9. The latest catalogue shows that the TDX21 Altano is currently one of a few selected models available in right-hand drive form. The left-hand variants of the Altano are the TX17, TX18 and TX19. *Andrew Rigby*

EDDIE BROWN

Eddie Brown Tours Ltd, 8 Tower Street, York, YO1 9SA

Reg	Chassis	Body	Seating	Year	Notes
A5WOH	Volvo B10M-60	Plaxton Expressliner	C57F	1990	Independent, Horsforth, 1997
A2WOH	Volvo B10M-60	Plaxton Paramount 3500 III	C57F	1991	Dorset Travel, 1998
A16EBT	Volvo B10M-60	Van Hool Alizée HE	C57F	1994	Wallce Arnold, Leeds, 1998
A15EBT	Volvo B10M-60	Van Hool Alizée HE	C49FT	1994	Wallce Arnold, Leeds, 1997
DAZ1570	Volvo B10M-62	Plaxton Première 320	S70F	1994	Ulsterbus, 2007
EAZ2574	Volvo B10M-62	Plaxton Première 320	S70F	1994	Ulsterbus, 2007
A7BKE	Scania K113 TRB	Irizar Century 12.37	C49FT	1995	Nicholson, Hesleden, 2008
FBZ4780	Volvo B10M-62	Plaxton Première 350	C53F	1995	
551ALW	Volvo B10M-62	Plaxton Première 350	C53F	1996	
UXI551	Mercedes-Benz Vario O814	Autobus Nouvelle 2	C33F	1997	Bysian Cwn Taf, Whitland, 2009
IIL7075	Volvo B10M-62	Plaxton Première 350	C49FT	1998	Steele, Stevenston, 2010
A14EBT	Mercedes-Benz Vario O814	Plaxton Cheetah	C24F	1998	Worth, Longnor, 2005
NJI5510	Volvo B10M-62	Van Hool Alizée HE	C49FT	1999	
A9EBT	Volvo B10M-62	Van Hool T9 Alizée	C53F	1999	
OCZ8001	Mercedes-Benz Vario O814	Plaxton Cheetah	C25F	2001	Flexibus, Belfast, 2006
A13EBT	Scania K114 IB4	Van Hool T9 Alizée	C49FT	2002	
A17EBT	Scania K114 IB4	Van Hool T9 Alizée	C49FT	2002	
YY51BNB	Volkswagen Caravelle	Volkswagen	M7	2002	
KM02EJE	Volkswagen Caravelle	Volkswagen	M7	2002	
KN03MSU	Volkswagen Caravelle	Volkswagen	M7	2003	private owner, 2006
B5EBT	Neoplan Starliner N516 SHD	Neoplan	C36FT	2004	Ellison, St Helens, 2008
B6EBT	Neoplan Starliner N516 SHD	Neoplan	C36FT	2004	Ellison, St Helens, 2008
WIJ551	Mercedes-Benz Vario O814	Plaxton Cheetah	C33F	2004	Procter's, Leeming Bar, 2007
R55EBT	Mercedes-Benz Vario O814	TransBus Cheetah	C33F	2004	Fourways, Kirkstall, 2007
KX04HPU	Optare Solo M990	Optare	N35F	2004	Landylines, Wellington, 2011
KX04HPY	Optare Solo M990	Optare	N35F	2004	Leeds NHS, 2011
YN05GXA	Scania L94 UB	Wright Solar	N43F	2005	Reading Buses, 2011
YN05GXB	Scania L94 UB	Wright Solar	N43F	2005	Reading Buses, 2011
YN05GXC	Scania L94 UB	Wright Solar	N43F	2005	Reading Buses, 2011
YN05GXD	Scania L94 UB	Wright Solar	N43F	2005	Reading Buses, 2011
YN05GXE	Scania L94 UB	Wright Solar	N43F	2005	Reading Buses, 2011
A3EBT	Volvo B12B	Plaxton Panther	C49FT	2005	Richardson, Midhurst, 2009

Taking a break in Stratford-upon-Avon is Plaxton Panther-bodied Volvo B9R GT11EBT from Eddie Brown's fleet.
Mark Doggett

London is the destination for CT06EBT, a Volvo B12M with Plaxton Panther bodywork. *Dave Heath*

Reg	Model	Body	Seating	Year	Notes
AT05EBT	Volvo B12B	Plaxton Panther	C49FT	2005	
BT05EBT	Volvo B12B	Plaxton Panther	C49FT	2005	
B2EBT	Volvo B12M 12.8m	Plaxton Panther	C50FT	2006	Logan, Dunloy, 2010
ET06EBT	Volvo B12M 12.8m	Plaxton Panther	C50FT	2006	Logan, Dunloy, 2010
CT06EBT	Volvo B12M 12.8m	Plaxton Panther	C42FT	2006	
DT06EBT	Volvo B12M 12.8m	Plaxton Panther	C42FT	2006	
YN06CYA	Mercedes-Benz Vario O814	Plaxton Cheetah	C33F	2006	Cropper, Guiseley, 2009
YN07DVG	Mercedes-Benz Vario O814	Plaxton Cheetah	C33F	2007	Happy Days, Stafford, 2010
YK07YFD	Mercedes-Benz Vito 120 cdi	Mercedes-Benz	M8	2007	Peel, Harrogate, 2010
YN08BKG	Mercedes-Benz Sprinter 515 cdi	Onyx	M16	2008	Holsworthy, Dolton, 2011
KX08OLO	MAN 12.240	Plaxton Centro	N38F	2008	Weavaway, Newbury, 2011
YN08NNC	Volvo B12M	Plaxton Panther	C53FT	2008	Logan, Dunloy, 2011
YN08NNE	Volvo B12M	Plaxton Panther	C53FT	2008	Logan, Dunloy, 2011
YN10EOL	Volvo B12M	Plaxton Panther	C57FT	2010	
FT11EBT	Volvo B9R	Plaxton Panther	C38FT	2011	
GT11EBT	Volvo B9R	Plaxton Panther	C38FT	2011	
HT11EBT	Volvo B9R	Plaxton Panther	C38FT	2011	
JT11EBT	Volvo B9R	Plaxton Panther	C38FT	2011	
BC12EBC	Irisbus EuroRider 397E.12.35	Beulas Spica 330	C49FT	2012	

Previous registrations:

551ALW	BD02HDF	B2EBT	YN06RWF
A2WOH	H351MLJ	B5EBT	YN04AVM, FDJ75
A3EBT	YN54WWR	B6EBT	YN53EXE, ONU77
A5WOH	G452JCC	ET06EBT	YN06RWJ
A7BKE	?	FBZ4780	M51WWT
A9EBT	S551JNW	IIL7075	A5FTG, R434MEH
A13EBT	From new	NJI5510	S2WOH
A14EBT	S699RWG	TXY978	P173NAK
A15EBT	L915NNW	UXI551	T86RJL
A16EBT	L907NWW	WIJ551	NX04GCV
A17EBT	From new	YK07YFD	YK07YFD, W4ASA

Depots: Bar Lane, Boroughbridge and Thirsk Road, Easingwold.
Web: www.eddiebrowntours.com

English Bus Handbook: Coaches

ELCOCK REISEN

M H Elcock & Son Ltd, Spring Hill, Wellington, Telford, TF1 3NA

Reg	Chassis	Body	Type	Year	History
EIL1607	Volvo B10M-62	Plaxton Première 320	C57F	1997	Woodstones, Kidderminster, 2004
HIL6584	Volvo B10M-62	Plaxton Première 320	C57F	1997	Woodstones, Kidderminster, 2004
5038NT	Volvo B10M-62	Plaxton Première 350	C53F	1997	
R922LAA	Volvo B10M-62	Plaxton Première 320	C57F	1998	Excelsior, Bournemouth, 2001
V200OER	Mercedes-Benz Sprinter 412	Autobus Classique	C16F	1999	
Y4REP	Volvo B10M-62	Van Hool T9 Alizée	C53F	2001	Repton, New Haw, 2009
KW02EZN	Volvo B10M-62	Van Hool T9 Alizée	C53F	2002	Richmond, Barley, 2009
3408NT	Volvo B12M	Van Hool T9 Alizée	C53F	2002	WA Shearings, Wigan, 2009
OIW7026	Volvo B12M	Van Hool T9 Alizée	C53F	2002	WA Shearings, Wigan, 2009
1577NT	Volvo B12M	Van Hool T9 Alizée	C53F	2002	WA Shearings, Wigan, 2009
3572NT	Volvo B12M	Van Hool T9 Alizée	C53F	2002	WA Shearings, Wigan, 2009
1398NT	Volvo B12B	Plaxton Panther	C49FT	2004	Logan, Dunloy, 2006
A2EXC	Volvo B12B	Plaxton Panther	C49FT	2004	Logan, Dunloy, 2006
CJE32	Volvo B12B	Plaxton Panther	C53F	2004	
SN54KYK	Mercedes-Benz Sprinter 413 cdi	KVC	M16	2005	
3419NT	Volvo B12B	Van Hool T9 Alizée	C49FT	2005	Nefyn Coaches, 2008
YN55KME	Volvo B12M	Plaxton Paragon	C57F	2005	
SN06AAE	Mercedes-Benz Atego 1523 L	UNVI/Esker Cimo	C32F	2006	
1389NT	Volvo B12B	Van Hool T9 Alizée	C57F	2006	
YN06MXE	Volvo B12B	Plaxton Panther	C49FT	2006	
YN06MXH	Volvo B12M	Plaxton Paragon	C57F	2006	
FJ07AAY	Volvo B7R	Plaxton Profile	C57F	2007	Woodstones, Kidderminster, 2010
HIG7790	Mercedes-Benz Vario O814	Plaxton Cheetah	C33F	2007	Blythswood, Glasgow, 2010
SF57JRO	Mercedes-Benz Vario O814	Plaxton Cheetah	C33F	2007	Fairline, Glasgow, 2010
YN57BVS	Volvo B12B	Plaxton Paragon	C49FT	2007	
YN57BVT	Volvo B12B	Plaxton Paragon	C49FT	2007	
SN08HUH	Mercedes-Benz Atego 1022L	UNVI Cimo	C35F	2008	Mearns Travel, East Kilbride, 2011
1932NT	Volvo B12B	Van Hool T9 Alizée	C49FT	2010	Snowdon, Easington Colliery, '11
YJ10JZC	Volvo B12B	Van Hool T9 Alizée	C49FT	2010	
SN11CTV	Mercedes-Benz Sprinter 616cdi	Unvi GT-R	C16F	2011	

Previous registrations:

1389NT	YJ06GNP		A2EXC	YN04WTU
1398NT	YN04WTR		CJE32	YN04WTE
1577NT	MV02ULX		EIL829	XEL14 R922LAA
1932NT	SN10DON, KT10UYN		EIL1607	A8EXC, R924LAA
3408NT	MV02ULS		HIG7790	SF57JPY
3419NT	CX05AHU		HIL6584	A9EXC, R923LAA
3572NT	MV02ULY		KW02EZN	851PYD
5038NT	P289ENT		OIW7026	MV02ULU

Depots: The Maddocks, Madeley, Telford and Spring Hill, Wellington, Telford

Elcock Reisen operates several tours to Austria and Germany which was the inspiration for the German tour name. Until recently the fleet included two UNVI Cimo midi-coaches although SN05YKS, seen here on the coast, has been replaced.
Tony Wilson

P & J ELLIS Ltd.

P & J Ellis Ltd, 3 Radford Estate, Old Oak Lane, North Acton, London, NW10 6UA

YN07OPS	Mercedes-Benz Vario O816	Plaxton Cheetah	C29F	2007
FJ08BYO	Volvo B12B	VDL Jonckheere SHV	C53FT	2008
FJ08BZY	Volvo B12B	VDL Jonckheere SHV	C53FT	2008
FN09APK	Volvo B12B	VDL Jonckheere SHV	C53FT	2009
FN09APU	Volvo B12B	VDL Jonckheere SHV	C53FT	2009
FN09APO	Volvo B7R	Sunsundegui Sideral 320	C53F	2009
FJ10DNO	Volvo B7R	Sunsundegui Sideral 320	C53F	2010
FJ10DRX	Volvo B7R	Sunsundegui Sideral 320	C53F	2010
FJ10DPE	Volvo B12B	VDL Jonckheere SHV	C53FT	2010
FJ10DPO	Volvo B12B	VDL Jonckheere SHV	C53FT	2010
FJ60EJE	Volvo B12B	Volvo 9700	C53FT	2010
FJ60EJG	Volvo B12B	Volvo 9700	C53FT	2010
BX11GUF	Volvo B7R	Sunsundegui Sideral 320	C49FT	2011
BX11GUK	Volvo B7R	Sunsundegui Sideral 320	C43FT	2011
BX11GUG	Volvo B9R	VDL Jonckheere SHV	C53FT	2011
BX11GUH	Volvo B9R	VDL Jonckheere SHV	C53FT	2011
BX11GUJ	Volvo B9R	VDL Jonckheere SHV	C53FT	2011
BX12CVC	Volvo B9R	VDL Jonckheere SHV	C53FT	2012
BX12CVD	Volvo B9R	VDL Jonckheere SHV	C53FT	2012
BX12CVE	Volvo B9R	VDL Jonckheere SHV	C53FT	2012
PO12CZV	Mercedes-Benz Vario O816	Unvi Compa GT	C29F	2012

Web: www.pjellis.co.uk

Marylebone Road is the setting for this view of P & J Ellis' FN09APU, a Volvo B12B with VDL Jonckheere bodywork. *Colin Lloyd*

ELLISON'S

W S Ellison Ltd; Gavin Murray Ltd, Queens Garage, 61 Boundary Road, St Helens, WA10 2LX

152JUP	Van Hool T916 Astron 12.6m	Van Hool	C36FT	2007
PSU970	Van Hool T916 Astron 12.6m	Van Hool	C53FT	2008
OJB53	Van Hool T916 Astron 12.6m	Van Hool	C36FT	2008
FJ08FZF	Volvo B12B 13.4m	VDL Jonckheere SHV	C36FT	2008
FJ08FZH	Volvo B12B 13.4m	VDL Jonckheere SHV	C36FT	2008
NLE145	Volvo B12B 13.4m	VDL Jonckheere SHV	C36FT	2008
74YKP	Volvo B12B 13.4m	VDL Jonckheere SHV	C35FT	2008
BN08OBV	Mercedes-Benz Tourino O510	Mercedes-Benz	C28FT	2008
ONU77	Neoplan Starliner N516 SHD	Neoplan	C36FT	2009
GFF405	Neoplan Starliner N516 SHD	Neoplan	C36FT	2009
DX59DHP	Mercedes-Benz Sprinter 515 cdi	Excel	M11	2009
RJ10VYO	Mercedes-Benz Sprinter 515 cdi	Excel	M11	2010
RV60DMZ	Mercedes-Benz Sprinter 515 cdi	Excel	M11	2010
3WSM	Neoplan Starliner 2 N5218 SHD	Neoplan	C36FT	2011
ODR29	Neoplan Starliner 2 N5218 SHD	Neoplan	C36FT	2011
MA61KLP	Neoplan Starliner 2 N5218 SHD	Neoplan	C32FT	2011
WSM3	Neoplan Starliner 2 N5218 SHD	Neoplan	C32FT	2011
FDJ75	Van Hool T918 Altano	Van Hool	C42FT	2011
LOT7E	Van Hool T918 Altano	Van Hool	C42FT	2011
PN61UOE	Neoplan Tourliner N2216 SHD	Neoplan	C32FT	2012
MT61HVE	Neoplan Tourliner N2216/3 SHD	Neoplan	C32FT	2012
MT61HVF	Neoplan Tourliner N2216/3 SHD	Neoplan	C32FT	2012
MT61HVG	Neoplan Tourliner N2216/3 SHD	Neoplan	C32FT	2012
MT61HVU	Neoplan Tourliner N2216/3 SHD	Neoplan	C32FT	2012
MT61HVW	Neoplan Tourliner N2216/3 SHD	Neoplan	C32FT	2012
MV12OEA	Neoplan Tourliner N2216/3 SHD	Neoplan	C32FT	2012
MV12OEB	Neoplan Tourliner N2216/3 SHD	Neoplan	C32FT	2012
MV12OEC	Neoplan Tourliner N2216/3 SHD	Neoplan	C32FT	2012

Previous registrations:

3WSM	MF11LUE	NLE145	GFF405, FJ57CYY
74YKP	FJ08ABU	ODR29	MF11LUH
152NUP	YJ07JUC	OJB53	YJ08VPY, FDJ75
FDJ75	YJ11UKL	ONU77	YN58OLU
GFF405	MX09CHZ, LOT7E	PSU970	YJ08VOY, FDJ75
LOT7E	YJ61EXX	WSM3	MU61AVX

Web: www.ellisonstravel.com

New vehicles
delivered to
Ellisons during
the last year have
been purchased
from Neoplan, a
company founded
by Gottlieb Auwärter
in Stuttgart in 1935.
An earlier Neoplan
shown here was
recently withdrawn
Transliner BJ05ELL.
Colin Martin

EPSOM COACHES

H R Richmond Ltd, Blenheim Road, Epsom, KT19 9AF

503	YN08DMV	Mercedes-Benz Vario O816	Plaxton Cheetah	C25F	2008
504	YN08DMX	Mercedes-Benz Vario O816	Plaxton Cheetah	C25F	2008
601	LX06FFA	Mercedes-Benz Sprinter	Mercedes-Benz	M16	2006
602	LX06FFB	Mercedes-Benz Sprinter	Mercedes-Benz	M16	2006
603	BF10VBX	Mercedes-Benz Sprinter	Mercedes-Benz	M16	2010
604	BF10VBY	Mercedes-Benz Sprinter	Mercedes-Benz	M16	2010
605	BF59NHN	Mercedes-Benz Sprinter	Mercedes-Benz	M16	2009
716	BU04EXV	Setra S315 GT-HD	Setra	C53F	2004
717	BU04EXW	Setra S315 GT-HD	Setra	C53F	2004
718	BU04EXX	Setra S315 GT-HD	Setra	C53F	2004
719	BX54ECF	Setra S315 GT-HD	Setra	C53F	2005
720	BX54ECJ	Setra S315 GT-HD	Setra	C53F	2005
816	BU04EXT	Setra S315 GT-HD	Setra	C48FT	2004
901	BU06CSF	Setra S416 GT-HD	Setra	C49FT	2006
902	BU06CSO	Setra S416 GT-HD	Setra	C49FT	2006
903	BX56VTY	Setra S416 GT-HD	Setra	C44FT	2007
904	BX56VTZ	Setra S416 GT-HD	Setra	C44FT	2007
905	BX58URT	Setra S416 GT-HD	Setra	C44FT	2009
906	BF60OFD	Setra S416 GT-HD	Setra	C53FT	2011
907	BF60OFE	Setra S416 GT-HD	Setra	C53FT	2011
EP01	FJ11GLF	Volvo B9R	Caetano Levanté	C48FT	2011
EP02	FJ11GMV	Volvo B9R	Caetano Levanté	C48FT	2011
EP03	FJ61EYK	Volvo B9R	Caetano Levanté	C48FT	2012
EP04	FJ51EYL	Volvo B9R	Caetano Levanté	C48FT	2012

Web: www.epsomcoaches.com
Depot: Blenheim Road, Epsom. The associated bus fleet in included in the *London Bus Handbook*.

In April 2012 the French operator RATP announced that it had acquired the bus company HR Richmond Ltd which operates Epsom Coaches. The firm was founded by Herbert Roderick Richmond and Jim Reeves in 1920. Representing the fleet is Setra 901, BU06CSF, the first of seven S416 GT-HD models. *Mark Doggett*

EXCALIBUR

Excalibur Coach Company Ltd, Nyes Wharf, Frensham Street, London, SE15 6TH

N950RBC	Volvo B10M-62	Plaxton Première 350	C49FT	1996	Phoenix, New Cross, 2009
Y177JSH	Scania K124 IB4	Irizar Century	C49FT	2001	Phoenix, New Cross, 2009
YN04UKB	Scania K114 IB4	Irizar Century	C53F	2004	Phoenix, New Cross, 2009
YN04UKC	Scania K114 IB4	Irizar Century	C53F	2004	Phoenix, New Cross, 2009
FJ55BXR	Volvo B12B	Caetano Enigma	C53F	2005	
YN06CHX	Scania K114 IB4	Irizar Century	C53F	2006	Phoenix, New Cross, 2009
YN06CFZ	Scania K114 EB6	Irizar Century Style	C65F	2006	
YN06CJF	Scania K114 EB6	Irizar Century Style	C63F	2006	
YN06CHL	Scania K114 EB4	Irizar Century Club	C49FT	2006	
YN06CKE	Scania K114 EB6	Irizar Century Style	C63F	2006	
YN06CKG	Scania K114 EB4	Irizar Century Club	C49FT	2006	
YN06JXA	Scania K114 EB4	Irizar Century Style	C53F	2006	
YN06NYO	Scania K114 EB6 13.7m	Irizar Century Style	C65F	2006	
YN06NYP	Scania K114 EB6 13.7m	Irizar Century Style	C65F	2006	
YN56FFX	Scania K114 EB4	Irizar PB	C49FT	2006	
YN57FWE	Scania K340 EB6	Irizar Century Style	C65FT	2008	
YN57FWF	Scania K340 EB6	Irizar Century Style	C65FT	2008	
YN08DFG	Scania K340 EB6	Irizar Century Style	C63FT	2008	
FN09AOH	Volvo B12B	Volvo 9700	C51FT	2009	
FN09AOM	Volvo B12B	Volvo 9700	C51FT	2009	
YT10OAX	Scania K360 EB6	Irizar Century Style	C63FT	2010	
YT10OAY	Scania K360 EB6	Irizar Century Style	C63FT	2010	
YJ10JYU	VDL Bova Futura FHD127.365	VDL Bova	C53FT	2010	
YJ10JYV	VDL Bova Futura FHD127.365	VDL Bova	C53FT	2010	
YJ60LBX	VDL Bova Futura FHD127.365	VDL Bova	C53FT	2010	
YT11LRK	Scania K340 EB4	Irizar Century Style	C53FT	2011	
YT11LRN	Scania K340 EB4	Irizar Century Style	C53FT	2011	
YT12YUA	Scania K360 EB4	Irizar i6	C53FT	2012	
YT12YUB	Scania K360 EB4	Irizar i6	C53FT	2012	
YT12YUC	Scania K360 EB4	Irizar i6	C53FT	2012	
YT12YUD	Scania K360 EB4	Irizar i6	C53FT	2012	
YT12YUE	Scania K360 EB4	Irizar i6	C53FT	2012	

Previous registration:
Y177JSH   B12DWA

Web: www.excalibur-coach-hire.com

Volvo's own coach body, the 9700, is built in Poland on the B12B in both two and three axle variants and is currently supplied in tri-axle form on the B13R. Showing the styling is FN09AOH. *Mark Doggett*

EXCELSIOR

Excelsior Coaches Ltd, Central Business Park, Bournemouth, BH1 3SJ

M16	A11XEL	Mercedes-Benz Sprinter 308CDi	Crest	M8	2002	
M17	A12XEL	Mercedes-Benz Sprinter 308CDi	Crest	M8	2002	
M18	A13XEL	Mercedes-Benz Sprinter 308CDi	Crest	M8	2002	
M19	A14XEL	Mercedes-Benz Sprinter 308CDi	Crest	M8	2002	
201	A3XEL	Mercedes-Benz Atego 1018	Esker Cimo	C28FT	2006	
202	A5XEL	Mercedes-Benz Atego 1018	Esker Cimo	C28FT	2006	
300	FN09AOS	Volvo B12B	Volvo 9700	C53FT	2009	
301	FN09AOT	Volvo B12B	Volvo 9700	C53FT	2009	
302	FN09AOU	Volvo B12B	Volvo 9700	C37FT	2009	
303	FN09AOV	Volvo B12B	Volvo 9700	C37FT	2009	
355	XEL254	Volvo B12B	Caetano Enigma	C53F	2005	
400	FJ08FYH	Volvo B12B	Sunsundegui Sideral 350	C48FT	2008	
401	FJ08FYF	Volvo B12B	Sunsundegui Sideral 350	C48FT	2008	
402	FJ08FYG	Volvo B12B	Sunsundegui Sideral 350	C48FT	2008	
611	A10XEL	Volvo B12M	Sunsundegui Sideral 350	C49FT	2005	
612	A7XEL	Volvo B12B	Plaxton Paragon	C50FT	2005	Logan, Dunloy, 2007
613	XEL158	Volvo B12B	Plaxton Paragon	C50FT	2005	Logan, Dunloy, 2007
614	A2XEL	Volvo B12B	Plaxton Paragon	C50FT	2005	Logan, Dunloy, 2007
615	YN57OTY	Volvo B12M	Plaxton Paragon	C51FT	2008	
616	YN57OTZ	Volvo B12M	Plaxton Paragon	C51FT	2008	
617	YN57OTX	Volvo B12M	Plaxton Paragon	C51FT	2008	
620	YN08NKK	Volvo B12M	Plaxton Parargon	C52FT	2008	
621	YN08NKL	Volvo B12M	Plaxton Paragon	C52FT	2008	
622	YN08NKM	Volvo B12M	Plaxton Paragon	C52FT	2008	
907	A15XEL	Volvo B12B	Jonckheere Mistral 50	C44FT	2003	
908	A16XEL	Volvo B12B	Jonckheere Mistral 50	C44FT	2003	
909	A17XEL	Volvo B12B	Caetano Enigma	C49FT	2006	
910	A18XEL	Volvo B12B	Caetano Enigma	C49FT	2006	
911	A19XEL	Volvo B12B	Caetano Enigma	C49FT	2006	
912	A20XEL	Volvo B12B	Caetano Enigma	C49FT	2006	
913	BU08CGG	Volvo B12B	Caetano Enigma	C49FT	2008	

Four tri-axle Volvo 9700 coaches are operated by Excelsior, having joined the fleet in 2009. Volvo has replaced the B12B with the two-axle B19R or the three-axle B13R. Seen in its home town of Bournemouth is 301, FN09AOT. *Steve Rice*

Seen in Birmingham while operating on National Express service is Excelsior 402, FJ08FYG, a Volvo B12B with Spanish-built Sunsundegui Sideral 350 bodywork. Sunsundegui has been supplying coaches to the British market since 2001, exclusively on Volvo chassis. *Steve Rice*

914	FJ60EHB	Volvo B9R	Caetano Levanté	C48FT	2010
915	FJ60EHC	Volvo B9R	Caetano Levanté	C48FT	2010
916	FJ60EHD	Volvo B9R	Caetano Levanté	C48FT	2010
917	FJ60EHE	Volvo B9R	Caetano Levanté	C48FT	2010
918	FJ60EHF	Volvo B9R	Caetano Levanté	C48FT	2010
919	FJ11GNP	Volvo B9R	Caetano Levanté	C48FT	2011
920	FJ11GNU	Volvo B9R	Caetano Levanté	C48FT	2011
921	FJ11GNV	Volvo B9R	Caetano Levanté	C48FT	2011
922	FJ11GNX	Volvo B9R	Caetano Levanté	C48FT	2011
923	FJ11GNY	Volvo B9R	Caetano Levanté	C48FT	2011
924	FJ11GNZ	Volvo B9R	Caetano Levanté	C48FT	2011

Previous registrations:

A2XEL	YN05VSM	A14XEL	A13EXC
A3XEL	YN55KWB	A15XEL	FN03DYA
A5XEL	YN55KWC	A16XEL	FN03DYB
A7XEL	YN05VSF	A17XEL	FJ55BXZ
A9XEL	-	A18XEL	FJ55BXV
A10XEL	FJ55XAX	A19XEL	FJ55BXW
A11XEL	A8EXC	A20XEL	FJ55BXY
A12XEL	A9EXC	XEL158	YN05VSL
A13XEL	A12EXC	XEL254	HF05AXS

Depot: Southcote Road, Bournemouth; **Web:** www.excelsior-coaches.com

GALLOWAY

Galloway European Coachlines Ltd, Denter's Hill, Mendlesham, Stowmarket, IP14 5RR

No.	Reg	Chassis	Body	Seating	Year	Notes
134	1482PP	DAF SB220	Ikarus CitiBus	B53F	1995	
170	5516PP	Mercedes-Benz Vario 0814	Plaxton Cheetah	C33F	2001	
186	W478KSG	Mercedes-Benz Vito 110 cdi	Mercedes-Benz	M7	2000	
188	1440PP	Dennis Dart SLF	UVG Compass	N44F	1997	Marchwood, Totton, 2003
198	5048PP	DAF SB4000	Van Hool T9 Alizée	C53F	2003	
204	AY53KRO	DAF SB4000	Van Hool T9 Alizée	C49FT	2003	
207	5611PP	DAF SB3000	Ikarus Blue Danube 350	C53F	1996	North Kent Express, 2004
208	4092PP	DAF SB3000	Ikarus Blue Danube 350	C53F	1997	North Kent Express, 2004
209	3860PP	DAF SB3000	Plaxton Première 320	C53F	1999	LB Camden, 2004
211	SC04XOW	Mercedes-Benz Vito 111 cdi	Mercedes-Benz	M8	2004	
217	EY53GPK	Mercedes-Benz Vario 0814	TransBus Beaver	B31F	2004	Golden Boy, Hoddesdon, 2004
220	2086PP	VDL Bus SB4000	Van Hool T9 Alizée	C49FT	2004	
221	2513PP	VDL Bus SB4000	Van Hool T9 Alizée	C49FT	2004	
223	3367PP	Mercedes-Benz Vario 0810	Plaxton Beaver 2	B31F	1997	NCP, Paisley, 2005
224	YJ05PXT	VDL Bus SB4000	Van Hool T9 Alizée	C49FT	2004	
227	AY05KVF	VDL Bus SB120	Wrightbus Cadet 2	N39F	2005	
228	AY55DGV	VDL Bus SB120	Wrightbus Cadet 2	N39F	2005	
229	5946PP	DAF DB250	Optare Spectra	B47/28F	2000	Marchwood Motorways, 2006
236	AY06BZM	Mercedes-Benz Vito 110 cdi	Mercedes-Benz	M8	2006	
239	AY06CPX	Van Hool Astron T916	Van Hool	C49FT	2006	
244	YR02ZYL	Scania L94 UB	Wrightbus Solar	N43F	2002	Anglian, Ellough, 2006
252	6399PP	VDL Bus SB4000	Van Hool T9 Alizée	C53F	2005	P&J Ellis, North Acton, 2007
253	1842PP	Leyland Olympian ON2R50C13Z4	Alexander RH	B47/31D	1993	Dublin Bus, 2007
258	1754PP	DAF SB220	Ikarus Citibus	B39F	1999	K-Line, Honley, 2007
262	AY57EZR	Setra S416 GT-HD	Setra	C49FT	2008	
265	AY08CRU	Mercedes-Benz Vario 0816	Plaxton Cheetah	C33F	2008	
266	AU08DXF	VDL Bus SB4000	Van Hool T9 Alizée	C49FT	2008	
267	HF54HLE	Mercedes-Benz Vario 0814	Plaxton Beaver 2	B33F	2004	West End, Loughborough, 2008
268	HF54HLG	Mercedes-Benz Vario 0814	Plaxton Beaver 2	B33F	2004	West End, Loughborough, 2008
269	AU08DZP	VDL Bus SB4000	Van Hool T9 Alizée	C49FT	2008	
270	3379PP	Mercedes-Benz Vario 0814	Plaxton Beaver 2	B31F	1999	Coakley Bus, Motherwell, 2008
271	AY05WRA	Ford Transit	Ford	M8	2005	
273	6037PP	DAF SB3000	Ikarus Blue Danube 350	C51FT	1997	M&C, Earl Stonham, 2008
274	AY09BWM	Temsa Safari HD	Temsa	C53F	2009	

The Ikarus Blue Danube model was a popular choice for DAF-based coaches in the late 1990s. Galloway's 4092PP illustrates the model in this view. *Mark Doggett*

Recently entered service with Galloway is Setra S416 GT-HD BN12EOO, seen here at the 2012 UK Coach Rally. The GT-HD model forms part of the 'Comfort Class' trim level and is currently the only class imported to Britain. In previous years the 'Top Class' models HD and HDH had been available. *Tony Greaves*

275	AY09BYZ	Van Hool T916 Astron 13m	Van Hool	C49FT	2009	
276	AY09DHG	Van Hool T916 Astron 13m	Van Hool	C49FT	2009	
278	AY09BYC	VDL Bus SB200	Plaxton Centra	N45F	2009	
279	MX53FDN	Optare M920	Optare	N33F	2004	Anglian, Ellough, 2009
281	GJ52GYD	Mercedes-Benz Vario O814	Plaxton Beaver 2	B31F	2002	Kent Coach Tours, 2009
282	KX53SCV	Optare M920	Optare	N33F	2004	Courtney, Bracknell, 2009
288	FL58HHJ	Ford Transit	Ford	M8	2008	
289	BV10ZKL	Setra S416 GT-HD	Setra	C53FT	2010	
291	FR59KMY	Ford Transit	Ford	M8	2010	
292	AN60TVO	Ford Transit	Ford	M8	2010	
293	BF60OGA	Mercedes-Benz Tourismo OC510	Mercedes-Benz	C53F	2010	
294	BF60OGB	Mercedes-Benz Tourismo OC510	Mercedes-Benz	C53F	2010	
296	YJ11GGV	Vab Hool T916 Alicron	Van Hool	C49FT	2011	
300	FJ61EVN	Volvo B9R	Caetano Levanté	C48FT	2011	
301	FJ61EVP	Volvo B9R	Caetano Levanté	C48FT	2011	
302	FJ61EVR	Volvo B9R	Caetano Levanté	C48FT	2011	
303	FJ61EVT	Volvo B9R	Caetano Levanté	C48FT	2011	
304	FJ61EVU	Volvo B9R	Caetano Levanté	C48FT	2011	
305	FJ61EVV	Volvo B9R	Caetano Levanté	C48FT	2011	
306	BX12CWC	Volvo B13B	Volvo 9700	C53FT	2012	
307	BT05GBT	Volvo B12B	Plaxton Panther	C57F	2005	Eddie Brown, Boroughbridge, '12
308	R80PSW	Dennis Dart SLF	PLaxton Pointer	N40F	1997	Paul S Winson, Loughborough,'12
309	BN12EOO	Setra S416 GT-HD	Setra	C49FT	2012	
310	YJ55YGK	Optare M880	Optare	N27F	2005	Far East, Ipswich, 2012

Previous registrations:

1440PP	R558UOT	4092PP	R176GNW
1482PP	N665JGV	5048PP	AY53EEX
1754PP	Y294HUA	5516PP	Y733OGV
1842PP	93D10159, L842SNO	5611PP	P157RWR
2086PP	YJ54CKN	5946PP	W231CDN
2513PP	YJ54CGE	6037PP	P211PWR
2986PP	-	6399PP	YJ04HHS
3367PP	P849YGB	HF54HLE	HP54WET
3379PP	T300CBC	HF54HLG	LP54WET
3860PP	S408JUA		

GEE-VEE

G C H Clark, 7 Kendrey Street, Barnsley, S70 1DB

Reg	Model	Make	Type	Year	Notes
N167ONH	Ford Transit	Ford	M8	1995	
PIL6833	Bova Futura FHD12.340	Bova	C49FT	1995	Freedom Travel, Piltdown, 2008
N2GVT	Bova Futura FHD12.340	Bova	C49FT	1996	Freedom Travel, Piltdown, 2008
P1GVT	Bova Futura FHD12.340	Bova	C51FT	1997	Silver Fox, Renfrew, 2003
KEZ7425	Bova Futura FHD12.340	Bova	C51FT	1997	P W Jones, Burley Gate, 2003
TIL5084	Bova Futura FHD12.330	Bova	C51FT	1997	Roper, Bradford, 2006
R1GVT	Bova Futura FHD12.340	Bova	C51FT	1998	
916VBH	Bova Futura FHD12.340	Bova	C49FT	1998	K M, Lundwood, 2010
W618CHJ	Ford Transit	Ford	M14	2000	Guest, Worsborough Dale, 2011
X4GVT	Bova Futura FHD12.340	Bova	C51FT	2000	
YK51KOW	Bova Futura FHD12.370	Bova	C49FT	2001	Evans, Normanton, 2009
YD02PXG	Bova Futura FHD12.340	Bova	C51FT	2002	
YD02PXV	Bova Futura FHD12.340	Bova	C49FT	2002	Lawman, Kettering, 2010
KU04JDP	VDL Bova Futura FHD12.340	VDL Bova	C49FT	2004	Moxon, Oldcotes, 2011
GT04GVT	VDL Bova Futura FHD12.340	VDL Bova	C53FT	2004	
GT05GVT	VDL Bova Futura FHD12.340	VDL Bova	C53FT	2005	
GT06GVT	VDL Bova Futura FHD12.340	VDL Bova	C51FT	2006	
GT11GVT	VDL Bova Futura FHD127.365	VDL Bova	C51FT	2011	

Previous registrations:

916VBH	S383JUG	P1GVT	P69BSB, SIL1102
GT11GVT	YJ11ANV	PIL6833	M30FTG
KEZ7425	P7JMJ	TIL5084	R3PER
KU04JDP	FIL7997	W618CHJ	00C15821
N2GVT	N73WSB, N2RED, JNZ5042	YK51KOW	YK51KOW, 74YKP

Depot: Stanley Road, Stairfoot

This smart fleet comprises solely of the Bova Futura model. The integral Bova products are produced at Valkenswaard, just south of Eindhoven. The Bova name is derived from Bots Valkenswaard, J D Bots being the founder of the firm in 1878. Coachbuilding commenced in 1969 and the company became part of VDL Groep in 2003. *Mark Doggett*

GODSONS

J M Godson; R J Godson, 3 Sandbed Lane, Crossgates, Leeds, LS15 8JH

TJI4929	DAF MB230	Plaxton Paramount 3500 II	C53F	1986	Hellyers, Fareham, 2001
G991KJX	DAF SB2305	Plaxton Paramount 3200 III	C57F	1990	Gray, Holland Common, 2011
H24YBV	Leyland Lynx LX2R11X15Z4R	Leyland Lynx	BC45F	1990	Preston Bus, 2008
H27YBV	Leyland Lynx LX2R11X15Z4R	Leyland Lynx	BC45F	1990	Preston Bus, 2008
TXI1348	Leyland Tiger TR2R56V16Z4	Alexander Q	BC53F	1991	Ulsterbus, 2010
TXI1357	Leyland Tiger TR2R56V16Z4	Alexander Q	BC53F	1991	Ulsterbus, 2010
M955HRY	Volvo B6	Caetano Algarve 2	C34F	1994	
N37EUG	Bova Futura Club FLD12.270	Bova	C53F	1995	
YD02RJX	DAF SB3000	OVI Versatile	C51FT	2002	
BJ03OUF	Mercedes-Benz Touro OC500	Mercedes-Benz	C49FT	2003	
FN04FSV	Volvo B12B	Caetano Enigma	C55F	2004	
YU04XJG	Irisbus EuroRider 397E.12.31	Plaxton Paragon	C53F	2004	
YU05VRY	Irisbus EuroRider 397E.12.31	Plaxton Paragon	C51FT	2005	
YJ08NRY	VDL Bova Magiq MHD122.410	VDL Bova	C53FT	2008	
PO11HVZ	Irisbus EuroRider 397E.12.33	Tata Hispano Divo	C56FT	2011	

Previous registration:
TJI4929   C788MVH

Depots: Sandbed Lane, Crossgates; Sandleas Way, Crossgates; Grangefield Road, Stanningley and Aviation Road, Sherburn-in-Elmet.

Photographs for inclusion in the *Bus Handbook* **series are always welcome, as we desire recent pictures to accompany the fleets. Here, City Circle 54, BD60XSR, is seen in Victoria Street in London. This is a Mercedes-Benz Tourismo, one of the models built in Turkey.** *Dave Heath*

GOLDEN BOY

Jetsie Ltd, John Terence House, Geddings Road, Hoddesdon, EN11 0NT

402	OO05BOY	Volvo B12B	Van Hool T9 Alizée	C53FT	2005	
403	W7BOY	Volvo B10MT	Van Hool T9 Alizée	C53F	1999	Kenzies, Royston, 2004
404	MU53BOY	Mercedes-Benz Vario 0814	Plaxton Beaver 2	BC33F	2004	
405	UU54BOY	Mercedes-Benz Vario 0814	Eurocoach LX33	C33F	2004	
407	OO12BOY	Van Hool TX16 Astron	Van Hool	C43FT	2012	
415	T99BOY	Volvo B10MT	Van Hool T9 Alizée	C53F	1999	Kenzies, Shepreth, 2004
417	XO12BOY	Mercedes-Benz Sprinter 516 cdi	UNVI Vega GT	C16F	2012	
418	XO08BOY	Volvo B12B	Van Hool T916 Alicron	C53FT	2008	
419	OO03BOY	Volvo B12B	Van Hool T9 Alizée	C49FT	2003	
423	EU58ACX	ADL Dart 4	ADL Enviro 200	N29F	2008	
425	XX57BOY	Volvo B12B	Van Hool T9 Alicron	C53F	2007	
427	XO59BOY	VDL Bova Futura FLD120.36	VDL Bova	S69F	2009	Garlochhead Coaches, 2011
428	XO02BOY	Volvo B12B	Van Hool T9 Alizée	C57F	2002	Kenzies, Royston, 2004
429	VV58BOY	Mercedes-Benz Vario 0816	Plaxton Cheetah	C33F	2008	
430	GB10BOY	Van Hool T916 Astronef	Van Hool	C53FT	2010	
431	GB12BOY	Van Hool TX16 Astronef	Van Hool	C53FT	2012	
432	OO57BOY	Volvo B12B	Van Hool T9 Alicron	C53FT	2007	
434	T44BOY	Volvo B10MT	Van Hool T9 Alizée	C53F	1999	Kenzies, Royston, 2004
435	W9BOY	Volvo B10MT	Van Hool T9 Alizée	C53F	2000	Kenzies, Royston, 2004
481	UU59BOY	Mercedes-Benz Sprinter 515 cdi	Ferqui Soroco	C19F	2010	
484	VO10BOY	Mercedes-Benz Tourismo OC510	Mercedes-Benz	C32F	2010	
485	OO10BOY	Van Hool T916 Astron	Van Hool	C53FT	2010	
487	OO08BOY	Volvo B12B	Van Hool T9 Alizée	C53F	2008	
491	UU57BOY	Mercedes-Benz Sprinter 515 cdi	Optare/Ferqui Soroco	C16F	2007	

Golden Boy was awarded the title *Coach Operator of the Year in 2010* **and has provided coaching services from Hoddesdon for over forty years. Representing the fleet is 485, OO10BOY, a Van Hool T916 Astron, seen passing the Earls Court events hall.** *Colin Lloyd*

492	OO51BOY	Mercedes-Benz Vario 0814	Plaxton Cheetah	C33F	2001
493	VV57BOY	Mercedes-Benz Vario 0816	Plaxton Cheetah	C33F	2007
494	UU07BOY	Mercedes-Benz Vario 0816	Plaxton Cheetah	C29F	2007
495	OO04BOY	Mercedes-Benz 0815DT	Sitcar Beluga	C29F	2004
496	UU55BOY	Mercedes-Benz Vario 0814	Plaxton Cheetah	C33F	2005
497	XO11BOY	Mercedes-Benz Vario 0816	Plaxton Cheetah	C29F	2011
498	XO10BOY	Mercedes-Benz Vario 0816	Plaxton Cheetah	C29F	2010

Previous registrations:

T44BOY	T85NEG		W9BOY	W91BAV
T99BOY	T86NEG		XO02BOY	AK02EWE
W7BOY	W89BAV		XO59BOY	SF59GZA

Web: www.goldenboy.co.uk

GORDONS

D J Gordon; Billies Coaches Ltd, Chesterton Road, Rotherham, S65 1SU

C9WGS	Volvo B10M-61	Plaxton Paramount 3200 II	C53F	1988	SO Travel, Manchester, 2011
B12WGS	EOS E180Z	EOS 90	C51FT	1999	Lyles, Batley, 2010
B14WGS	Volvo B10M-62	Van Hool Alizée	C49FT	1999	Baker, Westbury, 2010
B20WGS	Van Hool T917 Astron	Van Hool	C36FT	2004	Eavesway, Ashton-in-Makerfield
B13WGS	Volvo B12M 12.8m	Plaxton Paragon	C55F	2004	
B18WGS	Volvo B12B	Plaxton Paragon	C34FT	2005	
B15WGS	Volvo B12M 12.8m	Plaxton Panther	C55F	2005	
B10WGS	Volvo B12M 12.8m	Plaxton Panther	C53F	2006	Park's of Hamilton, 2008
F1WGS	Van Hool T917 Astron	Van Hool	C38FT	2009	
F2WGS	Van Hool T917 Astron	Van Hool	C54FT	2010	

Previous registrations:

B10WGS	LSK497, SF06WEH		B17WGS	YN06WVU
B12WGS	R993FNW, 98C23115, GSU340		B20WGS	YJ54CKO
B14WGS	3RWM, VIL1525, T588DGD, PIL4420		C9WGS	

Another fleet with its own collection of index marks is Yorkshire-based Gordons. Currently carrying B13WGS, is a Plaxton Paragon-bodied Volvo B12M. The Paragon body was launched alongside the Panther for the 2000 season, the Paragon featuring a more vertical front and an inswing door. *Mark Doggett*

GRAYWAY

Walls of Wigan Ltd, 237 Manchester Road, Wigan, WN2 2EA

XIL3674	Volvo B10M-62	Van Hool Alizée HE	C49FT	1995	Edinburgh Castle Coaches, 2002
P312VWR	Volvo B10M-62	Van Hool Alizée HE	C46FT	1997	Wallce Arnold, Leeds, 2000
R832CCK	Volvo B10M-62	Van Hool T9 Alizée	C55F	1997	Hilton, Newton-le-Willows, 2003
R997PEO	Volvo B10M-62	Van Hool T9 Alizée	C55F	1997	Hilton, Newton-le-Willows, 2003
R998PEO	Volvo B10M-62	Van Hool T9 Alizée	C55F	1998	Hilton, Newton-le-Willows, 2003
R147OYS	Volvo B10M-62	Jonckheere Mistral 50	C51FT	1998	Hilton, Newton-le-Willows, 2008
S299JRM	Mercedes-Benz Vario 0814	ACI Nouvelle	C33F	1999	Hilton, Newton-le-Willows, 2005
W657FRN	Volvo B10M-62	Jonckheere Mistral 50	C49FT	2000	Hilton, Newton-le-Willows, 2003
W682FRN	Volvo B10M-62	Jonckheere Mistral 50	C49FT	2000	Hilton, Newton-le-Willows, 2003
Y92HHG	Volvo B10M-62	Jonckheere Mistral 50	C49FT	2001	Hilton, Newton-le-Willows, 2004
Y709HWT	Volvo B10M-62	Jonckheere Mistral 50	C48FT	2001	Wallace Arnold, Leeds, 2003
Y711HWT	Volvo B10M-62	Jonckheere Mistral 50	C48FT	2001	Wallace Arnold, Leeds, 2003
Y257LRN	Volvo B10M-62	Jonckheere Mistral 50	C48FT	2001	Hilton, Newton-le-Willows, 2006
FP51EUL	Volvo B10M-62	Jonckheere Mistral 50	C51FT	2002	Lochs and Glens, Aberfoyle, 2005
FP51EUM	Volvo B12M	Jonckheere Mistral 50	C51FT	2002	Lochs and Glens, Aberfoyle, 2005
FC02EJV	Volvo B12M	Jonckheere Mistral 50	C49FT	2002	Hilton, Newton-le-Willows, 2006
SA52AXV	Mercedes-Benz Vario 0814	Essbee	C24FT	2002	
MW52UCS	Mercedes-Benz Vario 0814	Plaxton Cheetah	C33F	2003	
YJ04BNL	DAF SB4000	Van Hool T9 Alizée	C55F	2004	Anderson, London, 2007
YJ04BNN	DAF SB4000	Van Hool T9 Alizée	C51FT	2004	Anderson, London, 2007
SJ04KBF	Volvo B10M-60	VDL Jonckheere Mistral	C53F	2004	Première, Nottingham, 2010
FJ05AOP	Volvo B12BT	VDL Jonckheere Mistral 70	C57FT	2005	Lochs and Glens, Aberfoyle, 2008
YN55KLV	Mercedes-Benz Vario 0814	Plaxton Cheetah	C33F	2005	Hilton, Newton-le-Willows, 2008
YN06CFL	Mercedes-Benz Vario 0814	KVC	C24F	2006	Hilton, Newton-le-Willows, 2010
YN06CFM	Mercedes-Benz Vario 0814	KVC	C24F	2006	Hilton, Newton-le-Willows, 2010
SF06VYV	Volvo B12M	Jonckheere Mistral 50	C53F	2006	Park's of Hamilton, 2008
SF06VYX	Volvo B12M	Jonckheere Mistral 50	C53F	2006	Park's of Hamilton, 2008
SF06WMG	Volvo B12M	Jonckheere Mistral 50	C53FT	2006	Park's of Hamilton, 2008
SF06WNB	Volvo B12M	Jonckheere Mistral 50	C53F	2006	Park's of Hamilton, 2008
BX07HLM	Mercedes-Benz Tourismo OC510	Mercedes-Benz	C30FT	2007	Whitelaws, Stonehouse, 2010
YJ58FHV	VDL SB4000	Van Hool Alizée	C51FT	2009	
YJ09CXA	VDL SB4000	Van Hool Alizée	C51FT	2009	BM, Hayes, 2011
YJ09CZZ	VDL SB4000	Van Hool Alizée	C51FT	2009	City Circle, Hayes, 2011

Special event vehicles:

HEK88G	Bedford J2	Plaxton Embassy	C20F	1969	Eavesway, Ashton-in-Makerfield
RIB7856	Volvo B10M-61	Jonckheere Jubilee	C51FT	1985	Cass, Moreton, 2000

Previous registrations:

R147OYS	R77CCH, HSK857	SF06WNB	2WR
R832CCK	97LS1	SF06WMG	3HWS
R997PEO	97TN1	W657FRN	00KY4026
R998PEO	98WD1	W682FRN	00KY4025
RIB7856	C407LRP	Y92HHG	01G5429
SJ04KBF	LSK879, SJ04KBF, B17PTL	Y257LRN	01DL3345
SF06VYV	HSK656	XIL3674	HSK642, M592DSJ, CCZ9018
SF06VYX	HSK660		

Depot: Brown Street, Higher Ince, Wigan **Web:** www.grayway.co.uk

Grayways has emerged from amalgamation with the well-known Walls of Wigan operation. The most common model in the fleet is the Jonckheere Mistral-bodied Volvo. FP51EUL illustrating the combination.
Mark Doggett

GREYS OF ELY

D R & A C Grey, 41 Common Road, Witchford, Ely, CB6 2HY

B10MBD	Dennis Condor DDA1702	Duple Metsec	B63/43D	1989	Eurotaxis, Siston Common, 2008
B10MKC	Dennis Condor DDA1702	Duple Metsec	B63/43D	1989	Souls, Olney, 2007
B10MWC	Dennis Condor DDA1702	Duple Metsec	B63/43D	1989	Eurotaxis, Siston Common, 2008
H805BKK	Leyland Olympian ON2R56C16Z4	Northern Counties	B51/34F	1990	Stagecoach, 2010
H806BKK	Leyland Olympian ON2R56C16Z4	Northern Counties	B51/34F	1990	Stagecoach, 2010
WSU484	Volvo B10B	Plaxton Verde	B51F	1995	Atbus, Ashford, 2010
M687TDB	Dennis Dragon	Duple Metsec	BC55/37F	1995	Stagecoach, 2011
ESU374	Dennis Lance 11m	Optare Sigma	BC47F	1996	Brighton & Hove, 2006
ESU629	Dennis Lance 11m	Optare Sigma	BC47F	1996	Brighton & Hove, 2007
ESU307	Volvo B10B	Plaxton Verde	B45D	1997	City of Oxford, 2009
ESU308	Volvo B10B	Plaxton Verde	B45D	1997	City of Oxford, 2009
WSU485	Volvo B10B	Plaxton Verde	B45D	1997	City of Oxford, 2010
WGR565	Leyland Tiger TRCTL11/3R	Plaxton Paramount 3200	C53F	1983	Clarke, Thorpe Heasley, 2007
C783MVH	DAF SB2300	Plaxton Paramount 3200 II	C53F	1986	Souls, Olney, 2007
E303UUB	Volvo B10M-61	Plaxton Paramount 3500 III	C50F	1988	Souls, Olney, 2008
ESU350	Dennis Javelin 12m	SCC Cutlass	C57F	2000	Fords, Althorne, 2006
G16ELY	ADL Javelin 12m	Plaxton Profile	C53F	2005	
G2ELY	Volvo B12B	VDL Jonckheere Mistral 50	C51FT	2006	
ESU378	Mercedes-Benz Vario O816	Plaxton Cheetah	C29F	2008	
G14ELY	Volvo B7R	Sunsundegui Sideral 330	C57F	2008	
G12ELY	Volvo B12B	VDL Jonckheere SHV	C59FT	2008	
G10ELY	Volvo B12B	VDL Jonckheere SHV	C51FT	2009	
G17ELY	Volvo B12B	Van Hool T917 Acron	C55F	2009	Pierce Kavanagh, Urlingford, 2010
G20ELY	Mercedes-Benz Tourismo	Mercedes-Benz	C49F	2009	
ESU389	Mercedes-Benz Vario O816	Plaxton Cheetah	C33F	2010	
G15ELY	Volvo B9R	Plaxton Paragon	C59F	2011	
G18ELY	Volvo B9R	Plaxton Panther	C57F	2012	

Previous registrations:

B10MBD	EH9604(HK), G959FVX	G2ELY	from new
B10MKC	EE9168(HK), F287UJN	G10ELY	from new
B10MWC	EH6403(HK), G807FVX	G12ELY	from new
C783MVH	C783MVH, VUD483	G14ELY	from new
E303UUB	E303UUB, 751EKX	G15ELY	from new
ESU307	P634FFC	G16ELY	from new
ESU308	P631FFC	G17ELY	09KK684
ESU350	W386WPX	G18ELY	from new
ESU374	N420MPN	G20ELY	ESU350
ESU378	from new	M687TDB	KAG292E (Kenya)
ESU389	from new	WSU484	N779DRH
ESU394	-	WSU485	P642FFC
ESU629	N412MPN		

Web: www.greysofely.co.uk

Joining the fleet in 2009, some sixty years after the first coach, is Mercedes-Benz Tourismo G20ELY.
Mark Doggett

HAMILTON

D L Bennett, 589-591 Uxbridge Road, Hayes, UB4 8HP

FN07BYO	Toyota Coaster BB50R	Caetano Optimo V	C26F	2007
FJ08BZH	Volvo B12B	VDL Berkhof Axial 75	C65FT	2008
FJ08BZM	Volvo B12B	VDL Jonckheere SHV	C49FT	2008
FJ08BZN	Volvo B12B	Sunsundegui Sideral 330	C49FT	2008
WA11HXM	VDL Bova Futura FHD127.365	VDL Bova	C57FT	2011
MA11NYV	Neoplan Tourliner N2216/3 SHD	Neoplan	C61FT	2011
MA11NYW	Neoplan Tourliner N2216/3 SHD	Neoplan	C61FT	2011
MJ61AVT	Neoplan Tourliner N2216/3 SHD	Neoplan	C62FT	2011
ML61CXE	Neoplan Tourliner N2216/3 SHD	Neoplan	C62FT	2011
ML61CXF	Neoplan Tourliner N2216/3 SHD	Neoplan	C62FT	2011
MV12OED	Neoplan Tourliner N2216/3 SHD	Neoplan	C62FT	2012

Depot: Pronto Yard, Uxbridge Road, Uxbridge

Seen leaving London on Megabus service M20 is Hamilton's FJ08BZH, a Volvo B12B with VDL bodywork.
Colin Lloyd

HARRY SHAW

H Shaw (DM) Ltd, Mill House, Mill Lane, Binley, Coventry, CV3 2DU

Reg	Chassis	Body	Seating	Year	Notes
H15URE	Volvo B10M-62	Van Hool Alizée	C53F	1993	Mills, Gornal Wood, 2005
84KOV	Volvo B10M-62	Berkhof Axial 50	C49FT	2000	
KOV2	Volvo B10M-62	Berkhof Axial 50	C49FT	2000	
3KOV	Volvo B10M-62	Berkhof Axial 50	C49FT	2001	
MM02DBO	Mercedes-Benz Sprinter 311 cdi	Mercedes-Benz	M8	2002	
HST11	Volvo B12M	Berkhof Axial 50	C40FT	2003	
F5RST	Volvo B12BT 13.75m	VDL Jonckheere Mistral 70	C57FT	2005	Lochs & Glens, Aberfoyle, 2009
1KOV	Scania K340 EB4	Irizar PB	C49FT	2008	
SF09FXP	Volvo B12B	VDL Jonckheere SHV	C57F	2009	Stokes, Carstairs, 2010
H5HST	Mercedes-Benz Vito 111 cdi	Mercedes-Benz	M8	2010	
YJ10JYZ	VDL Bova Futura FHD 127.365	VDL Bova	C53FT	2010	
YJ11AMX	VDL Bova Futura FHD 127.365	VDL Bova	C53FT	2011	
YJ11ANX	VDL Bova Futura FHD 127.365	VDL Bova	C53FT	2011	
YT11AOF	VDL Bova Futura FHD 127.365	VDL Bova	C44FT	2011	
YT11LRE	Scania OmniExpress K400 EB6	Scania	C62FT	2011	
YT61FEF	Scania K360 EB4	Irizar i6	C49FT	2012	
-	VDL Bova Futura FHD 127.365	VDL Bova	C53FT	2012	

Previous registrations:

1KOV	YN57FWU	H15URE	LSK845, L636AYS
3KOV	FE51RBY	HST11	From new
84KOV	W91ANH	KOV1	YN07LHH
F5RST	FJ05AOR	KOV2	W92ANH
H5HST	DA10FFW	MM02DBO	MM02DBO, H15URE

Depots: Leicester Street, Bedworth and Mill Lane, Binley

1KOV is a plate owned by Harry Shaw for a number of years and has recently been transferred to a Scania coach. Representing the fleet is HST11, a Volvo B12M with Berkhof Axial bodywork. *Colin Martin*

HENRY COOPER

L & G Greaves, Lane End Garage, Annitsford, NE23 7DB

ESU110	Leyland Tiger TRCTL11/3R	Plaxton Paramount 3200 II	C57F	1986	Arriva North East, 1999
526VVK	Volvo B10M-60	Plaxton Excalibur	C49FT	1993	
EX180	Volvo B10M-62	Plaxton Excalibur	C51F	1997	
754GHO	Volvo B12BT	Plaxton Excalibur	C51FT	2000	
OBR297	Volvo B12B	Plaxton Panther	C51FT	2003	
HC04BBB	Volvo B6BLE	Plaxton Centro	N43F	2004	
671MBB	Volvo B12B	Plaxton Elite	C53FT	2009	
EFL629	Volvo B7R	Plaxton Profile	C57F	2011	

Special event vehicles:

PT2053	Daimler CJK22	Robson	B20F	1924	Baker, Quarrington Hill
MFF580	AEC Routemaster R2RH	Park Royal	B36/28R	1961	London Transport

Previous registrations:

754GHO	W542PTY	MFF580	WLT931
EFL629	NK11GRU	OBR297	from new
EX180	P397CCU	526VVK	L352MKU
ESU110	C131HJN		

Seen through a telefoto lens is Henry Coopers' 754GHO, a Plaxton Excalibur-bodied Volvo, the first example of this model on a tri-axle chassis and was used for the model's launch. *John Birtwistle*

HILLS COACHES

Hills Coaches Ltd, 8c Gibbons Grove, Newbridge, Wolverhampton, WV6 0JR

Reg	Chassis	Body	Seating	Year	History
F478WFX	Volvo B10M-61	Duple 340	C57F	1989	FHW, Willenhall, 2006
H290XNS	Volvo B10M-60	Van Hool Alizée H	C53F	1990	Southern, Barrhead, 1998
L100CLA	Volvo B10M-62	Van Hool Alizée H	C49FT	1994	Clarke's of London, 2002
L400CLA	Volvo B10M-62	Van Hool Alizée H	C49FT	1994	Clarke's of London, 2002
W317SBC	Volvo B10M-62	Caetano Enigma	C49FT	2000	
Y751OBE	Mercedes-Benz Vario O814	Autobus Nouvelle 2	C29F	2001	Browne, Yiewsley, 2008
BU03LYW	Setra S315 GT-HD	Setra	C49FT	2003	
YN04GOP	Scania K114 EB4	Irizar Intercentury 12.32	C55F	2004	
BX06JXO	Mercedes-Benz Sprinter 614 cdi	Excel	C24F	2006	
FJ06BOU	Volvo B7R	Plaxton Profile 70	S70F	2006	
FJ07ADU	Volvo B7R	Plaxton Profile 70	S70F	2007	Woodstones, Kidderminster, 2010
BX07NKM	Mercedes-Benz Tourino O510	Mercedes-Benz	C35F	2007	
FJ57CZK	Volvo B12B	Sunsundegui Sideral 330	C49FT	2007	
AT57LCT	Volvo B12B	Van Hool T9 Alizée	C49FT	2007	Leons, Stafford, 2009
YN08OCS	Scania K340 EB4	Irizar PB	C42FT	2008	
YN58BHX	Scania K340 EB4	Irizar PB	C49FT	2008	
BK58URF	Setra S416 GT-HD	Setra	C49FT	2008	
FN09AOK	Volvo B12B	VDL Jonckheere SHV	C51FT	2009	
YN59BKF	Mercedes-Benz Vario O816D	Plaxton Cheetah	C33F	2009	
YN60BZM	Volvo B7R	Plaxton Profile 70	S70F	2010	
BX11DGF	Volvo B9R	Sunsundegui Sideral 330	C53FT	2011	
BX12CVB	Volvo B13R	Volvo 9700	C53FT	2012	

Depot: Canalside, Horden Road, Wolverhampton **Web:** www.hillscoaches.co.uk

Two Setra coaches are currently in Hills' fleet, a S315 and a S415. The earlier vehicle is BU03LYW and features a graduated paint scheme. *Mark Doggett*

HODGE'S

Hodge's Coaches (Sandhurst) Ltd, 100 Yorktown Road, Sandhurst, GU47 9AD

Reg	Chassis	Body	Seating	Year	Notes
H973KDY	Volvo B10M-60	Van Hool Alizée	C57F	1991	Rambler, Hastings, 2008
7107PH	Toyota Coaster HZB50R	Caetano Optimo III	C21F	1995	
4631PH	Toyota Coaster HZB50R	Caetano Optimo III	C21F	1996	
2568PH	Volvo B10M-62	Berkhof Axial 50	C53F	1998	
5226PH	Volvo B10M-62	Berkhof Axial 50	C53F	1998	
2480PH	Volvo B10M-62	Caetano Enigma	C49FT	2001	
5134PH	Volvo B10M-62	Caetano Enigma	C49FT	2001	
9649PH	Volvo B10M-62	Caetano Enigma	C49FT	2001	
3556PH	Volvo B10M-62	Caetano Enigma	C53F	2001	
8990PH	Volvo B10M-62	Caetano Enigma	C49FT	2001	
1598PH	Volvo B12M	Berkhof Axial 50	C51FT	2003	
5881PH	Volvo B12M	Berkhof Axial 50	C51FT	2003	
1210PH	Ford Transit	Ford	M16	2005	Budget, Sale, 2008
9958PH	Toyota Coaster BB50R	Caetano Optimo IV	C22F	2006	
8874PH	Ford Transit	Ford	M16	2007	Clfton College, Bristol, 2011
6691PH	Scania K340 EB4	VDL Berkhof Axial 50	C53FT	2007	
8466PH	Scania K340 EB4	VDL Berkhof Axial 50	C53FT	2007	
3900PH	Scania K340 EB4	VDL Berkhof Axial 50	C53FT	2008	
4402PH	Scania K340 EB4	VDL Berkhof Axial 50	C53FT	2008	
5049PH	ADL Javelin 12m	Plaxton Profile	C57F	2009	Devine, Yateley, 2011
6967PH	MAN 18.240	Fast Starter L	N57D	2009	
8896PH	MAN 18.240	Fast Starter L	N57D	2009	
9489PH	MAN 18.240	Fast Starter L	N57D	2009	

Previous registrations:

1210PH	NC05PUE	6691PH	from new
1598PH	from new	6967PH	-
2480PH	from new	7107PH	from new
2568PH	R984PMO	8466PH	from new
3556PH	FN52MZJ	8874PH	GL07SJX
3900PH	from new	8896PH	-
4402PH	from new	8990PH	FN52MZL
4631PH	from new	9489PH	-
5049PH	YN09DYD	9649PH	from new
5134PH	from new	9958PH	from new
5226PH	R985PMO	H973KDY	H532WGH, FDY83, KDY814
5881PH	from new		

Depot: St John's Road, Sandhurst.
Web: www.hodges-coaches.co.uk

Taking a lunch break at the Scottish town of Moffatt while heading for Arran is PUA917 from Andrew's fleet. The Van Hool-bodied Volvo illustrates the T8 version of the Alizée.
Bill Potter

HODSONS

Hodson's Coaches Ltd, Chapel Lane, Navenby, Lincoln, LN5 9ER

W104CEO	Volkswagen Caravelle	Volkswagen	M7	2000	
SC51HOD	Mercedes-Benz Sprinter 413 cdi	Autobus	C16F	2001	
Y2HOD	Setra S315 GT-HD	Setra	C53F	2001	
AC03HOD	Setra S315 GT-HD	Setra	C49FT	2003	
VA53WHL	Vauxhall Movano	Vauxhall	M6	2004	
SO05HOD	Volkswagen Caravelle	Volkswagen	M7	2005	
WH05HOD	Setra S315 GT-HD	Setra	C49FT	2005	
OX05HOD	Mercedes-Benz Sprinter 411 cdi	Koch	N16F	2005	
CC06HOD	Mercedes-Benz Tourino O510	Mercedes-Benz	C34FT	2006	
S555HOD	Mercedes-Benz Vario O815	UNVI/Esker Riada 815	C28F	2006	
BX56ZKF	LDV Convoy	Onyx	M16	2006	Hutchinson, Easingwold, 2009
PX56AAF	Mercedes-Benz Sprinter 413 cdi	Onyx	M16	2006	Routeledge, Brigham, 2010
HO08SON	Mercedes-Benz Tourismo	Mercedes-Benz	C49FT	2008	
SL08HOD	Mercedes-Benz Sprinter 515 cdi	Koch	N16F	2008	

Previous registration:
SL08HOD   MX08NNR

Web: www.hodsoncoaches.co.uk

Seen passing the lions in Trafalgar Square is HO08SON, a Mercedes-Benz Tourismo. *Colin Lloyd*

HOLMESWOOD

Aspden's - Bostock's - Holmeswood - John Flanagan - Owens - Walker's

Holmeswood Coaches Ltd, Fallowfields, Sandy Way, Holmeswood, Rufford, L40 1UB

A914RRN	Leyland Tiger B43	Plaxton P'mount 3200 (1984)	C49F	1979	Mercers, Longridge, 1984
AAX300A	Leyland Tiger TRCTL11/3R	Berkhof Excellence 1000 ('95)	C55F	1984	Tellings - Golden Miller, 1992
TIB2574	Volvo B10M-61	Van Hool Alizée	C49FT	1984	GVM, London, 2011
5AAX	Volvo B10M-61	Berkhof Excellence 1000 ('97)	C57F	1986	Shearings, Wigan, 1993
A19HWD	Leyland Olympian ONLXB/1RH	Eastern Coach Works	BC42/30F	1987	London Central, 1998
A20HWD	Leyland Olympian ONCL10/2RZ	Northern Counties	B49/34F	1989	City of Nottingham, 2001
LIB6440	Volvo Citybus B10M-50	Northern Counties	B47/35F	1989	Pete's Travel, W Bromwich, 2003
MIL9576	Leyland Olympian ONCL10/1RZ	Alexander RL	B47/30F	1990	Armchair, Brentford, 2002
YXI7923	Leyland Olympian ONCL10/1RZ	Alexander RL	B47/30F	1990	Armchair, Brentford, 2002
G369YUR	Leyland Olympian ONCL10/1RZ	Alexander RL	B47/30F	1990	Armchair, Brentford, 2002
716GRM	Scania K113 CRB	Plaxton Paramount 3500 III	C57F	1990	Lewis, Greenwich, 2001
H2HWD	Leyland Olympian ON2R50C13Z4	Leyland	B47/31F	1991	Armchair, Brentford, 2003
PBV779	Leyland Olympian ON2R50C13Z4	Leyland	B47/31F	1991	Armchair, Brentford, 2003
848AFM	Dennis Javelin GX 12m	Caetano Algarve II	S70F	1992	O'Brien, Radcliffe, 2001
AIG8933	Volvo B10M-60	Van Hool Alizée	C57F	1992	Kent Coach Travel, 2011
IIL5133	Volvo B10M-60	Caetano Algarve II	C55F	1993	Belle Vue, Wakefield, 2001
L5HWD	Dennis Javelin 10m	Berkhof Excellence 1000L	C41F	1993	Owen, Oswestry, 2000
SIL2732	Dennis Javelin GX 12m	Neoplan Transliner	S70F	1995	Camden, West Kingsdown, 2001
N367TJT	Scania K113 CRB	Van Hool Alizée	C57F	1996	Chapmans, Tonyrefail, 2008
CLZ8353	Scania N113DRB	East Lancs	B45/31F	1996	Fraser Eagle, Burnley, 2010
P50HWD	Dennis Javelin 12m	Marcopolo Explorer	S70F	1996	McGowan, Neilston, 2004
N896KFA	Volvo B10M-62	Plaxton Première 320	C57F	1996	Charlie Irons, Kirknewton, 2010
P604HRM	Volvo B10M-62	Plaxton Première 350	C57F	1997	Wheeler, Kendal, 2011
464HYB	Dennis Javelin 12m	Plaxton Première 320	S70F	1997	Wilfreda-Beehive, Doncaster, 2006
R4HWD	Dennis Javelin GX 12m	Caetano Algarve II	C53F	1997	
P144GHE	Scania K113 CRB	Van Hool Alizée	C49FT	1997	South Coast, Southbourne, 2011
R870SDT	Scania L94 IB4	Irizar Century 12.35	C57F	1997	Luckett, Fareham, 2011
R454YDT	Scania K113 CRB	Van Hool Alizée	C57F	1998	Greenhill, Westcliffe-on-Sea, 2011
P2HWD	DAF SB3000	Ikarus Blue Danube 350	S67F	1997	Haytons, Burnage, 2008
YTY867	DAF SB3000	Ikarus Blue Danube 350	S67F	1997	Haytons, Burnage, 2009
A4HWD	Optare Solo M920	Optare	N33F	1998	Tees Valley, Hartlepool, 2010
R6HWD	Volvo B10M-62	Plaxton Première 350	S70F	1998	Wallce Arnold, Leeds, 2001
UTF119	Iveco EuroRider 391E.12.35	Beulas Stergo e	C53F	1999	SM Coaches, Harlow, 2009
296HFM	Iveco EuroRider 391E.12.35	Beulas Stergo e	C53F	1999	Logic, Broadley Common, 2009
KIB8111	Iveco EuroRider 391E.12.35	Beulas Stergo e	C53F	1999	McColl, Balloch, 2007
WYR562	Iveco EuroRider 391E.12.35	Beulas Stergo e	C53F	1999	McColl, Balloch, 2007
T206AUA	DAF SB3000	Van Hool T9 Alizée	C57F	1999	National Express, 2008
T208AUA	DAF SB3000	Van Hool T9 Alizée	C57F	1999	National Express, 2008
629LFM	Iveco EuroRider 391E.12.35	Beulas Stergo e	C53F	1999	McColl, Dunoon, 2007
T376JWA	Scania K113 TRB	Irizar Century	C49FT	1999	Greenhill, Westcliffe-on-Sea, 2011
V4HWD	Scania L94 IB	Van Hool T9 Alizée	C49FT	1999	
152ENM	Mercedes Benz Vario O814	Plaxton Beaver 2	B27F	1999	Epsom Coaches, 2005
V265HEC	Optare Solo M850	Optare	N27F	1999	Blackpool Transport, 2011
JHF825	Scania N113 CRB	East Lancs Cityzen	B47/31F	2000	Shire Coaches, St Albans, 2003
HBV682	Scania N113 CRB	East Lancs Cityzen	B47/31F	2000	Chambers, Bures, 2005
JBV529	Scania N113 CRB	East Lancs Cityzen	B47/31F	2000	Chambers, Bures, 2005
466YMG	Scania N113 CRB	East Lancs Cityzen	B47/31F	2000	Mayne, Manchester, 2004
ESK807	Scania N113 CRB	East Lancs Cityzen	B47/31F	2000	Mayne, Manchester, 2004
V430DRA	Dennis Trident	East Lancs Lolyne	N53/34F	2000	City of Nottingham, 2011
V433DRA	Dennis Trident	East Lancs Lolyne	N53/34F	2000	City of Nottingham, 2011
W4HWD	DAF SB3000	Ikarus Blue Danube	S70F	2000	Skyline, Oldbury, 2010
SBV703	Iveco EuroRider 391E.12.35	Beulas Stergo e	C51FT	2000	Cedar Coaches, Bedford, 2008
JHF824	Iveco EuroRider 391E.12.35	Beulas Stergo e	C51FT	2000	Cedar Coaches, Bedford, 2008
W148EEC	Volvo B10M-62	Jonckheere Mistral 50	C51FT	2000	Travellers Choice, Carnforth, '11
W151EEC	Volvo B10M-62	Jonckheere Mistral 50	C51FT	2000	Travellers Choice, Carnforth, '11
W152EEC	Volvo B10M-62	Jonckheere Mistral 50	C51FT	2000	Travellers Choice, Carnforth, '11
RIB8747	MAN 24.400	Marcopolo Explorer	C45FT	2000	Cerbydau, Cenarth, 2007
CNZ3824	Scania L94 IB4	Van Hool T9 Alizée	C49FT	2000	Whitestar, Barrhead, 2006
X4HWD	Scania L94 IB4	Van Hool T9 Alizée	C53F	2000	
ASV237	Irisbus EuroRider 391E.12.35	Beulas Stergo e	C57F	2001	Dover, Hetton-le-Hole, 2008
YSU991	Irisbus EuroRider 397E.12.35	Beulas Stergo e	C51FT	2001	Transport S, Peterborough, 2012

Holmeswood is a coach dealer as well as one of the principal coach operators in North West England with some hundred and seventy vehicles. Marcopolo-bodied MAN 18.350 PO55NXG illustrates the current group livery scheme. *Mark Doggett*

R3HWD	Optare Solo M850	Optare	N25F	2001	Rotherham MBC, 2009
L4HWD	Optare Solo M920	Optare	N31F	2001	Swanbrook, Cheltenham, 2009
Y744HWY	Volvo B10M-62	Plaxton Paragon	C49FT	2001	AAA, Kirknewton, 2008
Y706NVW	MAN 18.310	Marcopolo Viaggio 330	S70F	2001	Gilchrist, Quarrington Hill, 2006
BV51BOF	Mercedes-Benz Vito 110cdi	Mercedes-Benz	M6	2002	
FL02ZXZ	Volvo B12B	Berkhof Axial 50	C51FT	2002	AAA, Kirknewton, 2011
LV02LKC	Irisbus EuroRider 391E.12.35	Beulas Stergo e	C53F	2002	Coach Operations, 2007
LV02LKE	Irisbus EuroRider 391E.12.35	Beulas Stergo e	C53F	2002	Bailey's Hermitage, 2009
FN02VCJ	Irisbus EuroRider 391E.12.35	Beulas Stergo e	C49FT	2002	
FN02VCT	Irisbus EuroRider 391E.12.35	Beulas Stergo e	C49F	2002	
FM02KUR	Irisbus EuroMidi CC80E	Indcar Maxim 2	C29F	2002	Bailey, Newbury, 2011
184XNO	MAN 24.240	Marcopolo Continental 360	C49FT	2002	Catterall's, Southam, 2005
FG03JEJ	Irisbus EuroRider 397E.12.35	Beulas Stergo e	C49FT	2003	Patterson, Seahouses, 2008
FG03JAU	Irisbus EuroRider 397E.12.35	Beulas Stergo e	C49FT	2003	Bailey's, Hermitage, 2009
PL03BBZ	Mercedes-Benz Vito 110cdi	Mercedes-Benz	M7	2003	
PL03BCE	Mercedes-Benz Vito 110cdi	Mercedes-Benz	M7	2003	
YN53SVY	Optare Solo M850	Optare	N29F	2003	A1A, Birkenhead, 2011
YN53SVZ	Optare Solo M850	Optare	N29F	2003	A1A, Birkenhead, 2011
S9BOS	ADL Dart SLF	ADL Mini Pointer Dart	N29F	2004	Town & Country, Runcorn, 2007
HF04GXK	MAN 24.400	Noge Catalan Star	C53F	2004	Seaview, Parkstone, 2009
HF04GXL	MAN 24.400	Noge Catalan Star	C53F	2004	Seaview, Parkstone, 2009
HF04GXM	MAN 24.400	Noge Catalan Star	C53F	2004	Seaview, Parkstone, 2009
PN04NPA	VDL Bus SB4000	Marcopolo Viaggio 350	C55F	2004	
PN04NTX	MAN 13.220	Marcopolo Viaggio 330	C37F	2004	
PN04PFX	MAN 18.360	Marcopolo Viaggio 350	C55F	2004	Shore, Throop, 2008
PN04PFZ	MAN 11.220	Marcopolo Viaggio 330	C35F	2004	
PO54NAA	MAN 18.360	Marcopolo Viaggio 350	C49FT	2004	
PO54NAE	MAN 18.360	Marcopolo Viaggio 350	C55F	2004	
PO54NHB	MAN 18.360	Marcopolo Viaggio 350	C55F	2004	
PO54NLA	MAN 18.360	Marcopolo Viaggio 350	C55F	2004	
PO54NHA	MAN 11.220	Marcopolo Viaggio 330	C35F	2004	
PJ54VAE	Ford Transit	Ford	M8	2005	
MX05OUC	Optare Solo M850	Optare	N29F	2005	Enterprise, Peterborough, 2011

YJ05XMX	Optare Solo M780	Optare	N24F	2003	A1A, Birkenhead, 2011
YJ05XNX	Optare Solo M780	Optare	N24F	2003	A1A, Birkenhead, 2011
YN05HUZ	Irisbus EuroRider 397E.12.35	Plaxton Paragon	C49FT	2005	AAA, Kirknewton, 2010
RE05ANN	Irisbus EuroRider 397E.12.35	Beulas Stergo e	C49FT	2005	Wilfreda Beehive, Doncaster, 2011
PN05CVB	MAN 18.360	Marcopolo Viaggio 350	C55F	2005	
PN05CVC	Irisbus Daily 65C15	Indcar Wing	C22F	2005	
PN05CNA	Irisbus Daily 65C15	Indcar Wing	C22F	2005	
PN05CNC	VDL SB4000	Marcopolo Viaggio 350	C57FT	2005	Bailey, Newbury, 2011
A10SFC	VDL SB4000	Marcopolo Viaggio 350	C57FT	2005	Stainton, Kendal, 2011
PN05CVB	MAN 18.310	Marcopolo Viaggio 350	C55F	2005	
PN55NXF	MAN 18.310	Marcopolo Viaggio 350	C49FT	2005	
PO55NXG	MAN 18.350	Marcopolo Viaggio 350	C49FT	2005	
MX55WDZ	Enterprise Plasma EB01	Plaxton Primo	N28F	2005	Central Connect, 2009
PN06TVF	Irisbus Daily 65C17	Indcar Wing	C22F	2006	
A20EFA	Volvo B10M-62	Marcopolo Explorer	C45FT	2006	Applegate, Newport, 2008
PN06TVJ	MAN 18.360	Marcopolo Viaggio 350	C55FT	2006	
K4HWD	MAN 18.360	Marcopolo Viaggio 350	C57F	2006	Diplomat, Stockport, 2009
PN06TVL	MAN 18.360	Marcopolo Viaggio 350	C53FT	2006	
PN06TVT	Irisbus EuroRider 397E.12.35	Marcopolo Viaggio 350	C53FT	2006	Walton, Freckleton, 2010
PN06TVZ	MAN 18.360	Marcopolo Viaggio 350	C53FT	2006	
YB06VOK	Optare Solo M780 SL	Optare	N24F	2006	Veolia, 2012
YJ06YRM	Optare Solo M780 SL	Optare	N24F	2006	Veolia, 2012
YJ06YRN	Optare Solo M780 SL	Optare	N24F	2006	Veolia, 2012
YJ56AUE	Optare Solo M780 SE	Optare	N24F	2006	Veolia, 2012
YJ56AUF	Optare Solo M780 SE	Optare	N24F	2006	Veolia, 2012
YJ56AUM	Optare Solo M990	Optare	N33F	2006	Veolia, 2012
MX56AAY	Optare Solo M920	Optare	N33F	2006	Home James, Liverpool, 2012
PO56PBZ	MAN 14.280	Beulas Midi Cygnus	C35F	2006	
PO56PBY	Irisbus EuroRider 397E.12.35A	Marcopolo Viaggio 330	C53F	2006	
AY56EZM	Mercedes-Benz Vario O814	Plaxton Beaver 2	B29F	2006	Far East Travel, Ipswich, 2012
AY56EZO	Mercedes-Benz Vario O814	Plaxton Beaver 2	B29F	2006	Far East Travel, Ipswich, 2012
PJ56SVY	Mercedes-Benz Vito 111cdi	Mercedes-Benz	M8	2007	
PN56PCU	Irisbus Daily 65C17	Indcar Wing	C24F	2007	
MX56NHB	Enterprise Plasma EB01	Plaxton Primo	N28F	2007	EST, Llandow, 2011
MX56NHC	Enterprise Plasma EB01	Plaxton Primo	N28F	2007	EST, Llandow, 2011
AU07AFV	Enterprise Plasma EB01	Plaxton Primo	N28F	2007	Veolia, 2012
MX07LBG	Enterprise Plasma EB01	Plaxton Primo	N28F	2007	Mistral, Knutsford, 2009
YX07GVD	Enterprise Plasma EB01	Plaxton Primo	N28F	2007	Princess, West End, 2009
MX07JOA	Optare Solo M710	Optare	N23F	2007	A1A, Birkenhead, 2011
PN07EHW	Irisbus Daily 65C17	Indcar Wing	C24F	2007	
PN07EHF	Neoplan Skyliner N122/3L	Neoplan	C61/12CT	2007	
PN07EHG	Neoplan Skyliner N122/3L	Neoplan	C59/20CT	2007	
PN07EHD	MAN 18.310	Marcopolo Viaggio II 330	C53F	2007	
PN07EHB	Irisbus EuroRider 397E.12.35A	Marcopolo Viaggio II 330	C57FT	2007	
PN07EHC	Irisbus EuroRider 397E.12.35A	Marcopolo Viaggio II 330	C57F	2007	
PN07EHE	Irisbus EuroRider 397E.12.35A	Marcopolo Viaggio II 330	C57FT	2007	
PN07EHH	Irisbus EuroRider 397E.12.35A	Marcopolo Viaggio II 330	C57F	2007	
PN07EHJ	Irisbus EuroRider 397E.12.35A	Marcopolo Viaggio II 330	C53FT	2007	
PN07EHU	Irisbus EuroRider 397E.12.35A	Marcopolo Viaggio II 330	C53F	2007	
PN07EHO	Irisbus EuroRider 397E.12.35A	Marcopolo Viaggio II 330	C57F	2007	
PN07XDY	Irisbus EuroRider 397E.12.31A	Marcopolo Viaggio II 330	S70F	2007	
PN07XEB	Irisbus EuroRider 397E.12.35A	Marcopolo Viaggio II 330	S70F	2007	
PN57CUX	Irisbus EuroRider 397E.12.35A	Marcopolo Viaggio II 330	S70F	2007	
PN57CVB	Irisbus EuroRider 397E.12.35A	Marcopolo Viaggio II 330	C53F	2007	
PN57CUW	Irisbus EuroMidi CC80	Indcar Wing	C24F	2007	
CN57EFH	Enterprise Plasma EB01	Plaxton Primo	N29F	2007	Veolia, 2012
CN57EFJ	Enterprise Plasma EB01	Plaxton Primo	N29F	2007	Veolia, 2012
PN57CVD	MAN 14.280	Beulas Midi Cygnus	C35F	2007	
PN57CVE	MAN 14.280	Beulas Midi Cygnus	C35F	2007	
PN57CVF	MAN 18.360	Beulas Cygnus	C51F	2007	
PN08CMO	MAN 24.400	Beulas Cygnus	C51FT	2008	
PN08CMU	MAN 18.400	Beulas Cygnus	C50FT	2008	
PN08CMX	MAN 18.350	Marcopolo Viaggio II 330	S70F	2008	
PN08CNE	MAN 18.310	Marcopolo Viaggio II 330	C57F	2008	
PN08CNF	Irisbus EuroRider 391.12.35	Marcopolo Viaggio II 330	C57FT	2008	
PN08CNJ	Irisbus EuroRider 397.12.35A	Marcopolo Viaggio II 330	C49FT	2008	
PN08CNK	MAN 14.400	Beulas Cygnus	C49FT	2008	
PN08CMV	Mercedes-Benz Vario O816	Indcar Wing	C25F	2008	
PO58ACU	Mercedes-Benz Vario O816	Marcopolo Stella	C29F	2008	
PN09CXJ	Enterprise Plasma EB01	Plaxton Primo	N28F	2009	
PN09CXA	MAN 18.360	Marcopolo Viaggio III 350	C57F	2009	
PN09CXB	MAN 18.360	Beulas Cygnus	C57FT	2009	

Another MAN with Holmeswood is PN08CMU, this time an 18.400 with Beulas Cygnus bodywork. The Spanish coachbuilder Beulas was established in 1934 by Ramón Beulas and Narcís Pujol. The Cygnus model was introduced for the 2006 season and this example is seen passing Hyde Park in London. *Dave Heath*

	PN09CXC	Irisbus EuroRider 397E.12.38	Marcopolo Viaggio II 330	C57F	2009	
	PN09CWP	MAN 18.290	Marcopolo Viale HF	S70F	2009	
	PN10AFV	MAN 18.290	Marcopolo Viale HF	S74F	2010	
B	PN10AFJ	MAN 18.360	Beulas Cygnus	C53FT	2010	
	PN10AFF	Irisbus EuroRider 397E.13.45	Beulas Glory	C70/6F	2010	
	PN10AFE	VDL SB4000	Beulas Cygnus	C53FT	2010	
	PN10AFK	VDL SB4000	Marcopolo Viaggio III 330	C53FT	2010	
	PN10AGO	VDL SB4000	Marcopolo Viaggio III 330	C53FT	2010	
	PX10ABZ	Enterprise Plasma EB01	Plaxton Primo	N28F	2010	Reay's, Workington, 2011
	PX10ACE	Enterprise Plasma EB01	Plaxton Primo	N28F	2010	Reay's, Workington, 2011
	PX10ACF	Enterprise Plasma EB01	Plaxton Primo	N28F	2010	Reay's, Workington, 2011
	PO60HYR	MAN 18.400	Beulas Spica	C53F	2010	
	PO60HYP	VDL SB4000	Beulas Spica	C53F	2010	
	PO11HWG	VDL SB4000	Beulas Spica	C55F	2011	
	PO11HWC	Irisbus EuroRider 397E.12.38	Marcopolo Viaggio III 330	C53FT	2011	
	PO61KAA	VDL SB4000	Beulas Cygnus	C53FT	2011	
	PO61KAK	VDL SB4000	Beulas Cygnus	C44FT	2011	
	PO61KAE	VDL SB4000	Tata Hispano Xeros	C42FT	2011	
	PO12EOA	VDL SB4000	Beulas Spica	C53F	2012	
	PO12EOC	VDL SB4000	Beulas Aura	C44FT	2012	

Special event vehicles:

	539DTE	AEC Reliance MU3RV	Duple Britannia	C39C	1958	
	BHF291A	AEC Reliance 2MU3RV	Plaxton Panorama (1973)	C41F	1960	Valiant, London

Illustrating the Holmeswood VIP livery is PN10AFE. This Beulas Cygnus is based on the Dutch-built VDL SB4000 chassis. *John Marsh*

Previous registrations:

5AAX	C336DND, SPR124, C449GVM	LV52LKC	LV52LVC, TIL1257
152ENM	S454LGN	M6HWD	M335KRY
296HFM	T290CGU, 296HFM	MIL9576	G361YUR
464HYB	R202XKU	N367TJT	N367TJT, YTY867, C7OXF, J3EHD
466YMG	X119ABA	N896KPA	N300CHA
629LFM	T283CGU	NIL5675	
716GRM	H808RWJ, 686CXV, H582DMY	P2HWD	LV02LKE
848AFM	J915OAY, J8PJC	P50HWD	P211RUM
A4HWD	S289NRB	P604HRM	P604HRM, P2TYR, CJZ4231
A19HWD	D261FUL, 2CLT	PBV779	H561GKX
A20HWD	F128KTV	PN04PFX	PN04PFX, B3SLT
AAX300A	A257VWO	R3HWD	R437FWT
AIG8933	J452CEV	R6HWD	R427FWT
ASV337	Y55SUM, LEZ6921, Y212BBA	RIB8747	W751AAY
CLZ8353	P104HNC	S9BOS	MV54EEN
CNZ3824	V33CCH	SBV703	W31COM, W394BKN
ESK807	X118ABA	SIL2732	M911OVR
FN02VCJ	H19ATK	T366SDT	T366SDT, 99G2005, HBZ1974
FN52GVD	FN52GVD, 942AYA	TIB2574	A188MNE, YTP749, A568GBA
H2HWD	H559GKX	UTF119	T288CGU
HBV682	W87HRT	W4HWD	W736PPR
IIL5133	K588VBC	W148EEC	E148EEC, 3770RU
JBV529	W91HRT	W151EEC	W151EEC, XDO32
JHF824	X502AHE, R19CES	W152EEC	W152EEC, 6682WY
JHF825	V327EAL	WYR562	T293CGU
K4HWD	PN06TVK	Y706NVW	Y11PAT, Y706NVW, 296HFM
L4HWD	BU51OWL, VA51XFM	YSU991	Y822NAY, TTC86
L5HWD	L3SLT, L320CVM	YXI7923	G368YUR

Depots: Grappenhall Lane, Appleton (John Flanagan - F); Lancaster Street, Blackburn (Aspdens - A); Manor Street, Congleton (Bostock's - B); Sandy Way, Holmeswood (Holmeswood - H); Leyland (Holmeswood - H); Moss Street, Macclesfield (Bostock's - B) and Old Road, Northwich (Walker - W).
Web: www.Holmeswood.co.uk

HORSEMAN

Horseman Coaches Ltd, Whitley Wood Road, Reading, RG2 8GG

R204STF	Dennis Javelin	UVG S320	S69F	1997	
S192WAN	Volvo B10M-60	Berkhof Axial 50	C53F	1998	
S193WAN	Volvo B10M-60	Berkhof Axial 50	C53F	1998	
S484KJT	Volvo B10M-60	Berkhof Axial 50	C51F	1998	Chiltern Queens, Woodcote, 2002
T10DMB	Volvo B10M-60	Berkhof Axial 50	C51F	1999	Chiltern Queens, Woodcote, 2002
T20DMB	Volvo B10M-60	Berkhof Axial 50	C51F	1999	AWRE, Aldermaston, 2002
W56SJH	Toyota Coaster BB5CR	Caetano Optimo IV	C24F	2001	
W57SJH	Toyota Coaster BB5CR	Caetano Optimo IV	C24F	2001	
W59SJH	Toyota Coaster BB5CR	Caetano Optimo IV	C24F	2001	
RX51EXM	Volvo B10M-62	Plaxton Première 350	C49F	2001	
RX51EXN	Volvo B10M-62	Plaxton Première 350	C49F	2001	
RX51EXO	Volvo B10M-62	Plaxton Première 350	C55F	2001	
RX51EXP	Volvo B10M-62	Plaxton Première 350	C55F	2001	
FJ03ZTU	Irisbus EuroRider 397E.12.35	Beulas Stergo E	C53F	2003	Whittle, Kidderminster, 2006
FJ03ZTV	Irisbus EuroRider 397E.12.35	Beulas Stergo E	C53F	2003	Whittle, Kidderminster, 2006
FJ03ZTW	Irisbus EuroRider 397E.12.35	Beulas Stergo E	C53F	2003	Whittle, Kidderminster, 2006
FJ03ZTY	Irisbus EuroRider 397E.12.35	Beulas Stergo E	C53F	2003	Whittle, Kidderminster, 2006
RX06WVA	Volvo B12B	Plaxton Panther	C49FT	2006	
RX06WVB	Volvo B12B	Plaxton Panther	C49FT	2006	
RX06WVC	Volvo B12B	Plaxton Panther	C44FT	2006	
RX06WVD	Volvo B12B	Plaxton Panther	C49FT	2006	
RX06WVE	Volvo B12B	Plaxton Panther	C49FT	2006	
RX06WVL	Toyota Coaster BB50R	Caetano Optimo IV	C22F	2006	
RX06WVM	Toyota Coaster BB50R	Caetano Optimo IV	C22F	2006	
RX06WVN	Toyota Coaster BB50R	Caetano Optimo IV	C22FL	2006	
RX07KDF	Volvo B12B	Plaxton Panther	C57F	2007	
RX07KDJ	Volvo B12B	Plaxton Panther	C57F	2007	
RX07KDK	Volvo B12B	Plaxton Panther	C57F	2007	
RX07KDN	Volvo B12B	Plaxton Panther	C57F	2007	
RX07KDO	Volvo B12B	Plaxton Panther	C57F	2007	
RX07KDV	Volvo B12B	Plaxton Panther	C57F	2007	
RX07KDZ	Volvo B12B	Plaxton Panther	C57F	2007	
RX07KEJ	Volvo B12B	Plaxton Panther	C57F	2007	

Horseman has been operating coaches in the Reading area for some thirty years, with several school contracts currently undertaken. From the 2006 intake of Plaxton-bodied Volvo coaches, RX06WVC is departing from the Thurrock motorway services. *Dave Heath*

For the 2007 intake, electronic destination blinds were provided on the Plaxton Panthers. Seen in its home town is RX07KDO. *Dave Heath*

RX57GXL	Volvo B12B	Plaxton Panther	C57F	2007	
RX57GXM	Volvo B12B	Plaxton Panther	C57F	2007	
RX57GXN	Volvo B12B	Plaxton Panther	C57F	2007	
RX57GXO	Volvo B12B	Plaxton Panther	C57F	2007	
RX57GXP	Volvo B12B	Plaxton Panther	C57F	2007	
RX57GXR	Volvo B12B	Plaxton Panther	C57F	2007	
RX57GXS	Volvo B12B	Plaxton Panther	C57F	2007	
RX57GXT	Toyota Coaster BB50R	Caetano Optimo V	C26F	2008	
RX57GXU	Toyota Coaster BB50R	Caetano Optimo V	C26F	2008	
RX57GXV	Toyota Coaster BB50R	Caetano Optimo V	C26F	2008	
RX57GXW	Toyota Coaster BB50R	Caetano Optimo V	C26F	2008	
YN09HRG	Volvo B12B 13m	Plaxton Elite	C52FT	2009	Logan, Dunloy, 2011
YN11HXC	Volvo B9R	Plaxton Profile 70	S70F	2011	
RX61GDY	Mercedes-Benz Vario O816	Plaxton Cheetah	C33F	2011	
RX61GDZ	Mercedes-Benz Vario O816	Plaxton Cheetah	C33F	2011	
RX12HNP	Mercedes-Benz Vario O816	Plaxton Cheetah	C33F	2012	
RX12HNU	Mercedes-Benz Vario O816	Plaxton Cheetah	C33F	2012	
RX12HNV	Mercedes-Benz Vario O816	Plaxton Cheetah	C33F	2012	

Depots: Whitley Wood Road, Reading and The Green, Theale

IRVING'S of CARLISLE

Irving's Coach Hire Ltd, Jesmond Street, Greystoke Road, Carlisle, CA1 2DE

A182XCA	Volvo B10M-61	Van Hool Alizée	C53F	1984	Wright, Wrexham, 1986
EIG9423	Volvo B10M-61	Van Hool Alizée	C53F	1986	Scott, Oldham, 2011
PLZ3055	Volvo B10M-61	Jonckheere Jubilee P599	C49FT	1986	Plumley, Humshaugh, 2009
PIL9376	Volvo B10M-60	Van Hool Alizée	C53F	1989	Mawley, Cleobury Mortimer, 2011
V11BUS	VDL Bova Futura FHD13.340	VDL Bova	C49FT	2006	
V30BUS	Volvo B12B	Van Hool T917 Acron	C49FT	2006	Marbill, Beith, 2010
R8BUS	Volvo B12B	Van Hool T9 Alizée	C57F	2007	
YN11AWU	Volvo B7R	Plaxton Prima	C57F	2011	

Special event vehicle:

OHH977G	Bedford J2	Plaxton Embassy	C20F	1968	

Previous registrations:

EIG9423	C27OFL, KTL982	PLZ3055	C28GNK, TSV804, MLC5P
PIL9376	F953WSF, SV2923	V30BUS	SF06LKC

The bright orange livery on V11BUS of Irving's of Carlisle blends with the bright blue sky found in Blackpool where the only VDL product in the fleet and is seen during undertaking a local excursion. *Dave Heath*

JOHNSON BROS.

Johnson Bros. - Redfern Travel

Johnson Bros (Tours) Ltd, Portland House, Claylands Avenue, Worksop, S81 7BQ

Redfern Coaches (Mansfield) Ltd, Lindley Street, Mansfield, NG18 1QE

Buses:

OSF305G	Bristol VRT/SL/6LX	Eastern Coach Works	B43/31F	1969	Southern Vectis, 1986
NGM168G	Bristol VRT/SL/6LX	Eastern Coach Works	B43/31F	1969	Southern Vectis, 1986
PKE810M	Bristol VRT/SL/6LX	Eastern Coach Works	B43/34F	1974	Maidstone & District, 1988
HWE826N	Bristol VRT/SL2/6LX	Eastern Coach Works	B43/34F	1975	Yorkshire Traction, 1993
OWE854R	Bristol VRT/SL3/501(6LXB)	Eastern Coach Works	B43/31F	1977	Yorkshire Traction, 1993
OWE857R	Bristol VRT/SL3/501(6LXB)	Eastern Coach Works	B43/31F	1977	Yorkshire Traction, 1993
OWE858R	Bristol VRT/SL3/501(6LXB)	Eastern Coach Works	B43/31F	1977	Yorkshire Traction, 1993
RWT544R	Bristol VRT/SL3/6LX	Eastern Coach Works	B43/31F	1977	Moffat & Williamson, 1994
PTT98R	Bristol VRT/SL3/6LXB	Eastern Coach Works	B43/31F	1977	Solent Blue Line, 1997
ODL661R	Bristol VRT/SL3/6LXB	Eastern Coach Works	B43/31F	1977	Solent Blue Line, 1997
ODL662R	Bristol VRT/SL3/6LXB	Eastern Coach Works	B43/31F	1977	Solent Blue Line, 1997
ODL663R	Bristol VRT/SL3/6LXB	Eastern Coach Works	B43/31F	1977	Solent Blue Line, 1997
ODL664R	Bristol VRT/SL3/6LXB	Eastern Coach Works	B43/31F	1977	Solent Blue Line, 1997
TDT864S	Bristol VRT/SL3/501(6LXB)	Eastern Coach Works	B43/31F	1977	Yorkshire Traction, 1993
MIW2422	Bristol VRT/SL3/501(6LXB)	Eastern Coach Works	B43/31F	1978	Clarkson, South Elmsall, 1994
UDL668S	Bristol VRT/SL3/6LXB	Eastern Coach Works	B43/31F	1978	Solent Blue Line, 1997
YDL676T	Bristol VRT/SL3/6LXB	Eastern Coach Works	B43/31F	1979	Solent Blue Line, 2001
FDL677V	Bristol VRT/SL3/6LXB	Eastern Coach Works	B43/31F	1980	Solent Blue Line, 2001
FDL679V	Bristol VRT/SL3/6LXB	Eastern Coach Works	B43/31F	1980	Solent Blue Line, 2001
LVL804V	Bristol VRT/SL3/6LXB	Eastern Coach Works	B43/31F	1980	RoadCar, Lincoln, 1997
LVL807V	Bristol VRT/SL3/6LXB	Eastern Coach Works	B43/31F	1980	RoadCar, Lincoln, 1997
SVL177W	Bristol VRT/SL3/6LXB	Eastern Coach Works	B43/31F	1981	RoadCar, Lincoln, 1996
SVL178W	Bristol VRT/SL3/6LXB	Eastern Coach Works	B43/31F	1981	RoadCar, Lincoln, 1996
SVL179W	Bristol VRT/SL3/6LXB	Eastern Coach Works	B43/31F	1981	RoadCar, Lincoln, 1996
SVL180W	Bristol VRT/SL3/6LXB	Eastern Coach Works	B43/31F	1981	RoadCar, Lincoln, 1996
MWG940X	Bristol VRT/SL3/501(6LXB)	Eastern Coach Works	BC39/31F	1981	RoadCar, Lincoln, 2000
RTV438X	Leyland Atlantean AN68C/1R	Northern Counties	B47/33D	1981	Redfern, Mansfield, 1999
WDL694Y	Leyland Olympian ONLXB/1R	Eastern Coach Works	B45/30F	1983	Solent Blue Line, 2003
A697DDL	Leyland Olympian ONLXB/1R	Eastern Coach Works	B45/30F	1984	Solent Blue Line, 2003
A295FDL	Leyland Olympian ONLXB/1R	Eastern Coach Works	B45/30F	1984	Solent Blue Line, 2002
A133SMA	Leyland Olympian ONLXB/1R	Eastern Coach Works	B45/32F	1983	Daybird Roadline, , 2004
A530OKH	Leyland Olympian ONLXB/1R	Eastern Coach Works	B45/32F	1984	East Yorkshire, 2006
A531OKH	Leyland Olympian ONLXB/1R	Eastern Coach Works	B45/32F	1984	East Yorkshire, 2006
A532OKH	Leyland Olympian ONLXB/1R	Eastern Coach Works	B45/32F	1984	East Yorkshire, 2006
B533WAT	Leyland Olympian ONLXB/1R	Eastern Coach Works	B45/30F	1985	East Yorkshire, 2006
B534WAT	Leyland Olympian ONLXB/1R	Eastern Coach Works	B45/30F	1985	East Yorkshire, 2006
B535WAT	Leyland Olympian ONLXB/1R	Eastern Coach Works	B45/30F	1985	East Yorkshire, 2006
B503FFW	Leyland Olympian ONLXB/1R	Eastern Coach Works	B45/30F	1985	Stagecoach, 2008
B735GCN	Leyland Olympian ONCL10/RV	Eastern Coach Works	B45/32F	1985	Go North East, 2004
B736GCN	Leyland Olympian ONCL10/RV	Eastern Coach Works	B45/32F	1985	Go North East, 2004
B738GCN	Leyland Olympian ONCL10/RV	Eastern Coach Works	B45/32F	1985	Go North East, 2004
B741GCN	Leyland Olympian ONCL10/RV	Eastern Coach Works	B45/32F	1985	Go North East, 2004
B742GCN	Leyland Olympian ONCL10/RV	Eastern Coach Works	B45/32F	1985	Go North East, 2004
B744GCN	Leyland Olympian ONCL10/RV	Eastern Coach Works	B45/32F	1985	Go North East, 2004
C171ECK	Leyland Olympian ONLXB/1R	Eastern Coach Works	BC42/30F	1985	Harrogate Coach Company, 2008
C658LJR	Leyland Olympian ONCL10/1RZ	Eastern Coach Works	B45/32F	1985	Johnson, Greencroft, 2006
C661LJR	Leyland Olympian ONCL10/1RZ	Eastern Coach Works	B45/32F	1985	Johnson, Greencroft, 2006
C665LJR	Leyland Olympian ONCL10/1RZ	Eastern Coach Works	B45/32F	1985	Weardale, Stanhope, 2006
UJT366	Leyland Olympian ONCL10/1RZ	Eastern Coach Works	B45/32F	1985	Weardale, Stanhope, 2006
C332HWJ	Leyland Olympian ONLXB/1R	Eastern Coach Works	B45/32F	1985	Stagecoach, 2005
C536DAT	Leyland Olympian ONLXB/1RH	Eastern Coach Works	B45/31F	1986	East Yorkshire, 2006
F708SDL	Leyland Olympian ONCL10/1RZ	Leyland	B47/31F	1989	York Pullman, 2009
G754UYT	Leyland Olympian ONLXB/1RZ	Northern Counties	B45/30F	1989	Arriva North West & Wales, 2006
G755UYT	Leyland Olympian ONLXB/1RZ	Northern Counties	B45/30F	1989	Arriva North West & Wales, 2006
G762UYT	Leyland Olympian ONLXB/1RZ	Northern Counties	B45/30F	1989	Arriva North West & Wales, 2008
YSV604	Leyland Olympian ONLXB/1RZ	Northern Counties	B45/30F	1989	Arriva North West & Wales, 2006
G213SSL	Leyland Olympian ON2R56G13Z4	Alexander RL	BC51/31F	1989	Stagecoach, 2009
G804SMV	Leyland Olympian ON2R50C13Z4	Leyland	B47/31F	1990	Western Greyhound, 2009

Johnson Bros operates a mixed fleet of coaches and double-deck buses that are predominantly used on school contracts. Stratford is the location for this view of P3JBT, an Irisbus EuroRider with Plaxton Paragon bodywork. *Mark Doggett*

H807XMY	Leyland Olympian ON2R50C13Z4	Leyland	B47/31F	1990	Western Greyhound, 2009
H548VAT	Leyland Olympian ON2R56C13Z4	Northern Counties	B51/34F	1990	East Yorkshire, 2009
H550VAT	Leyland Olympian ON2R56C13Z4	Northern Counties	B51/34F	1990	East Yorkshire, 2009
J132HMT	Scania N113DRB	Northern Counties Palatine	B41/27F	1992	Stagecoach, 2009
J143HMT	Scania N113DRB	Northern Counties Palatine	B41/27F	1992	Stagecoach, 2009
J144HMT	Scania N113DRB	Northern Counties Palatine	B41/27F	1992	Stagecoach, 2009
J145HMT	Scania N113DRB	Northern Counties Palatine	B41/27F	1992	Stagecoach, 2009
K846LMK	Scania N113DRB	Northern Counties Palatine	B41/27F	1992	Stagecoach, 2009
K847LMK	Scania N113DRB	Northern Counties Palatine	B41/27F	1992	Stagecoach, 2009
K848LMK	Scania N113DRB	Northern Counties Palatine	B41/27F	1992	Stagecoach, 2009
K851LMK	Scania N113DRB	Northern Counties Palatine	B41/27F	1992	Stagecoach, 2009
K860LMK	Scania N113DRB	Northern Counties Palatine	B41/27F	1992	Stagecoach, 2009
K862LMK	Scania N113DRB	Northern Counties Palatine	B41/27F	1992	Stagecoach, 2009
K871LMK	Scania N113DRB	Northern Counties Palatine	B41/27F	1992	Stagecoach, 2009
K355DWJ	Leyland Olympian ON2R50C13Z4	Northern Counties	B47/29F	1992	Stagecoach, 2009
P274NRH	Optare Excel L1150	Optare	N45F	1997	East Yorkshire, 2002

Coaches

H5JBT	Volvo B10M-60	Van Hool Alizée H	C53F	1991	Shearings, Wigan, 1997
L3JBT	Volvo B10M-62	Jonckheere Deauville 45	C53F	1995	Clarkes of London, 2001
N1JBT	Volvo B10M-62	Van Hool Alizée HE	C44FT	1997	Red Arrow, Huddersfield, 2001
P1JBT	Volvo B10M-62	Van Hool Alizée HE	C46FT	1997	Wallce Arnold, Leeds, 2000
R54YDT	Ford Transit	Taurus	M8	1998	
63RT	MAN 24.350	Jonckheere Monaco	C53/15FT	1999	Stagecoach, 2007
T3JBT	MAN 24.350	Jonckheere Monaco	C53/15FT	1999	Stagecoach, 2007
T4JBT	Volvo B10M-62	Plaxton Excalibur	C49FT	1999	
Y2JBT	Iveco EuroRider 391E.12.35	Beulas Stergo E	C51FT	2002	
Y3JBT	Iveco EuroRider 391E.12.35	Beulas Stergo E	C51FT	2002	
YS02XED	Scania K114 EB4	Irizar Century 12.35	C49FT	2002	Mills, Gornalwood, 2005
M1JBT	Volvo B10M-62	Plaxton Panther	C53F	2002	
JBT16S	Volvo B12M	Jonckheere Mistral 50	C49FT	2003	
43RT	Mercedes-Benz Vario O814	TransBus Cheetah	C29F	2003	
YN03AVE	Neoplan Euroliner N316 SHD	Neoplan	C49FT	2003	
77RT	Neoplan Euroliner N316 SHD	Neoplan	C49FT	2004	

Joining the fleet in 2006, 6JBT is a Scania K114 with Irizar PB bodywork. The PB is 12.2 metres long in the standard 2-axle model and 13 metres on the 3-axle K-series chassis from Scania. *Mark Doggett*

K1JBT	Volvo B7R	TransBus Profile 70	S70F	2004	
YN04HJJ	Volvo B7R	TransBus Profile 70	S70F	2004	
79RT	Volvo B12M	VDL Berkhof Axial 50	C51FT	2004	
B8JBT	VDL Bova Futura FHD12.340	VDL Bova	C53FT	2004	
JBT3S	Neoplan Starliner N516 SHD	Neoplan	C53FT	2004	
123RT	Scania K114 EB6	Irizar PB	C49FT	2005	
76RT	Irisbus EuroRider 397E.12.31	Plaxton Paragon	C57F	2006	
P3JBT	Irisbus EuroRider 397E.12.31	Plaxton Paragon	C57F	2006	
YJ06YRA	Ford Transit	Optare/Ferqui	C16F	2006	
YN06OPG	Mercedes-Benz Vario 0814	Plaxton Cheetah	C33F	2006	
4JBT	Scania K114 EB6	Irizar PB	C49FT	2006	
96RT	Irisbus Daily 45C14	Excel	M16	2006	
5JBT	Scania K114 EB6	Irizar Century 12.35	C53F	2006	
6JBT	Scania K114 EB6	Irizar PB	C49FT	2006	
N1JBT	Volvo B12M	VDL Jonckheere Mistral	C53FT	2007	Park's of Hamilton, 2009
EN08ECE	Ford Transit	Ford	M14	2008	Maun, Huthwaite, 2008
YN58CFV	Mercedes-Benz Vario 0816	Plaxton Cheetah	C33F	2008	
YN58CGV	Mercedes-Benz Vario 0816	Plaxton Cheetah	C33F	2008	
94RT	VDL Bova Futura FHD127.365	VDL Bova	C53FT	2009	
71RT	Irisbus EuroRider 397E.12.35	Beulas Cygnus	C53FT	2009	
8JBT	Ayats Bravo 1 A3E/BR1	Ayats	C65/18DT	2009	
YN10AAE	Irisbus EuroRider 397E.12.35	Beulas Cygnus	C53FT	2010	
YN10AAF	Irisbus EuroRider 397E.12.35	Beulas Cygnus	C53FT	2010	
PN10AHD	Irisbus EuroRider 397E.12.43	Beulas Cygnus	C53FT	2010	
FJ60EGE	Volvo B9R	Caetano Levanté	C48FT	2010	
FJ60EGF	Volvo B9R	Caetano Levanté	C48FT	2010	
9JBT	Volvo B9R	Sunsundegui Sideral 330	C36FT	2010	
MF11LUJ	Neoplan Tourliner N2216/3 SHD	Neoplan	C61FT	2011	
MF11LUL	Neoplan Tourliner N2216/3 SHD	Neoplan	C61FT	2011	
MF11LUO	Neoplan Tourliner N2216 SHD	Neoplan	C50FT	2011	
YJ61FFS	Van Hool T917 Altano	Van Hool	C54FT	2011	

Johnsons maintains a collection of interesting coaches from days gone by including GAL967, a Bedford OWB with Duple coachwork. *John Marsh*

Special event vehicles

GAL967	Bedford OWB	Duple	C29F	1944	Gash, Newark
KAL578	Daimler CVD6	Massey	B33/28R	1948	Gash, Newark
YDK795	Ford 570E	Plaxton Embassy I	C41F	1961	Roberts, Rochdale
5188RU	Bedford VAL14	Plaxton Panorama	C52F	1963	Excelsior, Bournemouth
8488NU	Bedford VAL14	Plaxton Panorama	C52F	1964	Branson, Brompton
HPN487D	Bedford J2	Plaxton Embassy	C20F	1966	Bletchley Self Drive
KNK379H	Bedford VAL70	Plaxton Panorama Elite	C53F	1970	Thompson, London
NEC237K	Bedford VAL70	Plaxton Panorama Elite II	C53F	1972	Brown, Ambleside
KNS401N	Volvo B58	Plaxton Supreme IV	C57F	1979	Volvo demonstrator
LHE601W	Volvo B58-56	Plaxton Supreme IV	C53F	1981	
A283HAY	Bedford YMP	Plaxton Paramount 3200	C45F	1984	Smith, Kibworth

Previous registrations:

4JBT	YN06CHO	JBT3S	YN04AXA
5JBT	YN56NNO	JBT16S	FJ03AAK
6JBT	YN56NNP	K1JBT	YN04HJC
8JBT	YN59EYW	L3JBT	M327KRY
9JBT	FJ60EJL	M1JBT	YR52MEV
43RT	YJ53EJO	M2JBT	71RT, PN09CXS
76RT	YN04OPH	MIW2422	VHB679S
77RT	YN04AUX	N1JBT	LSK506, SF07XNU
79RT	FJ04ETT	OIB2917	KNS401V
94RT	YJ09FHZ	P1JBT	PN09CXR
96RT	FJ56HLN	P3JBT	YN06OPJ
123RT	YN05HBB	T3JBT	T55UBE, T617DWL
A283HAY	A283HAY, JIL5807	T616DWL	T50UBE
A295FOL	A702DDL, WDL142	UJT366	C672LJR
B8JBT	YJ05XXC	Y2JBT	FN02VCL
H5JBT	H184DVMS	Y3JBT	FN02VCM
		YSV604	G759UYT

JOHNSONS

Johnsons (Henley) Ltd, Liveridge House, Liveridge Hill, Henley-in-Arden, Solihull, B95 5QS

Buses

P914SUM	Optare Excel L1070	Optare	N48F	1997	BT Goonhilly, 2005
V145LGC	Volvo B7TL	Alexander ALX400	N47/27F	2000	Go-Ahead London, 2010
YD02RHZ	DAF SB220	East Lancs Myllennium	NC50F	2002	
YM52TSO	Optare Solo M850	Optare	N25F	2003	
YM52TSU	Optare Solo M850	Optare	N25F	2003	
YN53SVX	Optare Solo M920	Optare	N30F	2003	
YN53YHA	Optare Solo M850	Optare	N26F	2003	
YN53YHB	Optare Solo M850	Optare	N26F	2003	
KN04XCU	TransBus Dart	TransBus Pointer	N30F	2004	*Operated for Warwickshire CC*
YJ54UBX	Optare Solo M920	Optare	N33F	2005	
YJ55BMO	Optare Solo M850	Optare	N29F	2005	
YJ55BMU	Optare Solo M850	Optare	N29F	2005	
MX06BSU	Optare Solo M920	Optare	N33F	2006	Ace, Aintree, 2012
MX56LNR	Optare Solo M920	Optare	N33F	2007	Ace, Aintree, 2012
YN56NNE	Scania OmniCity N230 UB	Scania	N41F	2007	*Operated for Warwickshire CC*
YN56NNF	Scania OmniCity N230 UB	Scania	N41F	2007	*Operated for Warwickshire CC*
YN56NNG	Scania OmniCity N230 UB	Scania	N41F	2007	*Operated for Warwickshire CC*
YJ07EHG	Optare Tempo X1200	Optare	N36F	2007	
YJ07EHH	Optare Tempo X1200	Optare	N36F	2007	
YJ57EGU	Optare Tempo X1200	Optare	N40F	2008	Optare demonstrator, 2008
YJ57YCL	Optare Tempo X1200	Optare	N40F	2008	
YJ08PGY	Optare Tempo X1200	Optare	N40F	2008	
YJ08PGX	Optare Solo M850	Optare	N29F	2008	
PN09ELJ	Scania N230 UB	Optare Olympus	NC51/30F	2009	
PN09EMJ	Scania N230 UB	Optare Olympus	NC51/30F	2009	
PN09ENJ	Scania N230 UB	Optare Olympus	NC51/30F	2009	
YJ59GEU	Optare Tempo X1200	Optare	N43F	2009	
YJ59GEY	Optare Tempo X1200	Optare	N43F	2009	
YJ59GFA	Optare Tempo X1200	Optare	N43F	2009	
YJ59GFE	Optare Tempo X1200	Optare	N43F	2009	
YJ10MHA	Optare Tempo X1200	Optare	N43F	2010	
YJ11EJE	Optare Versa V1100 Hybrid	Optare	N37F	2011	
YJ11EJF	Optare Versa V1100 Hybrid	Optare	N37F	2011	
YJ11EJG	Optare Versa V1100 Hybrid	Optare	N37F	2011	
YJ11EJK	Optare Versa V1100 Hybrid	Optare	N37F	2011	
YJ11EJL	Optare Versa V1100 Hybrid	Optare	N37F	2011	

Over a hundred years have passed since, Johnsons of Henley-in-Arden started its business. The company now provides several commercial services in the surrounding area of Warwickshire and West Midlands. Ten Optare Tempo buses have joined the fleet, including YJ59GEU which is seen while operating the route to Banbury. *Mark Doggett*

Coaches

EN03OJF	Ford Transit Tourneo	Ford		M7	2002	
EX04AZL	Ford Transit	Ford		M8	2004	
EA05XBL	Ford Transit	Ford		M8	2005	
ET55KDX	Ford Transit	Ford		M12	2006	
ET55KGG	Ford Transit	Ford		M12	2006	
EN06XOO	Ford Transit	Ford		M8	2006	
EX56OSP	Ford Transit	Ford		M8	2006	
AD07CXJ	Ford Transit	Ford		M8	2007	
AK07URW	Ford Transit	Ford		M8	2007	
N10JRJ	Bova Futura FLD12.340	Bova		C49FT	1996	
E16JCT	Bova Futura FHD12.340	Bova		C49FT	1997	
E17JCT	Bova Futura FHD12.340	Bova		C49FT	1997	
E14JCT	Bova Futura FHD12.340	Bova		C49FT	1999	
E15JCT	Bova Futura FHD12.340	Bova		C49FT	1999	
E9JCT	Bova Futura FHD10.340	Bova		C37FT	1999	
E18JCT	Bova Futura FHD12.370	Bova		C53F	2000	Cummer, Galway, 2001
E19JCT	Bova Futura FHD12.370	Bova		C53F	2000	Cummer, Galway, 2001
E10JCT	Bova Futura FHD12.370	Bova		C49FT	2000	
E12JCT	Bova Futura FHD12.370	Bova		C49FT	2000	
E11JCT	Bova Futura FHD12.370	Bova		C49FT	2000	
Y656HWY	Bova Futura FHD12.370	Bova		C53F	2001	
Y657HWY	Bova Futura FHD12.370	Bova		C53F	2001	
YD02PXA	Bova Futura FHD12.340	Bova		C53F	2002	Anderson, London, 2007
YD02PXB	Bova Futura FHD12.340	Bova		C53F	2002	Anderson, London, 2007
YD02PXP	Bova Futura FHD12.370	Bova		C53F	2002	
YJ03GYB	Bova Futura FHD12.340	Bova		C44FT	2003	
YJ03GYC	Bova Futura FHD12.340	Bova		C49FT	2003	
YJ03GYD	Bova Futura FHD12.340	Bova		C49FT	2003	
YJ03GYE	Bova Futura FHD12.340	Bova		C49FT	2003	
YM03EOP	Volvo B7R	Plaxton Profile 70		S70F	2003	*Operated for Warwickshire CC*
YM03EOR	Volvo B7R	Plaxton Profile 70		S70F	2003	*Operated for Warwickshire CC*
YJ04GYA	VDL Bova Futura FHD12.340	VDL Bova		C44FT	2004	
YJ04GYB	VDL Bova Futura FHD12.340	VDL Bova		C44FT	2004	
YJ04GYC	VDL Bova Futura FHD12.340	VDL Bova		C49FT	2004	
YJ04GYD	VDL Bova Futura FHD12.340	VDL Bova		C49FT	2004	
YJ54EXL	VDL Bova Futura FHD14.430	VDL Bova		C61FT	2005	Shaw, Coventry, 2012
YJ05FXK	VDL Bova Futura FHD13.340	VDL Bova		C49FT	2005	
YJ05FXL	VDL Bova Futura FHD13.340	VDL Bova		C49FT	2005	
YJ07DWF	VDL Bova Magiq XHD122.410	VDL Bova		C44FT	2007	
YJ07DWG	VDL Bova Magiq XHD122.410	VDL Bova		C44FT	2007	

Johnsons was successful in its bid for funding for the Versas from the Government's Green Bus Fund, including YJ11EJK shown. These 11.1 metre 40-seater Versas are in service on the Stratford-upon-Avon Park & Ride scheme which also incorporates town service route 222. The driveline in the Versas combines the Siemens hybrid drive system using ultra-capacitors with the Mercedes-Benz OM904LA diesel engine to achieve outstanding fuel efficiency. *Mark Doggett*

Johnsons has been synonymous with the Bova Futura for several years and a further three coaches joined the fleet in 2011. In 2007 two Bova Magiq models were acquired two years after the product was re-introduced to Britain. Illustrating the Magiq is YJ07DWG. *Colin Lloyd*

YX08AOK	Mercedes-Benz Sprinter 515cdi	Optare/Ferqui Soroco	C15F	2008
YX08AOV	Mercedes-Benz Vario O816	Optare/Ferqui Toro	C23F	2008
YX08AOW	Mercedes-Benz Vario O816	Optare/Ferqui Toro	C23F	2008
YN08JAO	Scania K340 EB4	Irizar PB	C44FT	2008
YT09FLP	Scania K340 EB4	Irizar PB	C44FT	2009
YT09FLR	Scania K340 EB4	Irizar PB	C44FT	2009
YJ10JYC	VDL Bova Futura FHD127.365	VDL Bova	C49FT	2010
YJ10JYD	VDL Bova Futura FHD127.365	VDL Bova	C49FT	2010
YJ10JYE	VDL Bova Futura FHD127.365	VDL Bova	C53F	2010
YJ10JYF	VDL Bova Futura FHD127.365	VDL Bova	C53F	2010
YJ11AMO	VDL Bova Futura FHD127.365	VDL Bova	C49FT	2011
YJ11AMU	VDL Bova Futura FHD127.365	VDL Bova	C49FT	2011
YJ11ANR	VDL Bova Futura FHD127.365	VDL Bova	C49FT	2011
BW11CHG	Volkswagen Transporter	Volkswagen	M8	2011
YJ12KGA	VDL Bova Futura FHD127.365	VDL Bova	C49FT	2012
YJ12KGE	VDL Bova Futura FHD127.365	VDL Bova	C49FT	2012

Previous registrations:

B10JCT	ICOV, YJ54EXL	E15JCT	T936WWY
E9JCT	V505PCX	E16JCT	P256XUM
E10JCT	W484HJW	E17JCT	P257XUM
E11JCT	W162DYG	E18JCT	00G2353, V319LHS
E12JCT	W119DUA	E19JCT	00G3430, V320LHS
E14JCT	T935WWY		

Web: www.johnsonscoaches.co.uk
Depot: Liveridge Hill, Henley-in-Arden and Timothys Bridge Road, Stratford-upon-Avon.

KM Travel

KM Motors Ltd, Wilson Grove, Lundwood, Barnsley, S715JS

H3KMT	Ford Transit	Ford	M8	1994	
K4KMT	Scania K113 CRB	Van Hool Alizée	C49FT	1997	
4465KM	Scania K113 CRB	Van Hool Alizée	C49FT	1997	Bostock's, Congleton, 2001
S474MTF	Mercedes-Benz Vito 108	Mercedes-Benz	M8	1998	
JIL3581	Bova Futura FHD12.370	Bova	C49FT	2001	Moxon, Oldcotes, 2005
YD02PXM	Bova Futura FHD12.370	Bova	C49FT	2002	Moxon, Oldcotes, 2006
BV03RXN	Ford Transit	Ford	M8	2003	Tellings-Golden Miller, 2010
MP03FZJ	Mercedes-Benz Vito 110 cdi	Mercedes-Benz	M8	2003	
1516KM	VDL Bova Futura FHD13.340	Bova	C49FT	2005	Moxon, Oldcotes, 2010
YJ09FHP	VDL Bova Futura FHD13.420	Bova	C49FT	2009	
YJ10JYT	VDL Bova Futura FHD120.365	Bova	C49FT	2010	
ER11ZAR	Irizar i6	Irizar	C50FT	2012	

Previous registrations:

893KM	-	JIL3581	?
1516KM	YJ05FXO	K4KMT	-
4465KM	R7BOS, R578XBV	MP03FZJ	R953CET
J10KMT	T985WPN	YD02PXM	YD02PXM, M9XON

Irizar first supplied coaches for the British market in 1993 and until recently they have only been based on Scania chassis. The integral i6model was launched in Madrid in November 2010, its structure having been designed by taking into consideration the vehicle's resistance to frontal collisions and roll-overs, thus complying with the future R66.01 safety regulation. Several of the coaches, including ER11ZAR, are fitted with the Ecolife automatic gearbox. *Tony Greaves*

KENZIES

Kenzies Coaches Ltd, 6 Angle Lane, Shepreth, Royston, SG8 6QH

YJE3T	Bedford YMT	Plaxton Supreme IV	C53F	1979	
XVE8T	Volvo B58-61	Plaxton Supreme IV	C57F	1979	
CVE12V	Volvo B58-61	Plaxton Supreme IV	C50F	1980	
HFL14W	Bedford YMQ	Plaxton Supreme IV	C45F	1981	
LEW16W	Volvo B10M-61	Plaxton Supreme IV	C53F	1981	
C25KAV	Volvo B10M-61	Van Hool Alizée H	C57F	1985	
D30BEW	Volvo B10M-61	Van Hool Alizée H	C57F	1987	
F443PNC	Volvo B10M-60	Van Hool Alizée HE	C53F	1989	Robinson, Kimbolton, 2010
K51TER	Volvo B10M-60	Van Hool Alizée HE	C48FT	1993	
K52TER	Volvo B10M-60	Van Hool Alizée HE	C48FT	1993	
VVE885	Volvo B9M	Van Hool T9 Alizée	C36FT	2001	
S100CBK	Volvo B12B	Van Hool T9 Alizée	C48FT	2004	
K20CBK	Volvo B12B	Van Hool T9 Alizée	C49FT	2005	
K30CBK	Volvo B12B	Van Hool T9 Alizée	C49FT	2005	
K40CBK	Volvo B12B	Van Hool T9 Alizée	C49FT	2005	
K50CBK	Volvo B12B	Plaxton Panther	C49FT	2005	
K3CBK	Volvo B12B 13m	Van Hool T9 Alicron	C59F	2006	
H2CBK	Volvo B12B 13m	Van Hool T9 Alicron	C59FT	2008	
K10CBK	Volvo B12B 13m	Van Hool T9 Alicron	C59FT	2008	
CK10CBK	Volvo B12B	Van Hool T9 Alizée	C59FT	2010	

Special event vehicles:

u	EEL46	Bedford WTB	*chassis only*			
	JUE860	Bedford OB	Duple Vista	C29F	1950	Webb, Armcote
	JBY804	Bedford OB	Duple Vista	C29F	1951	Barber, Mitcham
	750DCD	Leyland Leopard L2	Harrington Grenadier	C28F	1963	Southdown
	GUP743C	Bedford VAL14	Plaxton Panorama	C52F	1965	Carr, New Silksworth
	CNW155C	Bedford VAL14	Harrington Legionnaire	C44F	1965	Heaps, Leeds
	KNK373H	Bedford J2SZ10	Plaxton Embassy	C15F	1969	Rickards, Brentford
	PJE999J	Bedford YRQ	Plaxton Panorama Elite	C45F	1971	
	PEB2R	Bedford YMT	Plaxton Supreme III	C45F	1977	
	B948ASU	Volvo B10M-56	Van Hool Alizée L	B51F	1984	Hutchison, Overtown

Previous registrations:

H2CBK	YJ08NSV		K3CBK	AE06OAD
F443PNC	F37DAV, 648EAU, A10CVR		K10CBK	YJ08NSY

Depots: Angle Lane, Shepreth and Barrington Road, Shepreth

Taking a break in Portsmouth is K10CBK, a Volvo B12B with Van Hool T9 Alicron bodywork. *Dave Heath*

KETTLEWELLS

Kettlewell (Retford) Ltd; Pegasus Coachways Ltd, Grove Street, Retford, DN22 6LA

JIL7899	Volvo B10M-61	Jonckheere Jubilee P90	C49/9FT	1983	Trathens, Plymouth, 1986
A50WVL	Scania K112 CRS	Deltaplan	C49FT	1984	
GIL7216	Leyland Tiger TRCL10/3ARZM	Plaxton Paramount 3500 III	C53F	1989	Rosemary Cs, Terrington, 1993
K300KET	Scania K124 IB	Irizar Century 12.35	C55F	1999	Blue Iris, Nailsea, 2005
V334EAK	Scania N113 DRB	East Lancashire Cityzen	BC47/31F	2000	
K500KET	Scania L94 IB	Irizar Century 12.35	C49FT	2000	
K600KET	Scania L94 IB	Irizar Century 12.35	C55F	2000	
K700KET	Scania K114 IB4	Irizar Century 12.35	C49FT	2003	Allan, Gorebridge, 2005
MF52UKD	Mercedes-Benz Sprinter 413 cdi	Concept	M16	2003	
KET6	Neoplan Starliner N516 SHD	Neoplan	C49FT	2005	
K155KET	Scania K340 EB6	Irizar PB	C53FT	2006	
K800KET	Scania K340 EB6	Irizar PB	C53FT	2006	Milligan, Mauchline, 2005
K900KET	Scania K340 EB6	Irizar PB	C49FT	2007	Happy Days, Stafford, 2009

Previous registrations:

A50WVL	A50WVL, KET6	K700KET	SN53RXF, B18DWA
GIL7216	G704HPW	K800KET	YN56FGF
JIL7899	A147JTA	K900KET	YN07EYF
K300KET	V301EAK	KET6	YN55NPK
K500KET	W5KET		
K600KET	W66KET		

Representing Kettlewells fleet is Scania K155KET, a Scania with Irizar PB bodywork. *Dave Heath*

Laguna operates a fleet comprised almost entirely of Scania coaches bodied in Spain by Irizar. Representing the fleet is YR10BBV. *Dave Heath*

The Shropshire-based Lakeside Coaches operates from the north of the county. Seen in London on a Ladies' Ghost outing is the latest arrival, BN11UGO, a Mercedes-Benz Tourismo. *Dave Heath*

LAGUNA

B M R & R Gwynne, Laguna Hotel, Suffolk Road South, Bournemouth, BH2 6AZ

Y8LAG	Ayats Bravo 1 A3E/BR1	Ayats	C57/18DT	2001	
YN05HFR	Scania K114 EB4	Irizar PB	C49FT	2005	
BX06UMS	Setra S416 GT-HD	Setra	C49FT	2006	James Gibson, Moffat, 2008
YN56NRX	Scania K114 EB4	Irizar Century Style	C49FT	2007	
YN57FYZ	Scania K114 EB4	Irizar Century Style	C49FT	2007	
YN57FWV	Scania K114 EB4	Irizar Century Capacity	C53F	2007	
YR58RVA	Scania K124 EB4	Irizar PB	C49FT	2008	
YR10BBV	Scania K340 EB4	Irizar Century Style	C49FT	2010	
YR10BAA	Scania K340 IB4	Irizar Century Capacity	S59DT	2010	
YT60OTH	Scania K340 IB4	Irizar Century Capacity	S59DT	2010	
YT12RNJ	Scania K340 IB4	Irizar Century	C49FT	2012	

LAKESIDE

Lakeside Coaches Ltd, Ellesmere Business Park, Oswestry Road, Ellesmere, SY12 0EW

V56KWO	Volvo B10M-62	Plaxton Première 320	C53F	2000	Bebb, Llantwit Fardre, 2002
X117BUJ	Volvo B10M-62	Plaxton Excalibur	C49FT	2001	
YR02PYV	Mercedes-Benz Sprinter 413 cdi	Excel	M16	2002	
DY52GYO	Volvo B12M	Plaxton Panther	C49FT	2003	
DX53YUG	Dennis Javelin 12m	TransBus Profile	C57F	2004	
BX54AEP	Toyota Coaster BB50R	Caetano Optimo V	C26F	2004	
YX54BGO	Mercedes-Benz Atego 1223L	Optare/Ferqui Solera	C39F	2004	
FJ55BXX	Volvo B12M	Caetano Enigma	C49FT	2006	
FJ55BYA	Volvo B12M	Caetano Enigma	C53F	2006	
YN56ORY	Volvo B12M 12.8m	Plaxton Panther	C57F	2006	
YN56ORZ	Volvo B12M 12m	Plaxton Panther	C49FT	2007	
SF07DLY	Volvo B12B	Caetano Enigma	C53FT	2007	Hamilton, Uxbridge, 2010
YX07AYE	Mercedes-Benz Vario O816	Ferqui Toro	C31F	2007	Sargeant, Hodnet, 2011
YJ07DWP	Mercedes-Benz Vario O815	Sitcar Beluga 2	C29F	2007	
FJ57KJK	Toyota Coaster BB50R	Caetano Optimo V	C26F	2007	
10GJD	Volvo B12M	Sunsundegui Sideral 350	C49FT	2008	Ulsterbus, 2011
YN57MDU	Volvo B12B	Plaxton Panther	C49FT	2008	
YD58GAU	Mercedes-Benz Sprinter 515 cdi	Mercedes-Benz	M15	2008	Sargeant, Hodnet, 2011
BU08BGF	Toyota Coaster BB50R	Caetano Optimo V	C26F	2008	
DD59LAK	Setra S415 Gt-HD	Setra	C49FT	2009	Silver Star, Caernarfon, 2011
JD09LAK	Volvo B12B	Plaxton Panther	C49FT	2009	
YN10AAJ	Volvo B12M	Plaxton Panther	C49FT	2010	
YN10AAK	Volvo B12M	Plaxton Panther	C49FT	2010	
BX11VOF	Volvo B9R	Plaxton Panther	C57F	2011	Hemmings, Holsworthy, 2012
BN11UGO	Mercedes-Benz Tourismo	Mercedes-Benz	C49FT	2011	

Previous registrations:

10GJD	IXI1000		
		DD59LAK	N20EDW

Web: www.hireameacoach.co.uk

LEONS

Happy Days - Leons

Leons Coach Travel (Stafford) Ltd, Douglas House, Tollgate Estate, Beaconside Stafford, ST16 3EE; Happy Days Coaches Ltd

	L	9346PL	Volvo B10M-61	Duple Laser	C57F	1983	FHW, Willenhall, 2006
	w	947JWD	Volvo B10M-61	Van Hool Alizée H	C53F	1984	Fisher, Bronington, 2001
195	H	HSV674	Volvo B10M-61	Van Hool Alizée H	C53F	1986	Fisher, Bronington, 2001
196	H	TDR725	Volvo B10M-61	Van Hool Alizée H	C53F	1985	Fisher, Bronington, 2001
	H	EIW7434	Volvo B10M-61	Jonckheere Jubilee	C53F	1986	Grace, Gomersal, 2008
	H	C514DND	Volvo B10M-61	Plaxton Paramount 3200	C53F	1986	?, 2009
	L	C270FBH	Volvo B10M-61	Plaxton Paramount 3200	C57F	1986	Elcock Reisen, Telford, 2011
	L	C822ARU	Volvo B10M-61	Plaxton Paramount 3200	C55F	1986	Elcock Reisen, Telford, 2011
	H	D93BNV	DAF MB230	Jonckheere Deauville	C53F	1987	Probus, West Bromwich, 2005
179	H	MIB580	DAF MB230	Van Hool Alizée	C53FT	1988	Brookes, Tipton, 2004
	L	SIB6719	Volvo B10M-61	Van Hool Alizée	C49FT	1988	Hills, Wolverhampton, 2007
177	H	G969KTX	Volvo B10M-60	Plaxton Expressliner	C51FT	1990	MRD, Catshill, 2006
	L	BNZ3505	Volvo B10M-60	Plaxton Paramount 3500	C49F	1990	Tappins, Didcot, 2011
	L	TIL4508	Volvo B10M-60	Plaxton Paramount 3500	C49F	1990	Tappins, Didcot, 2011
	L	GLZ4419	Volvo B10M-60	Plaxton Paramount 3500	C49F	1990	Tappins, Didcot, 2011
	L	G838UDV	Mercedes-Benz 811D	Carlyle C16	B33F	1990	Huxley, Threapwood, 2008
197	H	CAZ2818	Volvo B10M-60	Van Hool Alizée H	C53F	1991	Fisher, Bronington, 2001
	L	GIL3273	Volvo B10M-60	Plaxton Paramount 3200	C57F	1992	Hills, Wolverhampton, 2009
126	H	M945SUX	Mercedes-Benz 814D	Wadham Stringer Wessex 2	BC26F	1995	MoD, 2004
127	H	K11HDC	Mercedes-Benz 814D	Wadham Stringer Wessex 2	BC26F	1995	MoD, 2004
180	H	XWC18	Volvo B10M-62	Plaxton Première 350	C53F	1996	Newbury, Ledbury, 2001
181	H	HDC83E	Volvo B10M-62	Plaxton Première 350	C50F	1996	WA Shearings, Wigan, 2006
182	H	L1HDC	Volvo B10M-62	Plaxton Première 350	C50F	1996	WA Shearings, Wigan, 2006
183	H	KJF3V	Volvo B10M-62	Plaxton Première 350	C53F	1996	WA Shearings, Wigan, 2006
184	H	917DBO	Volvo B10M-62	Plaxton Première 350	C53F	1996	WA Shearings, Wigan, 2006
185	H	WHA325	Volvo B10M-62	Plaxton Première 350	C53F	1996	WA Shearings, Wigan, 2006
	L	R131LNR	Mercedes-Benz Vario O810	Plaxton Beaver 2	BC27F	1997	Elcock Reisen, Telford, 2010
	L	GIG5332	Mercedes-Benz Vario O810	Plaxton Beaver 2	B31F	1997	Pickford, Chippenham, 2010
	H	S252EGK	Mercedes-Benz Vario O814	Mellor	BC32F	1998	Hartley Travel, Aintree, 2011
209	H	H9HDC	Volvo B10M-62	Van Hool T9 Alizée	C53F	2001	WA Shearings, Wigan, 2010
210	H	H10HDC	Volvo B10M-62	Van Hool T9 Alizée	C53F	2001	WA Shearings, Wigan, 2010
223	H	SG02ONA	Scania K114 EB4	Irizar Century	C49FT	2002	Kingdom, Tiverton, 2011

Leons is based in Staffordshire and recent editions to the fleet have included several integral Van Hool coaches including AT11LCT, shown. This example is a T915 Alicron which is 3470mm high compared with the Acron at 3600mm and Atlon at 3210mm. *Mark Doggett*

Happy Days' livery continues on selected coaches including YN07EYG, a Scania with Irizar PB bodywork. The PB comes from the local language for new product which is Produukto Berria. *Mark Doggett*

158	L	ET05LCT	Mercedes-Benz Vario O614	Plaxton Pronto	C24F	2005
207	H	18XWC	Scania K114 EB4	Irizar Century	C48FT	2006
208	H	YN07EYG	Scania K114 EB6	Irizar PB	C48FT	2007
214	H	YJ08NTE	VDL Bova Futura FHD127.365	VDL Bova	C53F	2008
173	L	BT08LCT	VDL Bova Futura FHD127.365	VDL Bova	C55FT	2008
174	L	CT08LCT	Scania K114 EB4	Van Hool T9 Alizée	C53FT	2008
175	L	AT58LCT	LDV Maxus	LDV	M15	2008
176	L	YL57PUU	LDV Maxus	LDV	M15	2008
177	L	AT09LCT	Van Hool T916 Astron 13.2m	Van Hool	C53FT	2009
178	L	BT09LCT	Van Hool T916 Astron 13.2m	Van Hool	C53FT	2009
179	L	CT09LCT	Scania K340 EB4	Irizar Century	C49FT	2009
185	L	AT10LCT	Van Hool T916 Astron 13.2m	Van Hool	C53FT	2010
186	L	BT10LCT	Van Hool T916 Astron 13.2m	Van Hool	C53FT	2010
187	L	CT10LCT	Scania K340 EB4	Irizar Century	C49FT	2010
220	H	YN60BYY	Mercedes-Benz Vario O816	Plaxton Cheetah	C33F	2010
188	L	DT10LCT	Mercedes-Benz Vario O816	Plaxton Cheetah	C33F	2010
191	L	ET10LCT	Iveco Daily 45C15	Excel Excalibur	M16	2010
192	L	FT10LCT	Van Hool T915 Acron 12.2m	Van Hool	C51FT	2010
221	H	YT60OTD	Scania K400 EB4	Irizar PB	C49FT	2011
193	L	AT11LCT	Van Hool T915 Alicron 12.2m	Van Hool	C51FT	2011
197	L	AT61LCT	Van Hool T915 Acron 12.2m	Van Hool	C51FT	2011
198	L	BT61LCT	Van Hool T915 Acron 12.2m	Van Hool	C51FT	2011
222	H	MT61HUP	Neoplan Tourliner N2216 SHD	Neoplan	C53FT	2012
224	H	YR61RVP	Scania OmniExpress K400 EB4	Scania	C51FT	2012
199	L	CT12LCT	Van Hool T917 Altano 13.2m	Van Hool	C59FT	2012
200	L	AT12LCT	Van Hool T917 Altano 13.2m	Van Hool	C59FT	2012
201	L	BT12LCT	Van Hool T917 Altano 13.2m	Van Hool	C59FT	2012

Special event vehicle:

	H	VRE150	Johnstone Midget	Johnstone	-	1951

Previous registrations:

9346PL	EHG467Y	SIB6719	E281HRY
BNZ3505	G505LWU	TIL4508	G508LWU
C270FBH	C270FBH, EIL829	UBC464X	WBC464X, 9346PL
D93BNV	D93BNV, SBZ9698		
ET10LCT	BJ10FTX		
GIL3273	J256MFP		
GLZ4419	G419YAY		
H9FDC	Y301KBN		
H10FDC	Y302KBN		

Web: www.leons.co.uk

LODGE'S

JW Lodge & Sons Ltd, The Garage, High Easter, Chelmsford, CM1 4QS

YMJ555S	Bedford YMT	Duple Dominant	C53F	1978	
G294UYK	Leyland Olympian ONCL10/1RZ	Leyland	B47/31F	1989	East Yorkshire, 2008
G295UYK	Leyland Olympian ONCL10/1RZ	Leyland	B47/31F	1989	East Yorkshire, 2008
G296UYK	Leyland Olympian ONCL10/1RZ	Leyland	B47/31F	1989	East Yorkshire, 2008
G297UYK	Leyland Olympian ONCL10/1RZ	Leyland	B47/31F	1989	East Yorkshire, 2008
G299UYK	Leyland Olympian ONCL10/1RZ	Leyland	B47/31F	1989	East Yorkshire, 2008
J634CEV	Leyland Olympian ON3R56C18Z4	Alexander RH	BC57/45F	1992	Tausman, Gt Bromley, 2009
B3CEC	Dennis Javelin 12m	Plaxton Paramount 3200 III	C51FT	1992	Porter, Great Totham, 2008
F20DGE	Dennis Javelin 12m	Plaxton Paramount 3200 III	C51FT	1992	Porter, Great Totham, 2008
M73WYG	MAN 11.190	Optare Vecta	B42F	1995	Black Prince, Morley, 2003
N592BRH	Volvo Olympian	Alexander RH	B45/29F	1995	East Yorkshire, 2011
N593BRH	Volvo Olympian	Alexander RH	B45/29F	1995	East Yorkshire, 2011
E20DGE	Dennis Javelin 12m	Berkhof Axial 50	C53F	1997	Ford, Althorne, 2010
F20DGE	Dennis Javelin 12m	Berkhof Axial 50	C53F	1997	Ford, Althorne, 2010
R43GNW	Mercedes-Benz Vario 0810	Plaxton Beaver	B27F	1998	MacPherson, Donisthorpe, 2010
R710SLU	Iveco TurboDaily 59.12	Marshall C31	BC16F	1998	Pink Elephant Parking, 2006
V40DGE	Scania L94 IB	Van Hool T9 Alizée	C49FT	1999	Chambers, Moneymore, 2002
V118LVH	Optare Excel L1150	Optare	N24D	1999	Meteor, 2008
V936VUB	Optare Excel L1070	Optare	N30F	1999	Meteor, 2008
BX05UWS	Setra S416 GT-HD	Setra	C53FT	2006	Reynolds Diplomat, Watford, 2011
46AEW	Setra S416 GT-HD	Setra	C53FT	2006	The King's Ferry, Gillingham, 2011
AL06DGE	Setra S415 GT-HD	Setra	C49FT	2006	
BX06UMT	Setra S415 GT-HD	Setra	C49FT	2006	
TL07DGE	Setra S415 GT-HD	Setra	C49FT	2007	
AL08DGE	Mercedes-Benz Touro OC500	Mercedes-Benz	C49FT	2008	
BG58OLO	Mercedes-Benz Touro OC500	Mercedes-Benz	C53FT	2008	
JW10DGE	Setra S416 GT-HD	Setra	C49FT	2010	

Special event vehicles:

BXM568	Bedford WTL	Duple	C20F	1935	Dodds, Fareham, 2008
TMY700	Bedford OB	Duple Vista	C29F	1949	Essex County, Stratford
LTA752	Bedford OB	Duple Vista	C29F	1950	Western National
MJB481	Bedford SBG	Duple Vega	C37F	1956	Chiltonia, Chilton Foliat

Previous registrations:

46AEW	Y377UOM	J634CEV	FC1714 (HK)
BXM568	BXM568, CMN986	JW10DGE	BV10ZJX
E20DGE	P347KCF, P8AWF	V40DGE	V2CCH, CNZ3832
F20DGE	P899FMO		

Web: www.lodgecoaches.co.uk

Lodges retains a trio of interesting Bedford coaches including LTA752 which was new to Western National. During its time with Lincolnshire RoadCar its sides were opened up for use a coastal route to Butlin's camp at Skegness. *Mark Doggett*

LUCKETTS

H Luckett & Co Ltd, Broad Cut, Wallington, Fareham, PO16 8TB

Worthing Coaches Ltd, 117 King George V Road, Worthing, BN11 5SA

954	W	GB04EBL	Scania K114 EB4	Irizar Century 12.35	C49FT	2004	Flagship, Eastbourne, 2006
V10	L	HX07AJV	Mercedes-Benz Vito 110 cdi	Mercedes-Benz	M7	2007	
V11	L	HX07AJX	Mercedes-Benz Vito 110 cdi	Mercedes-Benz	M7	2007	
V12	L	DK06ZTT	Mercedes-Benz Vito 110 cdi	Mercedes-Benz	M7	2006	
V13	L	DK06ZTS	Mercedes-Benz Vito 110 cdi	Mercedes-Benz	M7	2006	
V14	L	HX58AXT	Mercedes-Benz Vito 110 cdi	Mercedes-Benz	M7	2008	
V15	L	HX58AXU	Mercedes-Benz Vito 110 cdi	Mercedes-Benz	M7	2008	
V16	L	HX58AXR	Mercedes-Benz Vito 110 cdi	Mercedes-Benz	M7	2008	
V17	L	HX58AXS	Mercedes-Benz Vito 110 cdi	Mercedes-Benz	M7	2008	
1601	L	BF59NHL	Mercedes-Benz Vito 110 cdi	Mercedes-Benz	M16	2009	
1903	L	BF60OEW	Mercedes-Benz Sprinter 515 cdi	Mercedes-Benz	C19F	2010	Evobus demonstrator, 2010
2108	L	W2HLC	Toyota Coaster BB50R	Caetano Optimo IV	C21F	2000	
2109	L	HX03BYT	Toyota Coaster BB50R	Caetano Optimo V	C21F	2003	
2110	L	A16HLC	Toyota Coaster BB50R	Caetano Optimo IV	C21F	1997	Hellyer's Fareham, 2006
2905	L	YN10EOP	Mercedes-Benz Vario O816	Plaxton Cheetah	C29F	2010	
	L	666VMX	Optare Excel L1070	Optare	N34F	1996	Johnsons, Henley-in-Arden, 2009
3603	L	A13HLC	Bova Futura FHD10.370	Bova	C34FT	2000	Maynes of Buckie, 2003
3801	L	A19LTG	Dennis Javelin 10m	Berkhof Axial 50	C38FT	1997	
4201	W	YR02ZZA	Scania K114 IB4	Irizar Century 12.35	C53FT	2002	
4202	W	YR02ZZC	Scania K114 IB4	Irizar Century 12.35	C53FT	2002	
4203		YS03ZLK	Scania K114 IB4	Irizar Century 12.35	C53F	2003	
4801	L	YN05HFK	Scania K124 EB6	Irizar PB	C48FT	2005	
4802	L	YN05HFL	Scania K124 EB6	Irizar PB	C48FT	2005	
4803	L	YN08DFF	Scania K420 EB6	Irizar PB	C48FT	2008	
4804	L	FJ11RDX	Volvo B9R	Caetano Levanté	C48FT	2011	
4805	L	FJ11RDY	Volvo B9R	Caetano Levanté	C48FT	2011	
4806	L	FJ61EWA	Volvo B9R	Caetano Levanté	C48FT	2011	
4807	L	FJ61EVW	Volvo B9R	Caetano Levanté	C48FT	2011	
4920	L	R4HLC	Dennis Javelin GX 12m	Berkhof Axial	C49FT	1998	
4921	W	T3HLC	Scania K124 IB4	Irizar Century 12.35	C49FT	1999	
4923	L	W3HLC	Mercedes-Benz O404	Hispano Vita	C53F	2000	
4924	L	W5HLC	Mercedes-Benz O404	Hispano Vita	C53F	2000	
4925	L	Y2HLC	Volvo B10M-62	Berkhof Axial 50	C49FT	2001	
4926	L	Y3HLC	Volvo B10M-62	Berkhof Axial 50	C49FT	2001	
4927	L	YN04GOH	Scania K114 IB4	Irizar Century 12.35	C49FT	2004	
4928	W	YN04GOJ	Scania K114 IB4	Irizar Century 12.35	C49FT	2004	
4929	W	YN04GOC	Scania K114 IB4	Irizar Century 12.35	C49FT	2004	
4930	L	YN04GOK	Scania K114 IB4	Irizar Century 12.35	C49FT	2004	
4941	L	YN56FGJ	Scania K114 EB4	Irizar Century Style	C49FT	2006	
4942	L	YN56FGK	Scania K114 EB4	Irizar Century Style	C49FT	2006	
4943	W	YN56FGM	Scania K114 EB4	Irizar Century 12.35	C49FT	2006	
4944	L	YN56FGO	Scania K340 EB4	VDL Berkhof Axial 50	C57FT	2006	
4945	L	YN07LJA	Scania K340 EB4	Irizar PB	C49FT	2007	
4946	L	YN08DFC	Scania K340 EB4	Irizar PB	C49FT	2008	
4947	W	YN08DFD	Scania K340 EB4	Irizar PB	C49FT	2008	
4948	W	YN08DFE	Scania K340 EB4	Irizar PB	C49FT	2008	
4949	L	DL03GSU	Scania K114 IB4	Irizar Century 12.37	C49FT	2003	Bakerbus, Biddulph, 2008
4950	W	DL03GRZ	Scania K114 IB4	Irizar Century 12.37	C49FT	2003	Bakerbus, Biddulph, 2008
4951	L	FJ58AHE	Scania K340 EB4	Irizar PB	C49FT	2009	
4952	L	FJ58AHF	Scania K340 EB4	Irizar PB	C49FT	2009	
4953	L	FJ58AHG	Scania K340 EB4	Irizar PB	C49FT	2009	
4954	L	FJ58AHK	Scania K340 EB4	Irizar PB	C49FT	2009	
4955	L	FJ58AHL	Scania K340 EB4	Irizar PB	C49FT	2009	
4956	L	FJ58AJY	Scania K340 EB4	Irizar PB	C49FT	2009	
4957	L	FJ58AKF	Scania K340 EB4	Irizar PB	C49FT	2009	
4958	L	FJ58AKG	Scania K340 EB4	Irizar PB	C49FT	2009	
4959	L	FJ58AHN	Scania K340 EB4	Irizar PB	C49FT	2009	
4960	L	FJ58AJX	Scania K340 EB4	Irizar PB	C49FT	2009	
4961	L	FJ58AHO	Scania K340 EB4	Irizar PB	C49FT	2009	

Representing the Lucketts fleet is Irizar Century number 4949, DL03GSU with a Scania K114 IB4 chassis. It is seen passing Hyde Park in London. *Steve Rice*

4962	L	FJ58AHP	Scania K340 EB4	Irizar PB	C49FT	2009	
4965	L	FJ59AOZ	Scania K340 EB4	Caetani Levanté	C49FT	2010	
4966	L	FJ59APF	Scania K340 EB4	Caetani Levanté	C49FT	2010	
4967	L	A18HLC	Bova Futura FHD12.370	Bova	C49FT	2000	Elkin Travel, Sutton Coldfield, 2010
4968	L	YN12BVR	Irizar i6 Ecolife	Irizar	C49FT	2012	
4969	L	YN12BVS	Irizar i6 Ecolife	Irizar	C49FT	2012	
5343	W	YR02ZZB	Scania K124 IB4	Irizar Century 12.35	C53F	2002	
5344	L	YR02ZZD	Scania K124 IB4	Irizar Century 12.35	C53F	2002	
5349	L	V200RAD	Scania L94 IB	Irizar Intercentury 12.32	C53F	2000	Radley, Brigg, 2004
5350	W	X498AHE	Scania L94 IB4	Irizar Century 12.35	C53F	2001	Flagship, Eastbourne, 2006
5353	L	R871SDT	Scania L94 IB4	Irizar Century 12.35	C49FT	1998	The Kings Ferry, Gillingham, 2006
5355	W	S373SET	Scania L94 IB4	Irizar Century 12.35	C53F	1998	The Kings Ferry, Gillingham, 2006
5358	L	YT11LPA	Scania OmniExpress K400 EB4	Scania	C53FT	2011	
5359	L	YT11LPC	Scania OmniExpress K400 EB4	Scania	C53FT	2011	
5360	L	YT11LPE	Scania OmniExpress K400 EB4	Scania	C53FT	2011	
5361	L	YT11LPU	Scania OmniExpress K400 EB4	Scania	C53FT	2011	
5362	L	YT11LPV	Scania OmniExpress K400 EB4	Scania	C53FT	2011	
5508	L	YT09FLW	Scania OmniExpress K340 EB4	Scania	C55FT	2009	
5509	L	YT09FLZ	Scania OmniExpress K340 EB4	Scania	C55FT	2009	
7001	L	T7HLC	Dennis Javelin 12m	Plaxton Première 320	S70F	1999	
7002	L	Y4HLC	Dennis Javelin 12m	Plaxton Première 320	S70F	2001	
7003	L	YR52MDV	Dennis Javelin 12m	Plaxton Première 320	S70F	2002	
7004	L	YN56NTE	Scania K230 IB4	Irizar S-kool	S70F	2006	
7005	L	YN56NTF	Scania K230 IB4	Irizar S-kool	S70F	2006	
7006	L	YN56NTG	Scania K230 IB4	Irizar S-kool	S70F	2006	
7401	L	A12HLC	Volvo B7TL	Alexander ALX400	N43/27F	2000	Go-Ahead London, 2010
7402	L	A17HLC	Volvo B7TL	Alexander ALX400	N43/27F	2000	Go-Ahead London, 2010
7403	L	A19HLC	Volvo B7TL	Alexander ALX400	N43/27F	2000	Go-Ahead London, 2010
8002	W	YN56FGG	Scania OmniCity N94 UD	East Lancs OmniDekka	NC49/32F	2006	
8301	L	YN04AVL	Neoplan Skyliner N122/3	Neoplan	C57/26DT	2004	

Previous registrations:

666VMX	P913SUM	DL03GRZ	8830RU
A12HLC	V122LGC	DL03GSU	9995RU
A13HLC	W500GSM	R871SDT	98D10279, R871SDT, A17HLC
A16HLC	P953DNR, A16HOF	S373SET	S373SET, A12HLC
A17HLC	V137LGC	X498AHE	00D83714
A18HLC	W652CYG, JUI9568		
A19LTG	P483GTF		

Depots: Birch Road, Eastbourne; Quarry Lane Ind Est, Gosport (Lucketts - L);
Broad Cut, Wallington (Lucketts - L) and Spencer Road, Worthing (Worthing Coaches - W).
Web: www.lucketts.co.uk

MARCHANTS

Marchants Coaches Ltd, 61 Clarence Street, Cheltenham, GL50 3LB

CWR512Y	Leyland Olympian ONLXB/1R	Eastern Coach Works	BC43/29F	1982	UK North, Manchester, 2003
E323PMD	Volvo B9M	Plaxton Derwent II	B40F	1988	Capital, West Drayton, 1999
F312JTY	Leyland Olympian ONLXB/1R	Alexander RH	BC43/30F	1988	Arriva North East, 2003
G918LHA	Leyland Olympian ONLXB/1RZ	East Lancs	B45/29F	1989	Val's, Chase Terrace, 2008
K361DWJ	Leyland Olympian ON2R50C13Z4	Alexander RL	BC43/27F	1992	Stagecoach, 2008
MCZ4413	DAF DB250	Optare Spectra	B48/29F	1994	Go South Coast, 2010
MCZ4426	DAF DB250	Optare Spectra	B48/29F	1994	Go South Coast, 2010
N101HGO	Volvo B6BLE	Wright Crusader	N36F	1995	Travel West Midlands, 2004
BIG8902	Neoplan Skyliner N122/3	Neoplan	C57/20DT	1996	The King's Ferry, Gillingham, 2002
P6WRS	Volvo B10M-62	Plaxton Première 350	C51F	1997	Spring, Evesham, 2003
R512KNJ	Volvo B6BLE	Wright Crusader	N28F	1995	National Express, 2009
MCZ4431	Volvo B10M-62	Plaxton Excalibur	C48FT	1998	Wallce Arnold, Leeds, 2000
MCZ4437	Volvo B10M-62	Plaxton Excalibur	C48FT	1998	Wallce Arnold, Leeds, 2000
MCZ4326	Volvo B10M-62	Plaxton Première 320	C53F	1998	Wallce Arnold, Leeds, 2000
V54HAX	Volvo B10M-62	Plaxton Première 320	C57F	1999	Wickson, Walsall Wood, 2006
V186OOE	Volvo B7TL	Alexander ALX400	N43/20D	1999	Dorset Heritage, 2011
MCZ4306	Volvo B10M-62	Plaxton Première 320	C57F	2000	Prentice, Haddington, 2010
MCZ7087	Volvo B10M-62	Van Hool Alizée	C57F	2001	Astra, Andover, 2012
VX51AWO	Mercedes-Benz Vario O814	Plaxton Cheetah	C25F	2001	
OV51OOC	Optare Solo M850	Optare	N29F	2001	Grayline, Bicester, 2010
SA02CCU	Volvo B7L	Wrightbus Eclipse	N41F	2002	Whitelaws. Stonehouse, 2006
SA02CDE	Volvo B7L	Wrightbus Eclipse	N41F	2002	Whitelaws. Stonehouse, 2006
MCZ5995	Mercedes-Benz Sprinter 413 cdi	Ferqui Soroco	C16F	2003	Foster, Winchcombe, 2010
YV03TZN	Volvo B12M	Plaxton Paragon Expressliner	C57F	2003	Stagecoach, 2010
MCZ4305	Volvo B12B	VDL Jonckheere Mistral 50	C51FT	2004	
MCZ4304	Volvo B12B	VDL Jonckheere Mistral 50	C51FT	2004	
GL05MAR	Volvo B12B	VDL Jonckheere Mistral 50	C51FT	2005	
GL05MCS	Volvo B12B	VDL Jonckheere Mistral 50	C53FT	2005	
AE55NLA	LDV Convoy	LDV	M15	2005	
BIG9803	Neoplan Skyliner N122/3	Neoplan	C59/24CT	2006	Hodson, Clitheroe, 2011
YN55NMM	Neoplan Skyliner N122/3	Neoplan	C59/24CT	2006	Veolia Cymru, 2012

Previous registrations:

BIG8902	P10TCC, P981HWF		MCZ4326	R452RWT
BIG9803	YN56BGF		MCZ4413	L122ELJ
JEY124Y	MSU593Y, VYB704		MCZ4426	L130ELJ
LIL9843	E214BOD		MCZ4431	R431FWT
MCZ4304	FJ54CZX		MCZ4437	R432FWT
MCZ4305	FJ54ZCV		MCZ7087	X578BYD
MCZ4306	HSK660, W493ASB, YCX320, B12DPC, W133TSX	P6WRS	P332VWR

Depot: Prestbury Road, Cheltenham Web: www.marchants-coaches.com

The Plaxton-bodied Mercedes coach is now in its third variant. Based on the Vario chassis it is normally deployed as a 29-seater. Marchants VX51AWO seats twenty-five and is seen in Park Lane, London.
Colin Lloyd

MARSHALLS

F W Marshall, Firbank Way, Leighton Buzzard, LU7 8YP

Reg	Chassis	Body	Seating	Year	History
KKY835P	Bristol VRT/SL3/501	Easterm Coach Works	B43/34F	1976	Johnson, Hodthorpe, 2010
MIL8340	Volvo B10M-61	East Lancs (1997)	BC45/35F	1981	Stephenson's, Rochford, 2003
KBZ2476	Volvo B10M-61	Plaxton Paramount 3200	C53F	1985	Naughton, London, 2009
WJI9363	Volvo B10M-61	East Lancs (1998)	BC45/35F	1986	Dunn-Line, Nottingham, 2004
E306NTC	Leyland Tiger TRCTL11/3RZ	Plaxton Derwent 2	S70F	1987	MoD, 2002
FDZ3715	Volvo B10M-61	Van Hool Alizée	C53F	1988	Mullany, Watford, 2008
SJI8100	Volvo B10M-60	Jonckheere Deauville P599	C49FT	1990	
H657GPF	Volvo Citybus B10M-50	East Lancs	B45/34F	1990	Arriva Midlands, 2004
K878CSF	Leyland Olympian ONR56C13Z4	Alexander RH	B51/30D	1992	Stephenson, Rockford, 2010
K858LMK	Scania N113 DRB	Northern Counties	B41/27F	1992	Johnson, Hodthorpe, 2009
M948TSX	Volvo B10M-62	Plaxton Première Interurban	BC51F	1994	Stagecoach, 2011
N446XVA	Volvo B10M-62	Plaxton Première 320	C49FT	1995	SDA Coach, Halstead, 2011
P792AHR	Dennis Javelin 12m	UVG Cutlass	S70F	1997	MoD, 2005
MKZ7190	Dennis Javelin 12m	Plaxton Prima	S69F	1998	
MKZ7186	Iveco EuroRider 391E.12.35	Beulas Stergo e	C49FT	1998	
S823AFG	Ford Transit	Ford	M7	1999	Titan, Redhill, 2003
T544CDM	Mercedes-Benz Sprinter 614	Crest	C20F	1999	Newbury Minibuses, 2002
H12FWM	Volvo B10M-62	Plaxton Paragon	C49F	2000	Logan, Dunloy, 2004
X642AKW	Dennis Javelin	Plaxton Prima	S70F	2000	
YR02ZLZ	Dennis Javelin	Plaxton Prima	S70F	2002	
SJI8106	Volvo B12M	Jonckheere Mistral 50	C49FT	2002	Park's of Hamilton, 2005
SJI8103	Volvo B12M	Jonckheere Mistral 50	C49FT	2002	Park's of Hamilton, 2005
FN52MZO	Volvo B10M-62	Caetano Enigma	C53F	2002	
SM9562	Neoplan Starliner N516 SHD	Neoplan	C53FT	2004	Reay, Wigton, 2009

Joining the Marshalls fleet in 2004 Plaxton-bodied H12FWM is seen on a shopping spree in Oxford Street.
Colin Lloyd

The Plaxton Profile was a development of the Première 320 and retained the 3.2m height. It was available on two chassis, the Volvo B7R and the Dennis Javelin. A Profile 70 variant was introduced for the 3+2 school bus market. Illustrating the model is SUI7803. *Dave Heath*

WA05DFG	VDL Bova Futura FHD 13.340	VDL Bova	C53FT	2005	Weavaway, Newbury, 2010
WA05JWM	VDL Bova Futura FHD 13.340	VDL Bova	C53FT	2005	Weavaway, Newbury, 2010
YN55WSX	Volvo B7R	Plaxton Profile 70	S70F	2006	
SUI7802	Volvo B7R	Plaxton Profile	C53F	2006	
SUI7803	Volvo B7R	Plaxton Profile	C53F	2006	
SUI7804	Volvo B12B	Plaxton Panther	C49FT	2006	
SUI7805	Volvo B12B	Plaxton Panther	C49FT	2006	
KE07HLP	Ayats Bravo 1 A3E/BR1	Ayats	C57/25DT	2006	
KE07HMO	Ayats Bravo 1 A3E/BR1	Ayats	C57/25DT	2006	
KE07KTN	Ayats Atlantis AT1	Ayats	C50FT	2007	

Previous registrations:

B43KAL	B43KAL, SJI8103	SJI8100	G166RBD
E306NTC	87KF12, D471TGS	SJI8103	SA02UCD
FDZ3715	E219JJF	SJI8106	SA02UCB
H12FWM	X626AKW	SM9562	C1UFC, 695CWR, PX04MPU
KBZ2476	B536BML	SUI7802	YN06OPR
MIL8340	NCS123W, WLT439, WGB853W	SUI7803	YN06OPW
MKZ7186	R8FWM	SUI7804	YN06OPV
MKZ7190	R12FWM	SUI7805	YN06PCV
M907OVR	M907OVR, XSU905	WA05DFG	WA05DFG, NBZ70
P792AHR	JT53AA	WA05JWM	WA05JWM, BKZ70
SA02UCD	HSK650, SA02UCD, SJI8103	WJI9363	D390PYS
SA02UCB	LSK845, SA02UCB, SJI8106		

Web: www.marshalls-coaches.co.uk

MAYNE

Mayne Coaches Ltd, The Coach Station, Battersby Lane, Warrington, WA2 7ET

11	F711LFG	Scania N113DRB	East Lancs	B47/33F	1989	Brighton & Hove, 2007
12u	C112UBC	Scania N112DRB	East Lancs	B46/33F	1988	Brighton & Hove, 2001
13u	C113UBC	Scania N112DRB	East Lancs	B46/33F	1988	Brighton & Hove, 2001
14	E704EFG	Scania N112DRB	East Lancs	B47/33F	1988	Brighton & Hove, 2002
15	S961YOO	Volvo Olympian	Alexander RH	B47/27F	1998	Dublin Bus, 2011
16	B424RNA	Leyland Tiger TRCLXCT/3RZ	Plaxton Paramount 3200	C55F	1985	
18	HJZ1918	Volvo B10M-62	Plaxton Première 350	C51FT	1999	Brighton & Hove, 2004
19	JIG6619	Volvo B10M-62	Plaxton Première 320	C57FT	1998	Rossendale, 2011
20	JIG6620	Volvo B10M-62	Plaxton Première 320	C57FT	1998	Rossendale, 2011
21	906GAU	Volvo B10M-62	Plaxton Première 320	C55F	1997	
22	289BUA	Volvo B10M-62	Plaxton Première 320	C55F	1997	
23	OED201	Scania K114 IB4	Irizar PB	C49FT	2004	Veolia, 2011
24	ASV764	Scania L94IB	Irizar Intercentury 12.32	C55F	1999	
25	M4YNF	Volvo B10M-62	Plaxton Première 320	C55F	2000	
26	M4YNC	Volvo B10M-62	Plaxton Première 320	C55F	2000	
27	YN57BWX	ADL Javelin 12m	Plaxton Profile	C55F	2007	
28	YN57BWY	ADL Javelin 12m	Plaxton Profile	C55F	2007	
29	SSV269	Scania K114IB4	Irizar Intercentury 12.32	C55F	2003	
30	403BGO	Scania K114IB4	Irizar Intercentury 12.32	C55F	2003	
31	UCE665	Scania K114IB4	Irizar Intercentury 12.32	C55F	2004	
32	NIB4162	Scania K114IB4	Irizar Intercentury 12.32	C55F	2004	
35	YN06JXF	Scania K114IB4	Irizar Century Capacity	C55F	2006	
36	YN06JXG	Scania K114IB4	Irizar Century Capacity	C55F	2006	
37	YN06JXH	Scania K114IB4	Irizar Century Capacity	C55F	2006	
51	YS02XDW	Scania L94IB4	Irizar InterCentury 12.32	C55F	2002	
52	NIL9774	Scania L94IB4	Irizar InterCentury 12.32	C55F	2002	
53	YN03WRW	Scania K114IB4	Irizar InterCentury 12.32	C55F	2003	

Following Mayne's disposal of bus services in Manchester, the coaching activities based in Warrington have expanded. Number 35, YN06JXF, is a Scania K114 with Irizar Century Capacity bodywork. It is seen at taking a break at Thorpe Park. *Dave Heath*

Pulham's fleet, shown on page 128, includes ten metre Javelin GL06PUL. The coach, which carries a Plaxton Profile body, is seen as the coach passes through its home town. *Tony Wilson*

BU06CVE	Mercedes-Benz Sprinter 411 cdi	Koch	N16F	2006	Translink, 2010
KC07PCC	Scania K230 EB	Irizar InterCentury 12.32	S70F	2007	
YN57GBX	Scania K380 EB4	Irizar Century Style	C49FT	2007	
YN08DGE	Scania K340 EB4	Irizar PB	C49FT	2008	Steton, Coventry, 2009
PC08PCC	Mercedes-Benz Vario O816	UNVI/Esker Riada GT	C33F	2008	Classic, Annfield Plain, 2008
SN09FFD	Scania OmniExpress K380 EB4	Scania	C51FT	2009	Milligan, Mauchline, 2011
SN09FFE	Scania OmniExpress K380 EB4	Scania	C51FT	2009	Milligan, Mauchline, 2011
LC11PCC	Scania OmniExpress K400 EB4	Scania	C51FT	2011	
PC11PCC	Scania OmniExpress K400 EB4	Scania	C51FT	2011	

Previous registrations:

217MYB	-		M99PCC	M247TAK
BRZ7174	Y2HCR, Y643NWP		N10PCC	N686AHL
BRZ7174	Y3HCR, Y642NWP		PUI6623	H813DKU
C12PCC	V303EAK		PUI6625	H811DKU
C14PCC	YN03DCY		PUI6684	H814DKU
ENZ7598	L542JJV		SK03DHJ	B11DWA, B13DWA
HSK845	G41HKY		T7PCC	B14DWA, SK03DHL
J1PCC	R880HCD			

Web: www.pccoaches.co.uk

PARRYS INTERNATIONAL

Parrys International Tours Ltd, Landywood Green, Cheslyn Hay, WS6 7AR

VK54LBE	Mercedes-Benz Vito 111 cdi	Mercedes-Benz	M8	2004
BV57VGO	Mercedes-Benz Sprinter 515 cdi	Mercedes-Benz	M16	2008
BV57VGR	Mercedes-Benz Sprinter 515 cdi	Mercedes-Benz	M16	2008
YJ09FJF	Van Hool T917 Astron	Van Hool	C48FT	2009
YJ10JYN	Van Hool T917 Astron	Van Hool	C48FT	2010
YJ10JYO	Van Hool T917 Astron	Van Hool	C48FT	2010
YJ10JYP	Van Hool T917 Astron	Van Hool	C48FT	2010
YJ10JYR	Van Hool T917 Astron	Van Hool	C48FT	2010
YJ10JYS	Van Hool T917 Astron	Van Hool	C48FT	2010
BJ10VTV	Setra S415 GT-HD	Setra	C49FT	2010
YJ60LCW	Van Hool T917 Astron	Van Hool	C48FT	2010
YJ11AOA	Van Hool T917 Astron	Van Hool	C48FT	2011
YJ11AOC	Van Hool T917 Astron	Van Hool	C48FT	2011
YJ11AOD	Van Hool T917 Astron	Van Hool	C48FT	2011
YJ11AOE	Van Hool T917 Astron	Van Hool	C48FT	2011
YJ12KFC	Van Hool TX17 Astron	Van Hool	C48FT	2012

Web: www.parrys-international.co.uk

Parrys' recent arrivals have been integral products from the Van Hool stable, with the first TX (tee-ten) model for the British market appearing at the UK Coach Rally this spring. From the 2011 delivery, YJ11AOC is seen on a tour to London. *Colin Lloyd*

PAUL S WINSON

Paul S Winson (Coaches) Ltd, The Coach Station, Royal Way, Loughborough, LE11 0XR

55	R5PSW	Dennis Javelin	Plaxton Première 320	S70F	1998	
57	T7PSW	Bova Futura FHD12.340	Bova	C53F	1999	
58	T8PSW	Bova Futura FHD12.340	Bova	C53F	1999	
63	V10PSW	Mercedes-Benz Vario 0814	Plaxton Beaver 2	BC29F	1999	
67	W9PSW	Bova Futura FHD12.370	Bova	C53F	2000	
90	BW04PSW	Volvo B12B	VDL Jonckheere Mistral 50	C53FT	2004	
95	G333NRC	Volvo Citybus B10M-50	Alexander RH	B47/35F	1989	City of Nottingham, 2004
96	G335PAL	Volvo Citybus B10M-50	Alexander RH	B47/37F	1989	City of Nottingham, 2004
98	CW05PSW	ADL Dart 8.8m	ADL Mini Pointer	N29F	2005	
99	DW05PSW	ADL Dart 8.8m	ADL Mini Pointer	N29F	2005	
100	TT06PSW	Volvo B12B	VDL Jonckheere Mistral 50	C53FT	2006	
101	XX06PSW	Volvo B12B	VDL Jonckheere Mistral 50	C53FT	2006	
103	G916LHA	Leyland Olympian ONLXB/1R	East Lancs	B45/29F	1989	Arriva North West & Wales, 2006
104	G917LHA	Leyland Olympian ONLXB/1R	East Lancs	B45/29F	1989	Arriva North West & Wales, 2006
105	BW53PSW	Bova Futura FHD13.340	Bova	C59FT	2003	Meirion, Aberystwyth, 2006
106	XX07PSW	VDL Bova Futura FHD13.365	VDL Bova	C59FT	2007	
108	HOD76	Scania N113 DRB	East Lancs Cityzen	BC47/31F	1999	Beeston's, Hadleigh, 2008
110	P318KTW	DAF DB250	Northern Counties Palatine 2	B47/30F	1996	Linkfast, Leigh-on-Sea, 2008
111	OO09PSW	ADL Dart 4 10.9m	ADL Enviro 200	N39F	2009	
112	XX09PSW	VDL Bova Futura FHD13.365	VDL Bova	C53F	2009	
113	XX56PSW	ADL Dart 4 10.7m	ADL Pointer	N37F	2006	SM Coaches, Harlow, 2009
115	YNR778	Dennis Trident	East Lancs Lolyne	N53/34F	1999	City of Nottingham, 2010
116	OO11PSW	Mercedes-Benz Vario 0816	Plaxton Cheetah	C33F	2011	
117	XX11PSW	Volvo B9R	Plaxton Elite	C53F	2011	
118	X663WCH	Dennis Trident	East Lancs Lolyne	N53/34F	2000	City of Nottingham, 2011
119	W647SNN	Dennis Trident	East Lancs Lolyne	N53/34F	2000	City of Nottingham, 2011
120	XX57PSW	Mercedes-Benz Tourino OC510	Mercedes-Benz	C36F	2008	Klarners, Colchester, 2011
121	XX12PSW	ADL E20D	ADL Enviro 200	N26F	2012	

Previous registrations:

BW53PSW	AF53MMF		
HOD76	V335EAK	XX56PSW	MX56HYB
R80PSW	R925RAU	XX57PSW	08CN969, EU57AXR
XX07PSW	YJ07DVU	YNR778	T420XVO

Web: www.winsoncoaches.co.uk

Paul S Winson Coaches is a family business formed in 1983 which now operates thirty-four vehicles offering between 29 and 78 coach seats from modern premises in Loughborough The flagship coach from Plaxton's product range is the Elite and XX11PSW joined the fleet last year. *John Marsh*

PEARCES

Pearce Private Hire Ltd, Tower Road, Wallingford, OX10 7LN

G227YLU	Toyota Hiace	Toyota	M8	1990	private owner, 2004
M300MFC	Toyota Coaster HZB50R	Caetano Optimo III	C21F	1994	
P1RWL	Toyota Coaster HZB50R	Caetano Optimo III	C21F	1997	
OU07FKA	Toyota Coaster BB50R	Caetano Optimo V	C26F	2007	
OU07FKB	Toyota Coaster BB50R	Caetano Optimo V	C26F	2007	
OU07FKD	ADL Javelin 10m	Plaxton Profile	C41F	2007	
OU07FKE	ADL Javelin 10m	Plaxton Profile	C41F	2007	
OU07HFR	Irisbus EuroRider 397E.12.35A	Plaxton Paragon	C53F	2007	
OU08EKJ	Irisbus EuroRider 397E.12.35A	Plaxton Panther	C61F	2008	
OU08EKK	Irisbus EuroRider 397E.12.35A	Plaxton Panther	C61F	2008	
OU09BZD	Irisbus EuroRider 397E.12.35A	Plaxton Panther	C61F	2009	
OU59BVO	Irisbus EuroRider 397E.12.33	Plaxton Panther	C61F	2009	
OU59BVP	Irisbus EuroRider 397E.12.33	Plaxton Panther	C61F	2009	

Special event vehicle:

OOU856G	Bedford VAL 70	Duple Viceroy 37	C53F	1968	Skinners, Oxted

Previous registrations:

M300MFC	M489HBC		
		P1RWL	P677CUD

Irisbus continues to provide the EuroRider, which was launched in 1995, for the British market. Seen heading for the racecourse at Epsom Downs is OU59BVP, an example with Plaxton Panther bodywork. *Dave Heath*

PETER CAROL

Peter Carol Travel Ltd, Bamfield House, Bamfield, Whitchurch, Bristol BS14 0XD

ROI1229	MAN 11.190	Caetano Algarve II	C35FT	1996	
ROI1913	Bova Futura FHD10.340	Bova	C27FT	2004	
ROI1417	Mercedes-Benz Touro OC500	Mercedes-Benz	C42FT	2004	
ROI8235	BMC Probus 850 RE	BMC	C35F	2005	
BX55FWC	Mercedes-Benz Touro OC500	Mercedes-Benz	C49FT	2005	Durham City, Brandon, 2009
UKZ2935	Mercedes-Benz Touro OC500	Mercedes-Benz	C49FT	2005	
UKZ2934	Mercedes-Benz Touro OC500	Mercedes-Benz	C53F	2006	
ROI2929	Mercedes-Benz Touro OC500	Mercedes-Benz	C53F	2006	
B15CTY	VDL Bova Futura FHD127.365	VDL Bova	C54FT	2010	
800XPC	Mercedes-Benz Tourismo	Mercedes-Benz	C49FT	2011	

Previous registrations:

800XPC	BK11CNO		
ROI1229	N790ORY		
ROI1417	BX54ECT	ROI7435	-
ROI1913	WA53SFY	ROI8235	WX55JNZ
ROI2929	WA08GSU	ROI8358	
ROI6774	BX54ECE	UKZ2934	BU06CTV
		UKZ2935	BX05UWU

Web: www.luxurycoach.co.uk

Representing Peter Carol Travel is Mercedes-Benz ROI1417. This is one of five Touros in the fleet which also includes one of the subsequent models, the Tourismo. *Colin Martin*

PRINCESS

Princess Coaches Ltd, Botley Road, West End, Southampton, SO30 3HA

549KYA	Scania L94 IB4	Irizar Century 12.35	C49FT	1998	Gwynn, Bournemouth, 2008
479COT	Scania L94 IB4	Irizar Century	C53F	1998	Gilchrist, Glasgow, 2004
489AOU	Scania L94 IB4	Irizar Century	C49FT	1999	Wilfreda-Beehive, Wakefield, 2004
PC05SFC	Mercedes-Benz Vario 0815	Sitcar Beluga	C29F	2005	Eassons, Southampton, 2010
YB06JON	Scania K114 EB4	Irizar Century Club	C49FT	2006	
EB56LOU	Scania K114 EB4	Irizar Century Club	C53F	2006	
MB56MAT	Scania K114 EB4	Irizar Century Style	C53F	2006	
987FOU	Scania K380 EB6	Irizar Century	C56FT	2007	The King's Ferry, Gillingham, 2009
406AOT	Scania K340 EB4	Irizar Century Style	C53F	2007	Lucketts, Fareham, 2007
YN08CCM	Scania K310 EB4	Irizar i4	C59F	2008	
PB09DEN	Scania K340 EB4	Irizar Century Club	C49FT	2009	
PC09SFC	Scania K340 EB4	Irizar Century Club	C49FT	2009	
DB09PAB	Scania K340 EB4	Irizar Century Club	C49FT	2009	
XL59BCL	Scania K480 EB6	Irizar PB	C59FT	2010	Burton's, Haverhill, 2011
EM10LOU	Scania K340 EB4	Irizar Century Style	C53F	2010	
YT12YUS	Scania K360 EB6	Irizar i6	C56FT	2012	

Previous registrations:

282GOT	98D37150, R467YDT	EB56LOU	YN56PEH
406AOT	YN07EWY	GIL1683	R876SDT, 479COT
489AOU	V315EAK	MB56MAT	YN56PEJ
549KYA	R22RED	PC05SFC	ES05ONS
987FOU	YN07LKD	SAZ4959	FX51BOF
991FOT	T738JHE	SJI6569	N2RED, ECL730, N516XDV

Web: www.princesscoaches.co.uk

Irizar Century Club PB09DEN illustrates this variant of the Irizar product in the livery of Princess Coaches. The Club is a high-specification version similar to the Century Style. It is seen in its home city of Southampton.
Dave Heath

PROSPECT

Prospect Coaches Ltd. 81 High Street, Lye, Stourbridge, DY9 8NG

Reg	Chassis	Body	Seats	Year	Notes
LCZ4009	Dennis Javelin 12m	Neoplan Transliner	C53F	1994	
N713AHP	Volvo B10M-62	Plaxton Première 350	C57F	1995	
LRU822	Dennis Javelin 12m	Plaxton Première 320	C57F	1996	Stort Valley
N912DWJ	Dennis Javelin 12m	Berkhof Excellence 1000L	C57F	1996	Bicknell, Guildford
N899KFA	Dennis Javelin 12m	Plaxton Prima	S70F	1996	Leons, Stafford, 2011
P425JDT	Dennis Javelin 12m	Plaxton Première 320	C57F	1997	
P440JDT	Dennis Javelin 12m	Plaxton Prima	C57F	1997	
P22TCC	Dennis Javelin 12m	Plaxton Première 350	C57F	1997	Travellers, Hounslow, 2010
P66TCC	Dennis Javelin 12m	Plaxton Première 350	C57F	1997	Travellers, Hounslow, 2010
P77TCC	Dennis Javelin 12m	Plaxton Première 350	C57F	1997	Travellers, Hounslow, 2010
P88TCC	Dennis Javelin 12m	Plaxton Première 350	C57F	1997	
R134CUX	Dennis Javelin 12m	Plaxton Prima	C57F	1997	Lakeside, Ellesmere
R714FLG	Dennis Javelin 12m	Plaxton Prima	S70F	1998	
R177TKU	Volvo B10M-62	Plaxton Première 350	C57F	1998	
VIL5317	Dennis Javelin 12m	Plaxton Prima	C57F	1998	
B10MNC	DAF SB3000	Plaxton Première 350	C55F	1998	Alfa, Preston
B10MHC	DAF SB3000	Plaxton Première 350	C57F	1998	Alfa, Preston
T637JWB	Dennis Javelin GX 12m	Plaxton Excalibur	C57F	1999	Stort Valley
T638JWB	Dennis Javelin GX 12m	Plaxton Excalibur	C57F	1999	Stort Valley
T645XNP	Dennis Javelin 12m	Plaxton Première 350	C53F	1998	Whittle, Kidderminster
V264DTE	Dennis Javelin 12m	Plaxton Première 350	C57F	1999	
V465ESL	Dennis Javelin 12m	Plaxton Première 350	C57F	2000	
W645MKY	Dennis Javelin 12m	Plaxton Première 350	C53F	2000	BSS Coaches
W561WKH	Dennis Javelin 12m	Plaxton Première 350	C57F	2000	
PN03OSF	Dennis Javelin GX	Marcopolo Continental 340	C53F	2003	
PR57LYE	ADL Javelin	Plaxton Profile	C57F	2007	
PR57PSV	ADL Javelin	Plaxton Profile	C57F	2007	
PR57TCC	ADL Javelin	Plaxton Profile	C57F	2007	
PR08BET	ADL Javelin	Plaxton Profile	S70F	2008	
PR08ECT	ADL Javelin	Plaxton Profile	S70F	2008	
PR08PET	ADL Javelin	Plaxton Profile	S70F	2008	
PC58NEC	ADL Javelin	Plaxton Profile	C57F	2008	
PR58BEC	ADL Javelin	Plaxton Profile	C57F	2008	
PR58WYN	ADL Javelin	Plaxton Profile	C57F	2008	
YN09DYA	ADL Javelin	Plaxton Profile	C53F	2009	
YN09DYB	ADL Javelin	Plaxton Profile	C53F	2009	
YN09HRX	ADL Javelin	Plaxton Profile	C53F	2009	
YN09HRZ	ADL Javelin	Plaxton Profile	C53F	2009	
PC09MOM	ADL Javelin	Plaxton Profile	C57F	2009	
PC10BOS	Volvo B12M	Plaxton Panther	C49FT	2010	
PC10BOS	Volvo B12M	Plaxton Panther	C49FT	2010	
PD11TRD	ADL Javelin	Plaxton Profile	S70F	2011	
PR11JES	ADL Javelin	Plaxton Profile	S70F	2011	
PR61ROS	Volvo B9R	Plaxton Elite	C51FT	2011	

Previous registrations:

B10MHC	R71GNW		
B10MNC	R72GNW	N912DWJ	N912DWJ, A10CVR
CLZ4009	M912OVR	R704FLG	R714FLG, KSV408
LRU822	N959DWJ	T645XNP	XKH455
N713AHP	95D41602	VIL5317	R755RVJ, WJ15015
N899KPA	629LFM	W645MKY	W645MKY, C7BSS
		W861WKH	W100ACK

Please see page 195 for the fleet picture.

PULHAM'S

Pulham & Sons (Coaches) Ltd, Station Road Garage, Bourton-on-the-Water, GL54 2EN

Reg	Chassis	Body	Seating	Year	History
DDD200T	Leyland Leopard PSU3E/4R	Plaxton Supreme IV	C53F	1979	Andybus, Dauntsey, 2009
HDF661	Volvo B10M-60	Plaxton Paramount 3200 III	C57F	1991	Supreme, Coventry, 1993
VAO141	Volvo B10M-60	Plaxton Paramount 3200 III	C57F	1991	Supreme, Coventry, 1993
XDG614	Volvo B10M-62	Plaxton Première 350	S70F	1994	Truemans, Fleet, 2001
WDD194	Volvo B10M-62	Van Hool Alizée HE	C49FT	1996	
FDF965	Volvo B10M-62	Plaxton Première 350	C57F	1997	Southern Vectis, 2000
NDD672	Volvo B10M-62	Plaxton Première 320	S70F	1997	Thornes-Independent, 2008
R70PUL	Volvo B10M-62	Plaxton Première 320	S70F	1998	Skyline, Derby, 2012
YPL764	Volvo B10M-62	Plaxton Première 320	C57F	1998	Mayne, Warrington, 2007
UDF936	Volvo B10M-62	Plaxton Première 350	C57F	1998	
PDF567	Volvo B10M-62	Plaxton Première 320	C57F	2002	
GL52PUL	Volvo B7R	Plaxton Prima	BC57F	2002	
HDF661	Volvo B12M	Plaxton Paragon	C48FT	2002	WA Shearings, Wigan, 2011
VAD141	Volvo B12M	Plaxton Paragon	C48FT	2002	WA Shearings, Wigan, 2011
ODF561	Volvo B12M	Plaxton Paragon	C53F	2003	Snaith, Otterburn, 2010
GL53PUL	Mercedes-Benz Vario 0814	TransBus Beaver	BC33F	2003	
LDD488	Volvo B7R	TransBus Profile	S70F	2003	
VDF365	Volvo B7R	TransBus Profile	S70F	2003	Hills, Wolverhampton, 2011
GL54PUL	Volvo B7R	TransBus Profile	BC53F	2004	
GL05PUL	Volvo B12M	Van Hool T9 Alizée	C49FT	2005	
VE05ZTR	Volkswagen Transporter	Volkswagen	M8	2005	
PL05PUL	Toyota Coaster BB50R	Caetano Optimo V	C22F	2005	
GL06PUL	ADL Javelin 10m	Plaxton Profile	C41F	2006	
YJ06YST	Optare Solo M950 SL	Optare	N29F	2006	
YJ06YSU	Optare Solo M950 SL	Optare	N29F	2006	
YJ56APZ	Optare Solo M950 SL	Optare	N29F	2006	

Newly into service with Pulham's is PU12HAM, a Volvo B9R with VDL Jonckheere bodywork. It is seen shortly after delivery. *Colin Martin*

Joining the fleet in 2010, ODF561 is a Volvo B12M with Plaxton Paragon bodywork. It is seen in Cheltenham.
Colin Martin

GL07PUL	Volvo B12B	Plaxton Panther	C49FT	2007	
WDF946	Volvo B12B	Plaxton Panther	C49FT	2007	Logan, Dunloy, 2009
YJ57EGV	Optare Solo M950	Optare	N33F	2007	Wilson, Rhu, 2011
GL58PUL	Volvo B12M	Plaxton Panther	C53FT	2008	
DW09PUL	Volvo B12BT	Van Hool T917 Acron	C55FT	2009	
PU10HAM	Mercedes-Benz Vario O816	Plaxton Cheetah	C29F	2010	
SL60PUL	Volvo B12M	Plaxton Panther	C53FT	2010	
LP12BUS	Optare Solo M980 SR	Optare	N31F	2012	
AP12BUS	Volvo B7RLE	MCV Evolution	N49F	2012	
KP12BUS	Volvo B7RLE	MCV Evolution	N49F	2012	
WP12BUS	Volvo B7RLE	MCV Evolution	N49F	2012	
PU12HAM	Volvo B9B	VDL Jonckheere SHV	C51FT	2012	

Previous registrations:

FDF965	P618FTV, 473CDL	R70PUL	R587NFX, A2XCL
H155HAC	H155HAC, HDF661	UDF936	R748SDF
H156HAC	H156HAC, PDF567, VAD141	VAD141	YC02CFJ
HDF661	YC02CFL	VDF365	ST03BZL
LDD488	VO03MWW	WDD194	N680RDD
NDD672	R200TMS	WDF946	YN07OPJ
ODF561	YM03EOS	XDG614	L671OHL
PDF567	VU51FGN	YPL764	R120CNE

RAMBLER

Rambler Coaches Ltd, Whitworth Road, St Leonards-on-Sea, TN37 7PZ

01	JG07RAM	Volvo B12B	Volvo 9700	C49FT	2007	
02	X500GDY	Mercedes-Benz O404	Hispano Vita	C49FT	2000	
03	BDY389	Volvo B10M-62	Plaxton Panther	C49FT	2002	
04	CR04RAM	Volvo B7R	Plaxton Profile	C53F	2004	
05	DDY557	Volvo B10M-62	Plaxton Panther	C53F	2002	
06	DDY222	Volvo B10M-62	Berkhof Axial 50	C49FT	2001	
07	N191LPN	Mercedes-Benz 709D	Alexander Sprint	BC25F	1996	Stagecoach, 2006
08	NDY962	Volvo B10M-62	Plaxton Première 350	C53F	1996	Bus Eireann, 2001
09	CR06EDY	Volvo B12B	VDL Berkhof Axial 50	C53FT	2006	
10	V222PDY	Mercedes-Benz Atego 01120L	Optare/Ferqui Solera	C35F	1999	
11	R710YWC	Dennis Dart SLF 10.2m	Plaxton Pointer	N34F	1007	Stagecoach, 2011
12	M525WHF	Volvo B10B	Wright Endurance	B53F	1994	Beestons, Hadleigh, 2011
14	JG04RAM	Volvo B7R	Plaxton Profile	C53F	2004	
15	T222ADY	Mercedes-Benz 614D	Autobus	C24F	1999	
16	ODY395	Volvo B10M-62	Jonckheere Deauville 45	C53F	1995	Shearings, Wigan, 2003
17	ODY607	Volvo B10M-62	Jonckheere Deauville 45	C53F	1995	Shearings, Wigan, 2003
18	LDY173	Volvo B10M-62	Plaxton Panther	C53F	2000	Amport & District, Thruxton, 2005
19	SDY788	Volvo B12B	Plaxton Panther	C49FT	2005	TGM Group, 2010
20	VDY468	Volvo B10M-62	Plaxton Première 320	C57F	1996	First, 2009
21	J505GCD	Dennis Dart 9.8m	Alexander Dash	B41F	1992	Stagecoach South, 2004
22	JG08RAM	Volvo B12B	Plaxton Panther	C49FT	2008	
23	LR07RAM	Volvo B12B	Van Hool T9 Alizée	C55FT	2007	Brown, Edinburgh, 2009
24	PE56XMJ	Mercedes-Benz 1022L	UNVI Cimo	C29F	2007	McCabe, Dundalk, 2011
25	GDY493	Volvo B10M-62	Plaxton Première 350	C53F	1996	Bus Eireann, 2001
26	TDY946	Volvo B10M-62	Plaxton Première 320	C57F	1996	First, 2009
27	N301XRP	Mercedes-Benz 709D	Alexander Sprint	B23F	1996	Stagecoach, 2006
28	S136RLE	Volvo Olympian	Alexander RH	B43/29F	1998	Ensign, Purfleet, 2009
29	FDY383	Leyland Olympian ON2R50C13Z4	Alexander RH	B47/27D	1981	Dublin Bus, 2006
30	GDY500X	Volvo B10M-62	Plaxton Paragon	C53F	2002	Princess, West End, 2009
31	RDY155	Volvo B10B	Plaxton Verde	B51F	1995	Gemini, Swansea, 2007
33	UDY910	Volvo B10B	Plaxton Verde	B51F	1995	Gemini, Swansea, 2007

Showing the livery of Grand UK Holidays is Rambler 22, JG08RAM. This Plaxton Panther joined the fleet in 2008. *Mark Doggett*

The Plaxton Cheetah has seen several changes, since it was introduced in 1997. It is based on the Mercedes-Benz Vario chassis, itself having seen engine modifications to meet new emission standards in the interim.. Rambler's 34, JG54RAM is shown. *Mark Doggett*

34	JG54RAM	Mercedes-Benz Vario 0814	Plaxton Cheetah	C33F	2004	
35	PDY272	Volvo B10M-62	Van Hool T9 Alizée	C49FT	1999	
36	CR12RAM	Mercedes-Benz Tourismo OC510	Mercedes-Benz	C49FT	2012	
37	JG12RAM	Volvo B9R	Plaxton Panther II	C49FT	2012	
38	CR08RAM	Volvo B12B	Volvo 9700	C49FT	2008	
39	KDY814	Mercedes-Benz Sprinter 413 cdi	Ferqui Soroco	C16F	2002	Chapeltown, 2009
40	RDY155	Volvo B10M-62	Plaxton Paragon	C53F	2001	TGM Group, 2010
41	UDY512	Volvo B10M-62	Plaxton Paragon	C53F	2001	TGM Group, 2010

Special event vehicles:

	NG2414	Bedford WLB	Economy	B20F	1932	Jarvis, Swaffham
	CMG30	Bedford WLB	Duple	C20R	1935	Taylor, Tintenhull
	UUD12	Bedford J2 SZ10	Plaxton Consort III	C20F	1961	Florey & Witney
	EDY565E	Bedford VAM14	Duple Viceroy	C45F	1967	Rambler, Hastings
	JDY888Y	Bedford VAS5	Plaxton Supreme IV	C29F	1983	Rambler, Hastings
	D133VJK	Bedford YMPS	Plaxton Paramount 3200	C33F	1987	

Previous registrations:

BDY389	GX02AEE	LR07RAM	SK07FUW
CMG30	CMG30, JTA608	N191LPN	N191LPN, UDY512
DDY222	Y222PDY	N301RP	TDY388
DDY557	GX02AED	NDY962	96D42485(EI), P427LJH
EDY565E	EDY565E, JUE244E	ODY395	M605ORJ
FDY83	-	ODY607	M613ORJ
FDY383	91D10123, J706CEV	PDY272	T222GDY
GDY493	96D42478(EI), P428LJH	PE56XMJ	07LH2460
GDY500X	YR52MEU	RDY155	YN51WGY
HDY405	-	SDY788	YN55WSW
HDY565	-	TDY388	
J505GCD	J505GCD, MDY397	TDY946	R330RVG
JDY673	-	UDY910	YN51WGZ
KDY814	FX02WHA	VDY468	N617AP
LDY173	W87RRU, XEL606		

REAYS

Reays Coaches Ltd , Strawberry Fields, Syke Road, Wigton, CA7 9NE

	Reg	Chassis	Body	Seating	Year	History
	B2LTC	DAF SB230	Van Hool Alizée	C51FT	1987	Campbell, East Kilbride, 2006
	N117YHH	Mercedes-Benz 709D	Alexander Sprint	B34F	1996	Ellendale, Aspatria, 2012
	B6CWR	Mercedes-Benz 709D	Alexander Sprint	B23F	1996	Stagecoach, 2009
	B7CWR	Mercedes-Benz 709D	Alexander Sprint	B23F	1996	Stagecoach, 2005
	B8CWR	Mercedes-Benz 709D	Alexander Sprint	B23F	1996	Stagecoach, 2009
	B10CWR	Mercedes-Benz 709D	Alexander Sprint	B23F	1996	Stagecoach, 2005
	B12CWR	Mercedes-Benz 709D	Alexander Sprint	B23F	1996	Stagecoach, 2005
	B13CWR	Mercedes-Benz 709D	Alexander Sprint	B23F	1996	Stagecoach, 2005
w	B14CWR	Mercedes-Benz 709D	Alexander Sprint	B23F	1996	Stagecoach, 2005
	B15CWR	Mercedes-Benz 709D	Alexander Sprint	B23F	1996	Stagecoach, 2005
	TFO532	Volvo B10M-62	Plaxton Paragon	C48FT	2001	WA Shearings, Wigan, 2010
	FPN259	Volvo B10M-62	Plaxton Paragon	C48FT	2001	WA Shearings, Wigan, 2010
	MH02NGG	Dennis Dart SLF 8.8m	Plaxton Pointer MPD	N29F	2002	Bu-Val, Smithybridge, 2011
	MH02NGN	Dennis Dart SLF 8.8m	Plaxton Pointer MPD	N29F	2002	Bu-Val, Smithybridge, 2011
	SN52PXH	Mercedes-Benz Vito 110 cdi	Mercedes-Benz	M8	2002	
	MP03CYF	Dennis Dart SLF 8.8m	Plaxton Pointer MPD	N29F	2002	Bu-Val, Smithybridge, 2011
	YSU871	Neoplan Starliner N516 SHD	Neoplan	C50FT	2004	Walton Swift, Preston, 2011
	YN04AVM	Neoplan Starliner N516 SHD	Neoplan	C50FT	2004	Ellison, St Helens, 2006
	YK04FVU	Bova Futura FHD 13.340	Bova	C57FT	2004	
	B4GWR	Mercedes-Benz Vario 0814	Plaxton Beaver 2	B31F	2004	TM Travel, Sheffield, 2011
	B5GWR	Mercedes-Benz Vario 0814	Plaxton Beaver 2	B31F	2004	TM Travel, Sheffield, 2011
	MB04DVJ	Transbus Dart 8.8m	Transbus Mini Pointer	N29F	2004	Bu-Val, Smithybridge, 2011
	GX54AOR	ADL Dart SLF 10.7m	Plaxton Pointer	N34F	2004	Handy, Merthyr Tydfil, 2012
	GX54AOU	ADL Dart SLF 10.7m	Plaxton Pointer	N34F	2004	Handy, Merthyr Tydfil, 2012
	4426BY	Volvo B12B	Plaxton Paragon	C34FT	2005	Gordon, Rotherham, 2010
	712GRM	VDL SB4000	Van Hool Alizée	C36FT	2005	Walton Swift, Preston, 2012
	YX07HPA	Enterprise Plasma EB01	Plaxton Primo	N28F	2007	Veolia, 2011
	YX07HPF	Enterprise Plasma EB01	Plaxton Primo	N28F	2007	Veolia, 2011

Reays' fleet has grown significantly in recent months, as it has expanded its service network into Carlisle and the English Lakes including an opentop service from Keswick. Bova Futura YJ08NSO is shown. *Mark Doggett*

USV628 is a Volvo B12B with Plaxton Panther bodywork. It was operating a tour of the Cotswolds when pictured. *Colin Martin*

Special event vehicle:

108GYC	Bedford SB3	Duple Super Vega	C41F	1960	Bowerman, Taunton

Previous registrations:

N2RED	N314BYA, N262PYS	USV577	R344GHS
R8PSV	W531EOL, T8GLC, G8TRU	USV605	-
T3RED	T300LCT	USV620	W456DYG, B8CWR, XIL7396, W524ORM
USV330	T129JBA	USV625	L590HSG
USV331	R939YNF	USV628	FB53GTX, SIL6438
USV462	X499AHE, USV859	USV630	BD05GLD, UFJ742
USV474	-	USV631	-
USV511	T125JBA	USV676	P131VYG
USV556	P345VWR	USV859	D532UGA, XIL1231
USV562	AK52MGE, T100TAJ, 2851RU	V2RED	V256JTO, A5BOB

Web: www.redwoodstravel.com

RICHMOND'S

H V Richmond Ltd, The Garage, Barley, Royston, SG8 8JA

W898YNK	Mercedes-Benz Vario 0814	Plaxton Beaver 2	B29F	2000	
239LYC	Bova Futura FHD12.340	Bova	C53F	2003	
275FUM	Bova Futura FHD12.340	Bova	C53F	2004	
426YRA	VDL Bus SB4000	Van Hool T9 Alizée	C53F	2005	
577HTX	VDL Bus SB4000	Van Hool T9 Alizée	C53F	2005	
YJ05XMY	Optare Solo M850	Optare	N27F	2005	
153WAR	Volvo B12B	Van Hool T9 Astromega	C61/18CT	2006	Ham, Flitwell, 2009
753LNU	VDL Bova Futura FHD10.340	VDL Bova	C39F	2006	
892LTV	VDL Bova Futura FHD10.340	VDL Bova	C39F	2006	
403NMM	VDL Bova Futura FHD10.340	VDL Bova	C38FT	2006	
729KTO	VDL Bova Futura FHD120.365	VDL Bova	C53F	2007	
WVJ539	Volvo B12B	Van Hool T9 Alicron	C53F	2007	
648EAU	Volvo B12BT	Van Hool T9 Acron	C53F	2008	
593FGF	Van Hool T916 Astron 13.2m	Van Hool	C53FT	2008	
438XYA	Van Hool T916 Astron 13.2m	Van Hool	C53FT	2008	
YER469	Van Hool T916 Astron 13.2m	Van Hool	C53FT	2009	
668PTM	Volvo B12B	Van Hool T9 Astromega	C61/18CT	2009	BM Coaches, Hayes, 2011
MX09AON	Optare Solo M710 SE	Optare	N23F	2009	
851FYD	VDL Bova Futura FHD120.365	VDL Bova	C53F	2010	
424KPP	VDL Bova Futura FHD120.365	VDL Bova	C53F	2010	
649ETF	Mercedes-Benz Vario 0815	Sitcar Beluga 2	C29F	2010	
HDT375	Mercedes-Benz Vario 0815	Sitcar Beluga 2	C29F	2011	
316UVX	VDL Bova Futura FHD10.365	VDL Bova	C38FT	2012	

Previous registrations:

153WAR	DW55HAM		668PTM	WA09AZJ

Depots: The Garage, Barley and Church End, Barley. Web: www.richmonds-coaches.co.uk

One of the older coaches with Richmond's is Bova Futura 239LYC, seen here in London's Park Lane. The Futura's styling has changed little since its introduction n 1982. The model is still produced at Valkenswaard, some six kilometres south of Eindhoven. *Dave Heath*

ROBINSONS

O&C Holdsworth Ltd, Park Garage, Great Harwood, Blackburn, BB6 7SP

210	PF57XHS	Volkswagen Transporter	Volkswagen	M8	2007	
211	PF57XHT	Volkswagen Transporter	Volkswagen	M8	2007	
212	PN09XCX	Volkswagen Transporter	Volkswagen	M8	2009	
214	PK09XDB	Volkswagen Transporter	Volkswagen	M8	2009	
215	PN11EYP	Volkswagen Transporter	Volkswagen	M8	2011	
216	PN11EYR	Volkswagen Transporter	Volkswagen	M8	2011	
217	PE11XBK	Volkswagen Transporter	Volkswagen	M8	2011	
258	S258JFR	Volvo B10M-62	Plaxton Excalibur	C49FT	1998	
259	S259JFR	Volvo B10M-62	Plaxton Excalibur	C49FT	1998	
260	S260JFR	Volvo B10M-62	Plaxton Excalibur	C49FT	1998	
269	FN04JZU	Volvo B12B	VDL Jonckheere Mistral 50	C48FT	2004	
270	FN04JZV	Volvo B12B	VDL Jonckheere Mistral 50	C48FT	2004	
271	FN04JZW	Volvo B12B	VDL Jonckheere Mistral 50	C48FT	2004	
274	GM03JVE	Neoplan Starliner N516 SHD	Neoplan	C48FT	2003	Buzzlines, Hythe, 2007
275	GK04LUZ	Neoplan Starliner N516 SHD	Neoplan	C48FT	2003	Buzzlines, Hythe, 2007
276	YN08FYE	Volvo B12M	Plaxton Panther	C50FT	2008	
277	YN08FYF	Volvo B12M	Plaxton Panther	C50FT	2008	
278	FN09APV	Volvo B9R	Sunsundegui Sideral 330	C53F	2009	
279	MX59KTL	Neoplan Tourliner N2216/3 SHD	Neoplan	C49FT	2010	
280	MX59KTU	Neoplan Tourliner N2216/3 SHD	Neoplan	C57FT	2010	
281	MX10DDF	Neoplan Tourliner N2216/3 SHD	Neoplan	C57FT	2010	
282	MX10DDJ	Neoplan Tourliner N2216/3 SHD	Neoplan	C57FT	2010	
283	PO61MYW	Volvo B13B 14m	VDL Jonckheere SHV	C59FT	2012	

Previous registrations:

GK04LUZ	KB04BUZ		GM03JVE	NU03BUZ

Robinsons Holidays have set out from East Lancashire towns ever since the company was established in 1923. The latest arrival is PO61MYW, an early B13B model with VDL Jonckheere bodywork. *Volvo Bus*

ROSELYN

Roselyn Coaches Ltd, Middleway Garage, St Blazey Road, Par, PL24 2JA

Reg	Model	Body	Seating	Year	History
SUI1478	Leyland Olympian ONLXB/1R	Eastern Coach Works	B42/26D	1986	Arriva North East, 2008
YEZ6670	Leyland Olympian ONLXB/1R	Eastern Coach Works	B42/26D	1987	Arriva North East, 2008
E2RCL	Leyland Olympian ONCL10/1RZA	Alexander RH	O51/28F	1988	Lothian Buses, 2011
TIL6878	Leyland Olympian ONCL10/1RZA	Northern Counties	B47/31F	1989	South Gloucester B&C, 2008
EKZ5322	Leyland Olympian ONCL10/1RZ	Leyland	B47/31F	1989	East Yorkshire, 2008
SUI3159	Leyland Olympian ONCL10/1RZ	Leyland	B47/31F	1989	Stephensons of Essex, 2008
JNK2425	Leyland Olympian ON2R50C13Z4	Leyland	B47/31F	1989	East Yorkshire, 2008
237AJB	Volvo B10M-61	Van Hool Alizée	C53F	1988	
KSU454	Volvo B10M-60	Plaxton Paramount 3500 III	C49FT	1990	New Enterprise, 2009
MHZ1473	Leyland Olympian ON2R50C13Z4	Alexander	BC45/27F	1992	Landylines, Wellington, 20108
YUU556	Volvo B10M-60	Plaxton Excalibur	C49FT	1994	Stoneman, Nanpean, 2006
L157LBW	Volvo B10M-62	Jonckheere Deauville	C49FT	1994	Stagecoach, 2011
HIG5712	Volvo B10M-55	Alexander PS	BC48F	1994	Stagecoach, 2009
PUI8031	Volvo B10M-55	Alexander PS	BC48F	1994	Landylines, Wellington, 2010
UFH277	Volvo B10M-55	Alexander PS	BC48F	1994	Stagecoach, 2009
M611APN	Volvo B10M-55	Alexander PS	BC48F	1994	Stagecoach, 2009
M537WHF	Volvo B10B	Wright Endurance	B53F	1994	Arriva NW & Wales, 2010
M687HPF	Volvo Olympian	East Lancs	B44/30F	1994	Pointmost, Ivybridge, 2010
TIL5637	Scania N113 DRB	Northern Counties	B42/29F	1995	Pointmost, Ivybridge, 20
TIL5704	Scania N113 DRB	Northern Counties	B42/29F	1995	Pointmost, Ivybridge, 2010
LIB226	Scania K113 CRB	Van Hool T8 Alizée	C53F	1995	Arriva The Shires, 2009
RUI2125	Dennis Lance 11m	Optare Sigma	B47F	1995	Pointmost, Ivybridge, 2010
EKZ3999	Dennis Lance 11m	Optare Sigma	B47F	1995	Pointmost, Ivybridge, 2010
YOR456	Volvo B10M-62	Jonckheere Deauville 45	C53F	1995	Clarkes of London, 2001
513SRL	Volvo B10M-62	Van Hool T8 Alizée	C53F	1995	Pride of the Clyde, 2004
UIA29	Volvo B10M-62	Van Hool T8 Alizée	C53F	1995	Pride of the Clyde, 2004
728FDV	Volvo B10M-62	Plaxton Première 350	C57F	1995	Skills, Nottingham, 2002
P802BTA	Volvo B10M-62	Plaxton Première 320	C57F	1996	Stagecoach, 2012

Roselyn Coaches can trace its heritage back some ninety years, the last sixty of which have been with the same family. Cheltenham Racecourse is the location for this view of Roselyn's FSK866, a Volvo B10M with a trailing third axle and Van Hool T9 Alizée body. *Colin Martin*

Reg	Chassis	Body	Type	Year	Source
N388OTY	Scania N113 DRB	East Lancs	BC43/31F	1995	Arriva North East, 2010
N395LPN	Volvo Olympian	Alexander RH	BV47/29F	1996	Stagecoach, 2011
N399LPN	Volvo Olympian	Alexander RH	BV47/29F	1996	Stagecoach, 2012
S126RLE	Volvo Olympian	Alexander RH	B43/29F	1998	Ensign, Purfleet, 2010
S128RLE	Volvo Olympian	Alexander RH	B43/29F	1998	Ensign, Purfleet, 2010
S132RLE	Volvo Olympian	Alexander RH	B43/27F	1998	Ensign, Purfleet, 2010
S138RLE	Volvo Olympian	Alexander RH	B43/27F	1998	Ensign, Purfleet, 2010
YAF872	Volvo B10M-62	Plaxton Première 350	C49FT	1999	National Holidays, 2005
239AJB	Volvo B10M-62	Plaxton Première 350	C49FT	1999	National Holidays, 2005
701UDE	Volvo B10M-55	Van Hool T9 Alizée	C53F	1999	Richmond, Barley, 2010
FSK866	Volvo B10M-55	Van Hool T9 Alizée	C53F	1999	Richmond, Barley, 2010
NUF276	Volvo B10M-55	Van Hool T9 Alizée	C49FT	1999	Richmond, Barley, 2010
647PYC	Volvo B10M-62	Caetano Enigma	C49FT	2001	Classic, Anfield Plain, 2008
W8EDE	DAF SB3000	Van Hool T9 Alizée	C49FT	2001	Hammond, Mallow, 2005
WB03EDE	Volvo B12M	Van Hool T9 Alizée	C49FT	2003	
244AJB	Volvo B12M	Van Hool T9 Alizée	C51FT	2004	
NM07EDE	Volvo B12BT	Van Hool T9 Acron	C51FT	2007	
BU57RCL	VDL Bova Magiq MHD122.410	VDL Bova	C49FT	2008	

Special event vehicles:

Reg	Chassis	Body	Type	Year	Source
RFO361	AEC Regent V	Park Royal	H41/32F	1962	AERE, Harwell
TUT888H	Bedford VAL70	Plaxton Panorama Elite	C53F	1970	Weston, Leicester
ODL770V	Bedford YMT	Duple Dominant II	C53F	1979	
KAF129W	Volvo B58	Plaxton Supreme IV	C53F	1981	

Previous registrations:

237AJB	E44SAF	MHZ1473	K237NHC, NUF276
239AJB	-	NUF276	W704YBD
241AJB	-	PUI8031	L630TDY
242AJB	WA04MHJ	RUI2125	N388OTY
513SRL	LSK513, M42HSU	S128RLE	S128RLE, WJY759
647PYC	FJ51JYN	SUI1478	D198FYM
701UDE	424KPP, T711VJN	SUI3159	G305UYK
728FDV	M34TRR	TIL5704	M178LYP
E2RCL	E308MSF	TIL6878	G509SFT
EKZ3999	N395LPN	UIA29	M981HNS, LSK507
EKZ5322	G292UYK	UFH277	L347KCK, 417DCD
FSK866	HDT375, T368ORP	W8EDE	OIC1702, Y877GDV
JNZ2425	G311UYK	YAF872	T519EUB
KSU454	G801BPG	YEZ6670	D223FYM
LIB226	M53AWW	YOR456	M325KRY
M611APN	M611APN, 411DCD	YUU556	L939NWW, 244AJB

Web: www.roselyncoaches.co.uk. **Depots:** St Blazey Road, Par and Roach Road, St Austell.

A further tri-axle Volvo B10M is NUF276, seen at Victoria, London in September 2011. *Dave Heath*

ROYALE

J A Kent, Ash Court, C Phoenix Way, Heston, TW5 9NB

S20YAL	Volvo B12T	Jonckheere Monaco	C57/14CT	2002	Park's of Hamilton, 2007
RE54JAK	Volvo B12B	Van Hool T9 Alizée	C53FT	2005	Deros, Killarney, 2009
RE06JAK	Volvo B12B	VDL Berkhof Axial 70	C53F	2006	Pierce Kavanagh, Urlingford, 2008
RE56JAK	Volvo B12BT	Van Hool T925 Astrobel	C61/18CT	2006	
SF07OSC	Volvo B12B 13.5m	VDL Berkhof Axial 100	C65/18CT	2007	
RE57JAK	Mercedes-Benz Tourino 0510	Mercedes-Benz	C34FT	2007	
RE08PSV	Volvo B12B	Van Hool T9 Alizée	C57FT	2008	
KX58BJU	Mercedes-Benz Sprinter 515 cdi	KVC	M9	2008	
KX58BKA	Mercedes-Benz Sprinter 515 cdi	KVC	M9	2008	
WA10KNL	VDL Bova Futura FHD127.365	VDL Bova	C57FT	2010	
RE12JAC	Neoplan Tourliner N2216/3 SHD	Neoplan	C55FT	2012	
RE12JAK	Neoplan Tourliner N2216/3 SHD	Neoplan	C61FT	2012	

Previous registrations:

A20YAL	KSK986, SE02UWD	RE56JAK	WA56ENO
RE06JAK	06KK3040, WU06EZJ	SF07OSC	KSK983
RE54JAK	05KK3490, WA05WOY		

Neoplan Tourliner RE12JAK carries the Royale livery as it passes Marble Arch in summer sunshine. Launched in 2007 the Tourliner is built in Turkey with two models available for the British market, a 12.2metre 2 axle and a 13.7 metre tri-axle. *Dave Heath*

SCOTLAND & BATES

RM & GA Bates, Heath Road, Appledore, Ashford, TN26 2AJ

BKO447Y	Volvo B10M-61	Plaxton Supreme V	C57F	1982
M420VYD	Volvo B10M-62	Van Hool Alizée	C55F	1995
N756CYA	Volvo B10M-62	Van Hool Alizée	C55F	1996
P728JYA	Volvo B10M-62	Van Hool Alizée	C55F	1997
R634VYB	Volvo B10M-62	Van Hool T9 Alizée	C55F	1998
T760JYB	Volvo B10M-62	Van Hool T9 Alizée	C55F	1999
W567RYC	Volvo B10M-62	Van Hool T9 Alizée	C55F	2000
Y224NYA	Volvo B10M-62	Van Hool T9 Alizée	C53FT	2001
WJ02KDN	Volvo B12M	Van Hool T9 Alizée	C51FT	2002
WA03HPY	Volvo B12M	Van Hool T9 Alizée	C51FT	2003
WA04EWR	Volvo B12M	Van Hool T9 Alizée	C51FT	2004
WA54KTP	Volvo B12M	Van Hool T9 Alizée	C51FT	2004
WA06CDO	Volvo B12M	Van Hool T9 Alizée	C51FT	2006
WA07BHK	Volvo B12B	Van Hool T9 Alizée	C51FT	2007
WA08GSO	Volvo B12B	Van Hool T9 Alizée	C51FT	2008
WA09AZG	Volvo B12B	Van Hool T9 Alizée	C51FT	2009
WA10CFV	Volvo B12B	Van Hool T9 Alizée	C49FT	2010
WA60DWP	Volvo B12B	Van Hool T9 Alizée	C49FT	2011
WA61GRU	Mercedes-Benz Vario O815	Sitcar Beluga 2	C29F	2012

Web: www.scotlandandbates.co.uk

Just one Plaxton coach remains with Scotland & Bates following the latest arrival in the fleet, WA60DWP, a Volvo B12B with Van Hool T9 Alizée bodywork. It is seen in Lambeth. *Dave Heath*

SEA VIEW

Sea View Coaches (Poole) Ltd, 10 Fancy Road, Parkstone, BH12 4QZ

120	MF11LVD	Neoplan Tourliner N2216 SHD	Neoplan	C48FT	2011	
121	GN11EEP	King Long XMQ6800	King Long	C29FT	2011	
122	PN57CVS	MAN 18.400	Beulas Cygnus	C53FT	2007	
123	PN57CVT	MAN 18.400	Beulas Cygnus	C53FT	2007	
124	YN07EBX	MAN 18.400	Noge Catalan Star 350	C53FT	2007	
125	YN07EBV	MAN 18.400	Noge Catalan Star 350	C53FT	2007	
126	PN57CVU	MAN 18.400	Beulas Cygnus	C53FT	2008	
127	YN07EBZ	MAN 24.400	Noge Titanium	C53FT	2007	
128	BN58BJU	Mercedes-Benz Tourino O510	Mercedes-Benz	C33FT	2008	
129	PN09CWT	MAN 18.400	Beulas Cygnus	C53F	2009	
130	PN09CWU	MAN 18.400	Beulas Cygnus	C53F	2009	
131	PN09CWV	MAN 18.400	Beulas Cygnus	C53F	2009	
132	HF06ETD	MAN 18.350	Noge Catalan Star 350	C36FT	2006	
133	MX10OFD	Neoplan Tourliner N440X SHD	Neoplan	C49FT	2010	
134	MX10OFE	Neoplan Tourliner N440X SHD	Neoplan	C49FT	2010	
135	MX10OFF	Neoplan Tourliner N440X SHD	Neoplan	C49FT	2010	
136	MX10OFG	Neoplan Tourliner N440X SHD	Neoplan	C49FT	2010	
137	MF12HGK	Neoplan Tourliner N2216 SHD	Neoplan	C48FT	2012	
138	MF11LVE	Neoplan Tourliner N2216 SHD	Neoplan	C48FT	2011	
139	MF11LVG	Neoplan Tourliner N2216 SHD	Neoplan	C48FT	2011	
717	N807KRL	Ford Transit	Ford	M14	1996	Vosper VH, Plymouth, 2000
718	YR02UOA	Mercedes-Benz Sprinter 412 cdi	Optare/Ferqui	C16F	2002	Hallmark, Birmingham, 2003
719	X719WPR	Mercedes-Benz 412D	Ferqui	M16	2000	
722	YN57EOE	Mercedes-Benz Sprinter 515 cdi	Mercedes-Benz	M16	2007	

Web: www.seaviewcoaches.com

Representing Sea View Coaches is 131, PN09CWV, one of three MAN 18.400s with Beulas Cygnus bodywork added to the fleet in 2009. Beulas has been building coaches in Spain for over seventy years. *Steve Rice*

SELWYNS

Selwyn's - Haytons

Selwyns Travel Ltd, Cavendish Farm Road, Runcorn, WA7 4LU

37	FJ06GGA	MAN 14.280	Caetano Enigma	C39F	2006	
38	FJ06GGO	MAN 14.280	Caetano Enigma	C39F	2006	
48	SEL23	DAF SB4000	Van Hool T9 Alizée	C51FT	2004	
49	SEL133	DAF SB4000	Van Hool T9 Alizée	C51FT	2004	
69	SEL702	DAF SB3000	Van Hool Alizée HE	C57F	1998	Armchair, Brentford, 2002
90	SEL36	DAF SB3000	Van Hool T9 Alizée	C55F	2002	
100	SEL73	DAF SB3000	Van Hool Alizée HE	C57F	1999	Armchair, Brentford, 2002
103	TJI6925	DAF SB4000	Van Hool T9 Alizée	C49FT	2003	
104	SEL392	DAF SB4000	Van Hool T9 Alizée	C53F	2003	
105	SEL853	DAF SB4000	Van Hool T9 Alizée	C49FT	2004	
106	352STG	DAF SB4000	Van Hool T9 Alizée	C53F	2004	
107	YJ04BYH	VDL Bus SB4000	Van Hool T9 Alizée	C49FT	2004	
109	YJ54CFD	VDL Bus SB4000	Van Hool T9 Alizée	C49FT	2004	
111	YJ05PWE	VDL Bus SB4000	Van Hool T9 Alizée	C49FT	2005	
112	YJ05PWF	VDL Bus SB4000	Van Hool T9 Alizée	C49FT	2005	
113	FN06EBO	Volvo B12B	Caetano Levanté	C49FT	2006	
114	FJ06PAO	Volvo B12B	Caetano Levanté	C49FT	2006	
115	FJ06PBF	Volvo B12B	Caetano Levanté	C49FT	2006	
116	FJ06PBO	Volvo B12B	Caetano Levanté	C49FT	2006	
119	YN56OSG	Mercedes-Benz Vario 0814	Plaxton Cheetah	C29F	2006	
120	YN56OSJ	Mercedes-Benz Vario 0814	Plaxton Cheetah	C29F	2006	
122	YJ04BOV	VDL Bus SB4000	Van Hool T9 Alizée	C49FT	2004	Ashton, St Helens, 2007
123	YJ04HHZ	VDL Bus SB4000	Van Hool T9 Alizée	C49FT	2004	Arriva Bus & Coach, 2007
124	YJ04HHY	VDL Bus SB4000	Van Hool T9 Alizée	C49FT	2004	Arriva Bus & Coach, 2007
126	YJ04BJF	VDL Bus SB4000	Van Hool T9 Alizée	C49FT	2004	Fishwick, Leyland, 2008
127	YJ05PXF	VDL Bus SB4000	Van Hool T9 Alizée	C49FT	2005	Gain Travel, Wibsey, 2008
128	YJ06LFV	VDL Bus SB4000	Van Hool T9 Alizée	C51FT	2006	Ciy Circle, Edinburgh, 2008
129	YJ08DGY	VDL Bus SB4000	VDL Berkhof Axial 50	C57FT	2008	
130	YJ08DHF	VDL Bus SB4000	VDL Berkhof Axial 50	C57FT	2008	
131	FJ58AJU	Scania K340 EB4	Caetano Levanté	C49FT	2009	
132	FJ58AJV	Scania K340 EB4	Caetano Levanté	C49FT	2009	
137	YN09KHO	Mercedes-Benz Vario 0816	Plaxton Cheetah	C29F	2009	
138	YN09KHP	Mercedes-Benz Vario 0816	Plaxton Cheetah	C29F	2009	
139	FJ59APX	Scania K340 EB4	Caetano Levanté	C49FT	2009	
140	FJ59APY	Scania K340 EB4	Caetano Levanté	C49FT	2009	

Carrying the latest Hayton's livery is BD08DZX, a Mercedes-Benz Tourismo which arrived in the Selwyn group fleet when Hayton's was acquired in 2011.
Paul Riley

Seen arriving on the Epsom Downs is Selwyns SEL133, a DAF SB4000 with Van Hool T9 Alizée bodywork.
Dave Heath

141	YN10FKM	Volvo B9R	Plaxton Elite	C48FT	2010	
142	YN10FKO	Volvo B9R	Plaxton Elite	C48FT	2010	
143	YN10FKP	Volvo B9R	Plaxton Elite	C48FT	2010	
144	YN10FKR	Volvo B9R	Plaxton Elite	C48FT	2010	
145	YN10FKS	Volvo B9R	Plaxton Elite	C48FT	2010	
146	YN10FKT	Volvo B9R	Plaxton Elite	C48FT	2010	
147	YN10FKV	Volvo B9R	Plaxton Elite	C48FT	2010	
149	MX60EGK	Mercedes-Benz Sprinter 413 cdi	KVC	C16F	2010	
150	DK60AMX	Mercedes-Benz Sprinter 413 cdi	KVC	C16F	2010	
151	MX60EKH	Mercedes-Benz Sprinter 413 cdi	KVC	C16F	2010	
152	YN60FMO	Mercedes-Benz Vario O816	Plaxton Cheetah	C29F	2011	
153	YN11AYA	Volvo B9R	Plaxton Elite	C48FT	2011	
154	YN11AYB	Volvo B9R	Plaxton Elite	C48FT	2011	
155	YN11AYC	Volvo B9R	Plaxton Elite	C48FT	2011	
156	YN11AYD	Volvo B9R	Plaxton Elite	C48FT	2011	
159	YN11FTU	Mercedes-Benz Vario O816	Plaxton Cheetah	C29F	2011	
160	YN11FTV	Mercedes-Benz Vario O816	Plaxton Cheetah	C29F	2011	
161	FJ11MLV	Volvo B9R	Caetano Levanté	C48FT	2011	
162	YN06TFY	Scania K114 EB4	VDL Berkhof Axial 50	C57FT	2006	Haytons, Manchester, 2011
163	MHZ9321	Volvo B12M	Jonckheere Mistral 50	C39FT	2002	Haytons, Manchester, 2011
164	MHZ9322	Volvo B12M	Jonckheere Mistral 50	C39FT	2002	Haytons, Manchester, 2011
165	FJ61EWF	Volvo B9R	Caetano Levanté	C48FT	2011	
166	FJ61EWG	Volvo B9R	Caetano Levanté	C48FT	2011	
167	FJ61EWH	Volvo B9R	Caetano Levanté	C48FT	2011	
168	FJ61EWK	Volvo B9R	Caetano Levanté	C48FT	2011	
169	FJ61EWL	Volvo B9R	Caetano Levanté	C48FT	2011	
170	FJ61EWM	Volvo B9R	Caetano Levanté	C48FT	2011	
171	FJ61EWB	Volvo B9R	Caetano Levanté	C48FT	2011	
172	FJ61EWZ	Volvo B9R	Caetano Levanté	C48FT	2011	
173	FJ61EXK	Volvo B9R	Caetano Levanté	C48FT	2011	
174	FJ61EXL	Volvo B9R	Caetano Levanté	C48FT	2011	
175	W201EAG	Volvo B10M-62	Plaxton Panther	C53F	2000	Haytons, Manchester, 2011
176	SH51MHO	Optare Solo M920	Optare	N30F	2002	Haytons, Manchester, 2011
177	SH51MHU	Optare Solo M920	Optare	N30F	2002	Haytons, Manchester, 2011
178	SH51MKO	Optare Solo M920	Optare	N30F	2002	Haytons, Manchester, 2011
179	FY02OTF	Mercedes-Benz Atego 1223L	Ferqui Solara	C39F	2002	Haytons, Manchester, 2011
180	LB52UYK	Volvo B12M	Plaxton Panther	C49FT	2003	Haytons, Manchester, 2011
181	YP52KRZ	Volvo B12M	Plaxton Panther	C49FT	2002	Haytons, Manchester, 2011

Selwyns provides several coaches on National Express work and is one of only two operators to use the Plaxton Elite product on such services. Illustrating the type is 155, YN11AYC. *Mark Doggett*

182	YN55WSO	Volvo B12B	Plaxton Panther	C49FT	2005	Haytons, Manchester, 2011
183	PO56PCF	MAN 18.310	Maropolo Viaggio 350	S70F	2007	Haytons, Manchester, 2011
184	BD08DZX	Mercedes-Benz Tourismo	Mercedes-Benz	C36FT	2008	Haytons, Manchester, 2011
185	WA08APO	VDL SB4000	VDL Bova Synergy 100	C63/20DT	2008	Haytons, Manchester, 2011
186	FJ60EFU	Volvo B9R	Caetano Levanté	C48FT	2010	Haytons, Manchester, 2011
187	FJ60EFV	Volvo B9R	Caetano Levanté	C48FT	2010	Haytons, Manchester, 2011
188	FJ60EFW	Volvo B9R	Caetano Levanté	C48FT	2010	Haytons, Manchester, 2011
190	DE52NWY	Tecnobus	Tecnobus Pantheon	N11C	2002	
191	DE52NXU	Tecnobus	Tecnobus Pantheon	N11C	2002	
192	DE52NXV	Tecnobus	Tecnobus Pantheon	N11C	2002	
193	DE52NXW	Tecnobus	Tecnobus Pantheon	N11C	2002	
194	DE52NYX	Tecnobus	Tecnobus Pantheon	N11C	2002	
195	DE52NYY	Tecnobus	Tecnobus Pantheon	N11C	2002	
800	YN51KUX	Dennis Trident	Aleander ALX400	N43/19D	2001	*On loan from Abellio*
801	YN51KVG	Dennis Trident	Aleander ALX400	N43/19D	2001	*On loan from Abellio*
802	YN51KVJ	Dennis Trident	Aleander ALX400	N43/19D	2001	*On loan from Abellio*
804	YN51KVC	Dennis Trident	Aleander ALX400	N43/19D	2001	*On loan from Abellio*
805	YN51KVD	Dennis Trident	Aleander ALX400	N43/19D	2001	*On loan from Abellio*
806	YN51KUW	Dennis Trident	Aleander ALX400	N43/19D	2001	*On loan from Abellio*
807	YN51KUY	Dennis Trident	Aleander ALX400	N43/19D	2001	*On loan from Abellio*
808	YN51KUV	Dennis Trident	Aleander ALX400	N43/19D	2001	*On loan from Abellio*
809	YN51KVA	Dennis Trident	Aleander ALX400	N43/19D	2001	*On loan from Abellio*

Previous registrations:

352STG	YJ53VDO		SEL133	YJ04HHC-
MHZ9321	GT02WAG		SEL392	YJ03PPZ
MHZ9322	GT02WAM		SEL702	R39GNW, 98D70419
SEL23	YJ04HHB		SEL853	YJ53VDN
SEL36	YJ51EKX		TJI6925	YJ03PPY
SEL73	T185AUA			

Depots: Melbourne Avenue, Manchester Airport; Cavendish Farm Road, Runcorn and Sherdley Road Ind Estate, St. Helens.
Web: www.selwyns.co.uk

SHARPES

Sharpes of Nottingham, 10 Canalside Ind Park, Cropwell Bishop, Nottingham, NG12 3BE

ROX634Y	MCW Metrobus DR102/27	MCW	B43/30F	1983	Travel West Midlands, 2008
A676UOE	MCW Metrobus DR102/27	MCW	B43/30F	1983	Travel West Midlands, 2008
A699UOE	MCW Metrobus DR102/27	MCW	B43/30F	1983	Travel West Midlands, 2008
B836AOP	MCW Metrobus DR102/27	MCW	B43/30F	1984	Travel West Midlands, 2008
MIB6571	MCW Metrobus DR102/27	MCW	B43/30F	1984	Travel West Midlands, 2008
NLZ116	MCW Metrobus DR102/48	MCW	B43/30F	1985	Travel West Midlands, 2008
OKZ7928	MCW Metrobus DR102/27	MCW	B43/30F	1985	Travel West Midlands, 2008
KAZ7305	Volvo Citybus B10M-50	Alexander RV	B46/34D	1988	2-Travel, Pentre-chwyth, 2004
MIB658	Volvo B10M-61	Van Hool Alizée	C53F	1988	Brown, Roecliffe, 2004
SIL706	Volvo B10M-55	Alexander PS	B49F	1993	Stagecoach, 2010
UXI476	Volvo B10M-55	Alexander PS	BC48F	1993	Stagecoach, 2010
TIW113	Volvo B10M-55	Alexander PS	B49F	1993	Stagecoach, 2010
60YWX	Volvo Olympian	Alexander RH	B51/30D	1996	Lothian Buses, 2009
55XY	Volvo Olympian	Alexander RH	B51/30D	1996	Lothian Buses, 2009
NBZ301	Volvo Olympian	Alexander RH	B51/30D	1996	Lothian Buses, 2009
60XYT	Volvo Olympian	Alexander RH	B51/30D	1996	Lothian Buses, 2009
HBZ651	Volvo B10M-62	Van Hool Alizée	C53F	1996	Shearings, Wigan, 2004
CLZ208	Volvo B10M-61	Van Hool Alizée	C53F	1997	Brown, Roecliffe, 2004
VCZ155	Volvo Olympian	Alexander RH	B47/31F	1999	Bus Eireann, 2010
22CDX	Volvo Olympian	Alexander RH	B47/31F	1999	Bus Eireann, 2010
ACZ103	Volvo B12B	Van Hool T9 Alizée	C53F	2004	Maynes of Buckie, 2007
KBZ801	Volvo B12M	Berkhof Axial 70	C49FT	2004	Brown, Broxburn, 2007
RIL516	Volvo B12M	Berkhof Axial 70	C49FT	2004	Brown, Broxburn, 2007

Sharpes operates two interesting double-deck coaches both shown. Below is Van Hool TD927 Astromega 3TYX and opposite VDL Synergy 8XNE. The Synergy model is now available with both Bova and Berkhof branding and is built in the Netherlands. *John Marsh/Dave Heath*

LAZ130	Volvo B12B	Van Hool T9 Alizée	C53F	2005	Maynes of Buckie, 2007
YIB827	Volvo B12B	Van Hool T9 Alizée	C53F	2005	Maynes of Buckie, 2007
HJZ113	Volvo B12B	Van Hool T9 Alizée	C59F	2005	Highland Heritage, 2011
BHZ122	Volvo B12B	Van Hool T9 Alizée	C49FT	2006	Maynes of Buckie, 2009
NLZ708	Volvo B12B+	Van Hool T9 Alizée	C49FT	2006	Maynes of Buckie, 2009
2SXV	Volvo B12B	Van Hool T9 Alizée	C49FT	2007	Mearns, East Kilbride, 2012
8XNE	VDL SB4000	VDL Bova Synergy	C59/16DT	2007	
YP07WFJ	Ford Transit	Ford	M16	2007	
7JXO	Van Hool T917 Astron	Van Hool	C48FT	2008	Parry, Cheslyn Hay, 2010
7OWX	Van Hool T917 Astron	Van Hool	C48FT	2008	Parry, Cheslyn Hay, 2010
AJ09OTT	Ford Transit	Ford	M16	2009	
3TYX	Van Hool TD927 Astromega	Van Hool	C61/22DT	2011	

Previous registrations:

2SXV	SM07GSM	MIB658	E629UNE, LSK807
7OWX	YJ08NTY	MIB6571	A764WVP
8XNE	WA56ONS	NBZ301	N405GSX
22CDX	99D449, S214CRR	NLZ116	C906FON
55YXS	N406GSX	NLZ708	DM06GSM
60XYT	N403GSX	OKZ7928	B837AOP
60YWX	0411KSX	RIL516	FN04JZD
ACZ103	KM04GSM	SIL706	K731DAO
BHZ122	KM06GSM	TIW112	FN04JZE
CLZ208	D51LWW, NJI5510	TIW113	K760DAO
HBZ651	P813GBA	UXI476	K774DAO
HJZ113	SN05DWA	VCZ155	99D454
KAZ7305	F121PHM	VJI625	N655EWJ
KBZ801	FN04JZF	YIB827	MM05GSM
LAZ130	KN05GSM		

SHEARINGS

Shearings - Euro Tourer - Grand Tourer - National Holidays

Shearings Ltd, Miry Lane, Wigan WN3 4AG

101-110 Setra S416 GT-HD Setra C48FT 2009

101	GT	BK09RMV	104	GT	BK09RMX	107	GT	BK09RMZ	109	GT	BK09RNF
102	GT	BK09RMO	105	GT	BK09RNA	108	GT	BK09RNE	110	GT	BK09RNJ
103	GT	BK09RMU	106	GT	BK09RMY						

111-130 Setra S416 GT-HD Setra C52FT 2009

111	SH	BN09FXA	116	SH	BN09FXG	121	SH	BK09LUH	126	SH	BK09LUR
112	SH	BN09FXB	117	SH	BN09FXF	122	SH	BK09LUJ	127	SH	BK09LUT
113	SH	BN09FXC	118	SH	BN09FXH	123	SH	BK09LUL	128	SH	BK09LUW
114	SH	BN09FXE	119	SH	BN09FXJ	124	SH	BK09LUO	129	SH	BK09LUZ
115	SH	BN09FXD	120	SH	BN09FXK	125	SH	BK09LUP	130	SH	BK09LUY

151-165 Setra S415 GT-HD Setra C48FT 2009

151	NH	NH09BRH	155	NH	NH09GRH	159	NH	NH09LRH	163	NH	NH09PRH
152	NH	NH09CRH	156	NH	NH09HRH	160	NH	NH09MRH	164	NH	NH09RRH
153	NH	NH09DRH	157	NH	NH09JRH	161	NH	NH09NRH	165	NH	NH09SRH
154	NH	NH09FRH	158	NH	NH09KRH	162	NH	NH09ORH			

201-210 Setra S416 GT-HD Setra C48FT 2010

201	GT	BK10EJA	204	GT	BK10EJE	207	GT	BK10EJJ	209	GT	BK10EJN
202	GT	BK10EJC	205	GT	BK10EJF	208	GT	BK10EJL	210	GT	BK10EJO
203	GT	BK10EJD	206	GT	BK10EJG						

211-230 Setra S416 GT-HD Setra C52FT 2010

211	SH	BK10VCA	216	SH	BK10VCJ	221	SH	BK10VCO	226	SH	BK10VCW
212	SH	BK10VCC	217	SH	BK10VCK	222	SH	BK10VCP	227	SH	BK10VCX
213	SH	BK10VCD	218	SH	BK10VCL	223	SH	BK10VCT	228	SH	BK10VCY
214	SH	BK10VCE	219	SH	BK10VCM	224	SH	BK10VCU	229	SH	BK10VCZ
215	SH	BK10VCG	220	SH	BK10VCN	225	SH	BK10VCV	230	SH	BK10VDA

After many years operating Volvo coaches with Van Hool or Plaxton bodywork, Shearings took Setra integral coaches for the 2009 season and the company has continued with this supplier for subsequent deliveries. For the 2012 season some vehicles have been contracted from other operators and these carry Shearings livery. One of the initial Setra S416 coaches is 126, BK09LUR. *Tony Wilson*

The Setra coaches for Shearings and Grand Tourer work are the tri-axle S416 GT-HD while those liveried for National Holidays are the two-axle S415 GT-DH. Seen in London is 327, BK11CRV. *Dave Heath*

251-265

			Setra S415 GT-HD			Setra			C48FT	2010		
251	NH	NH10BSH	255	NH	NH10GSH	259	NH	NH10LSH	263	NH	NH10PSH
252	NH	NH10CSH	256	NH	NH10HSH	260	NH	NH10MSH	264	NH	NH10RSH
253	NH	NH10DSH	257	NH	NH10JSH	261	NH	NH10NSH	265	NH	NH10SSH
254	NH	NH10FSH	258	NH	NH10KSH	262	NH	NH10OSH			

301-310

			Setra S416 GT-HD			Setra			C48FT	2011		
301	GT	BK11GJE	304	GT	BK11GJJ	307	GT	BK11GJV	309	GT	BK11GJY
302	GT	BK11GJF	305	GT	BK11GJO	308	GT	BK11GJX	310	GT	BK11GJZ
303	GT	BK11GJG	306	GT	BK11GJU						

311-330

			Setra S416 GT-HD			Setra			C52FT	2011		
311	SH	BK11COA	316	SH	BK11CPF	321	SH	BK11CPX	326	SH	BK11CRU
312	SH	BK11COH	317	SH	BK11CPN	322	SH	BK11CPY	327	SH	BK11CRV
313	SH	BK11COJ	318	SH	BK11CPO	323	SH	BK11CPZ	328	SH	BK11CRX
314	SH	BK11COU	319	SH	BK11CPU	324	SH	BK11CRF	329	SH	BK11CRZ
315	SH	BK11CPE	320	SH	BK11CPV	325	SH	BK11CRJ	330	SH	BK11CSF

351-365

			Setra S415 GT-HD			Setra			C48FT	2011		
351	NH	NH11BTH	355	NH	NH11GTH	359	NH	NH11LTH	363	NH	NH11PTH
352	NH	NH11CTH	356	NH	NH11HTH	360	NH	NH11MTH	364	NH	NH11RTH
353	NH	NH11DTH	357	NH	NH11JTH	361	NH	NH11NTH	365	NH	NH11STH
354	NH	NH11FTH	358	NH	NH11KTH	362	NH	NH11OTH			

506-520

			Volvo B12M			Van Hool T9 Alizée			C48FT	2003		
506	SH	MX03AAV	508	SH	MX03AAZ	516	SH	MX03ACJ	520	SH	MX03ACZ
507	SH	MX03AAY	510	SH	MX03ABK	519	SH	MX03ACY			

527	NH	MX03AED	Volvo B12M	Jonckheere Mistral 50	C48FT	2003
528	NH	MX03AEE	Volvo B12M	Jonckheere Mistral 50	C48FT	2003
537	NH	MX03AET	Volvo B12M	Plaxton Paragon	C48FT	2003
538	NH	MX03AEU	Volvo B12M	Plaxton Paragon	C48FT	2003
539	NH	MX03AEV	Volvo B12M	Plaxton Paragon	C48FT	2003
540	NH	MX03AEW	Volvo B12M	Plaxton Paragon	C48FT	2003
551	NH	MX03AEF	Volvo B12M	Jonckheere Mistral 50	C48FT	2003
552	NH	MX03AEG	Volvo B12M	Jonckheere Mistral 50	C48FT	2003

Grand Tourer livery is shown on Van Hool-bodied Volvo B12M 604, MX04AED. *Mark Doggett*

553-582		Volvo B12M			Plaxton Paragon			C48FT	2003		
553	NH	YJ03VMH	**560**	NH	YJ03VMW	**567**	NH	YJ03VND	**576**	NH	YJ03VOD
554	NH	YJ03VMK	**561**	NH	YJ03VMX	**568**	NH	YJ03VNE	**577**	NH	YJ03VOF
555	NH	YJ03VML	**562**	NH	YJ03VMY	**569**	NH	YJ03VNF	**578**	NH	YJ03VOG
556	NH	YJ03VMM	**563**	NH	YJ03VMZ	**570**	NH	YJ03VNG	**579**	NH	YJ03VOH
557	NH	YJ03VMP	**564**	NH	YJ03VNA	**571**	NH	YJ03VNS	**580**	NH	YJ03VOK
558	NH	YJ03VMR	**565**	NH	YJ03VNB	**574**	NH	YJ03VOB	**581**	NH	YJ03VOM
559	NH	YJ03VMT	**566**	NH	YJ03VNC	**575**	NH	YJ03VOC	**582**	NH	YJ03VOP

601-610		Volvo B12M			Van Hool T9 Alizée HE			C42FT	2004		
601	SH	MX04AEA	**604**	SH	MX04AED	**607**	SH	MX04AEG	**609**	SH	MX04AEK
602	SH	MX04AEB	**605**	SH	MX04AEE	**608**	SH	MX04AEJ	**610**	SH	MX04AEL
603	SH	MX04AEC	**606**	SH	MX04AEF						

611-626		Volvo B12M			Plaxton Panther			C48FT	2004		
611	SH	MX04AEM	**617**	SH	MX04AEW	**621**	NH	MX04AFE	**624**	NH	MX04AFK
613	SH	MX04AEP	**618**	SH	MX04AEY	**622**	SH	MX04AFF	**625**	NH	MX04AFN
615	SH	MX04AEU	**619**	NH	MX04AEZ	**623**	NH	MX04AFJ	**626**	NH	MX04AFU
616	SH	MX04AEV	**620**	SH	MX04AFA						

651-660		Volvo B12M			Plaxton Panther			C48FT	2004		
651	NH	NH04BCH	**654**	NH	NH04ECH	**657**	NH	NH04HCH	**659**	NH	NH04KCH
652	NH	NH04CCH	**655**	NH	NH04FCH	**658**	NH	NH04JCH	**660**	NH	NH04LCH
653	NH	NH04DCH	**656**	NH	NH04GCH						

701-715		Volvo B12M			Van Hool T9 Alizée			C42FT	2005		
701	GT	MX05AFU	**705**	GT	MX05AGO	**709**	GT	MX05AGZ	**713**	GT	MX05AHE
702	GT	MX05AFV	**706**	GT	MX05AGU	**710**	GT	MX05AHA	**714**	GT	MX05AHF
703	GT	MX05AFY	**707**	GT	MX05AGV	**711**	GT	MX05AHC	**715**	GT	MX05AHG
704	GT	MX05AFZ	**708**	GT	MX05AGY	**712**	GT	MX05AHD			

716-720		Volvo B12M			VDL Jonckheere Mistral 50		C42FT	2005		
716	GT	MX05AHJ	**718**	GT	MX05AHL	**719**	GT	MX05AHN	**720**	GT	MX05AHO
717	GT	MX05AHK								

721-730

		Volvo B12M			Plaxton Panther			C42FT	2005		
721	NH	MX05AHP	**723**	NH	MX05AHV	**724**	NH	NH05GDH	**725**	NH	NH05HDH
722	NH	MX05AHU									

751-755

		Volvo B12M			Plaxton Panther			C48FT	2005		
751	NH	NH05BDH	**753**	NH	NH05DDH	**754**	NH	NH05EDH	**755**	NH	NH05FDH
752	NH	NH05CDH									

801-810

		Volvo B12M			Van Hool T9 Alizée			C36FT	2006		
801	GT	MX06AKN	**804**	GT	MX06AKU	**807**	GT	MX06AKZ	**809**	GT	MX06ALU
802	GT	MX06AKO	**805**	GT	MX06AKV	**808**	GT	MX06ALO	**810**	GT	MX06AMK
803	GT	MX06AKP	**806**	GT	MX06AKY						

851-860

		Volvo B12M			Plaxton Panther			C48FT	2006		
851	NH	NH06BEH	**854**	NH	NH06EEH	**857**	NH	NH06HEH	**859**	NH	NH06KEH
852	NH	NH06CEH	**855**	NH	NH06FEH	**858**	NH	NH06JEH	**860**	NH	NH06LEH
853	NH	NH06DEH	**856**	NH	NH06GEH						

MO56-62

		Ford Tourneo			Ford			M9	2009		
56	SH	MF09ZLN	**58**	SH	MK59LXV	**60**	SH	MK59LXU	**62**	SH	MK59LXR
57	SH	MF09ZMO	**59**	SH	MK59LXW	**61**	SH	MK59LXP			

Ancillary vehicle:

999	K17FTG	Volvo B10M-60	Plaxton Excalibur	TV	1993	Woods, Wigton, 2009

Previous registrations:

NH04BCH	GT04AST	NH05FDH	MX05AKF
NH04CCH	GT04BST	NH05GDH	MX05AHY
NH04DCH	GT04CST	NH05HDH	MX05AHZ
NH04ECH	GT04DST	NH06BEH	MX06AMO
NH04FCH	GT04EST	NH06CEH	MX06AMU
NH04GCH	GT04NNN	NH06DEH	MX06AMV
NH04HCH	GT04RRR	NH06EEH	MX06ANF
NH04JCH	GT04UUU	NH06FEH	MX06ANP
NH04KCH	GT04YYY	NH06GEH	MX06ANR
NH04LCH	GT04ZZZ	NH06HEH	MX06ANU
NH05BDH	MX05AJO	NH06JEH	MX06ANV
NH05CDH	MX05AJU	NH06KEH	MX06AOA
NH05DDH	MX05AJV	NH06LEH	MX06AOB
NH05EDH	MX05AJY		

Web: www.washearings.com; www.national-holidays.co.uk

Many of the Grand Tourer coaches spend much of their time on the continent and are often seen in convoy heading for the channel ports. Still in Britain when pictured is 109, BK09RNF. *Mark Doggett*

SIESTA

Siesta International Holidays Ltd, Siesta House, Newport South Business Park, Lamport Street, Middlesbrough, TS1 5QL

R4SCC	Scania K124 IB4	Berkhof Axial 50	C40FT	1998
R14SCC	Scania K124 IB4	Berkhof Axial 50	C40FT	1998
YN53GDX	Scania K114 EB6	Berkhof Axial 100	C51/12CT	2003
YN53PBX	Scania K114 EB6	Berkhof Axial 100	C51/12CT	2003
DE03XDR	Ford Transit	Ford	M16	2003
YN04AHZ	Scania K114 EB6	Berkhof Axial 100	C51/12CT	2004
YN07LGF	Scania K470 EB6	Berkhof Axial 70	C48FT	2007
YJ12KFX	Van Hool TDX27 Astromega	Van Hool	C59/12FT	2012
YJ12KFY	Van Hool TDX27 Astromega	Van Hool	C59/12FT	2012
YJ12KFZ	Van Hool TDX27 Astromega	Van Hool	C59/12FT	2012

Depot: Parliament Road, Middlesbrough; **Web:** www.siestainternationalholidays.com

New arrivals for the 2012 season are three Van Hool TDX27 Astromega coaches. Representing these is YJ12KFX. *Siesta Holidays*

SILVERDALE

Silverdale Tours (Nottingham) Ltd, Little Tennis Street South, Nottingham, NG2 4EU

Silverdale Tours (London) Ltd, 3 Radford Estate, Old Oak Lane, Acton, London, NW10 6UA

Reg	Chassis	Body	Type	Year	Notes
G363SRB	Scania N113 DRB	Alexander RH	BC45/29F	1990	Bellamy, Nottingham, 2009
G365SRB	Scania N113 DRB	Alexander RH	BC45/29F	1990	Bellamy, Nottingham, 2009
G366SRB	Scania N113 DRB	Alexander RH	BC45/29F	1990	Bellamy, Nottingham, 2009
EIG4331	Volvo Olympian	Alexander RH	B47/31F	1995	Dublin Bus, 2008
M339UKN	Volvo Olympian	Alexander RH	B47/31F	1995	Dublin Bus, 2008
M343UKN	Volvo Olympian	Alexander RH	B47/31F	1995	Dublin Bus, 2008
M939JJU	Volvo B10M-62	Plaxton Première 350	C49FT	1995	
N127RJF	Volvo B10M-62	Plaxton Première 350	C53F	1996	
SIL7949	Volvo B10M-62	Van Hool Alizée	C49FT	1997	Bellamy, Nottingham, 2011
P168RWR	DAF SB3000	Plaxton Première 350	C53F	1997	Bellamy, Nottingham, 2011
FIG7338	Volvo Citybus B10M-50	East Lancs	BC47/35F	1997	City of Nottingham, 2005
R471RRA	Volvo Olympian	East Lancs	B49/35F	1997	City of Nottingham, 2005
R474RRA	Volvo Olympian	East Lancs	B49/35F	1997	City of Nottingham, 2005
S45KSM	Volvo B7R	Plaxton Prima	C55F	1998	Bellamy, Nottingham, 2011
R841FWW	Mercedes-Benz Atego O1120L	Optare/Ferqui Solera	C35F	1998	
FIG9180	DAF SB3000	Plaxton Première 320	C57F	1999	
T322UCH	Volvo B10M-62	Plaxton Première 350	C53F	1999	Bellamy, Nottingham, 2011
Y744NAY	MAN 11.220	Caetano Enigma	C35F	2001	
FN02VBL	Iveco EuroRider 391E.12.35	Beulas Stergo E	C51FT	2002	
RUI8266	Iveco EuroRider 391E.12.35	Beulas Stergo E	C51FT	2002	
BJ03OUB	Mercedes-Benz Touro OC500	Mercedes-Benz	C36FT	2003	
FJ03ABK	Volvo B12M	Sunsundegui Sideral 350	C53FT	2003	Bellamy, Nottingham, 2010
MCT612	Volvo B12M	Caetano Enigma	C49FT	2004	
JFZ8616	Volvo B12M	Caetano Enigma	C49FT	2004	
WRC419	Volvo B12B	Caetano Enigma	C49FT	2005	
JFZ8617	Volvo B12B	Caetano Enigma	C49FT	2005	
YJ55KZO	VDL Bus SB4000	Van Hool T9 Alizée	C36FT	2005	
FJ55DYW	Volvo B12B	Plaxton Panther	C49FT	2006	
JFZ8618	Volvo B12B	VDL Jonckheere Mistral 50	C53FT	2007	
JFZ8619	Volvo B12B	VDL Jonckheere Mistral 50	C53FT	2007	
FN07AEA	Mercedes-Benz Vario O814	Plaxton Cheetah	C33F	2007	
JFZ8620	Irisbus EuroRider 397E.12.35A	Beulas Cygnus	C55FT	2007	
JFZ8621	Irisbus EuroRider 397E.12.35A	Beulas Cygnus	C53F	2008	
YJ08NTK	VDL Bova Futura FHD127.365	VDL Bova	C45FT	2008	Hamlin,Torquay, 2008

Having a depot in England's capital city as well as its home base, ensures frequent sightings of Silverdale's coaches. YN07ECD is an Irisbus with Beulas Cygnus bodywork and is seen in Park Lane. *Dave Heath*

Recent changes on index numbers has seen Caetano-bodied Volvo FJ05HYG gaining WRC419 plates. It is seen with its new number while passing through London. *Dave Heath*

FJ58AJO	Scania K114 EB4	Caetano Enigma	C45FT	2008
FJ09DWY	Scania K340 EB4	Caetano Levante	C49FT	2009
FJ09DXT	Scania K340 EB4	Caetano Levante	C49FT	2009
FJ09DXU	Scania K340 EB4	Caetano Levante	C49FT	2009
FJ10EZT	Scania K340 EB4	Caetano Levante	C49FT	2010
FJ10EZU	Scania K340 EB4	Caetano Levante	C49FT	2010
MX10DDA	Neoplan Tourliner N2216 SHD	Neoplan	C49FT	2010
MX10DDL	Neoplan Tourliner N2216 SHD	Neoplan	C49FT	2010
MX10DFL	Neoplan Tourliner N2216/3 SHD	Neoplan	C61FT	2010
MX10DFN	Neoplan Tourliner N2216/3 SHD	Neoplan	C61FT	2010
PN10AFY	MAN 18.360	Beulas Sygnus	C53FT	2010
PN10AFZ	MAN 18.360	Beulas Sygnus	C53FT	2010
FJ61EWP	Volvo B9R	Caetano Levante	C48FT	2012
FJ61EWR	Volvo B9R	Caetano Levante	C48FT	2012
FJ61EWS	Volvo B9R	Caetano Levante	C48FT	2012
FJ61EWT	Volvo B9R	Caetano Levante	C48FT	2012
FJ61EWV	Volvo B9R	Caetano Levante	C48FT	2012
FJ61EWW	Volvo B9R	Caetano Levante	C48FT	2012
MV12ODS	Neoplan Tourliner N2216/3 SHD	Neoplan	C61FT	2012
MV12ODT	Neoplan Tourliner N2216/3 SHD	Neoplan	C61FT	2012
MV12ODU	Neoplan Tourliner N2216/3 SHD	Neoplan	C61FT	2012
MV12ODW	Neoplan Tourliner N2216/3 SHD	Neoplan	C61FT	2012
MV12ODX	Neoplan Tourliner N2216/3 SHD	Neoplan	C61FT	2012
MV12ODY	Neoplan Tourliner N2216/3 SHD	Neoplan	C61FT	2012

Previous registrations:

BJ03OUB	BJ03OUB, BU51OUR	JFZ8619	FJ07ACU
MCT612	-	JFZ8620	YN07ECD
EIG4331	95D205, M331UKN	JFZ8621	YN08ATO
M339UKN	95D209	P168RWR	P168RWR, WRC419
M343UKN	95D207	SIL7949	HSK657, P262YGG
FIG7338	R338RRA	T322UCH	99D41314
FIG9180	T180AUA	RUI8263	FN02VBL
JFZ8616	FJ04SNZ	RUI8266	FN02VBT
JFZ8617	FJ05HYH	WRC419	FJ05HYG
JFZ8618	FJ07ACO		

Web: www.silverdaletours.co.uk

SKILLS

Skill's Motor Coaches Ltd, Belgrave Road, Bulwell, Nottingham, NG6 8LY

	OUH269X	Van Hool T815	Van Hool	C53F	1982	Newhaven Carnival, 2007
95	E476SON	MCW Metrobus DR102/63	MCW	B45/30F	1987	East Yorkshire, 2006
96	E480UOF	MCW Metrobus DR102/65	MCW	B45/30F	1988	East Yorkshire, 2006
12	UJI6312	Volvo B10M-60	Plaxton Paramount 3500 III	C53F	1991	Motorvation, Netherfield, 2008
22	H922LOX	Dennis Dart 9.8m	Carlyle Dartline	B40F	1991	Gardner, Spennymoor, 2007
97	KJZ4397	Dennis Javelin 10m	Berkhof Excellence 1000	C32FT	1993	Motorvation, Netherfield, 2008
59	KJZ8508	Mercedes-Benz 709	Plaxton Beaver	B22F	1993	Motorvation, Netherfield, 2008
57	KJZ8509	Scania K113 CRB	Van Hool Alizée	C53FT	1994	Motorvation, Netherfield, 2008
47	SIL7947	Volvo B10M-62	Van Hool Alizée HE	C53F	1996	Park's of Hamilton, 2000
85	M418UKN	Volvo Olympian	Alexander RH	B47/27D	1996	Dublin Bus, 2008
86	M419UKN	Volvo Olympian	Alexander RH	B47/27D	1996	Dublin Bus, 2008
87	M420UKN	Volvo Olympian	Alexander RH	B47/27D	1996	Dublin Bus, 2008
88	M421UKN	Volvo Olympian	Alexander RH	B47/27D	1996	Dublin Bus, 2008
97	M438BRR	Volvo Olympian	Alexander RH	B47/27D	1996	Dublin Bus, 2008
98	M658VRR	Volvo Olympian	Alexander RH	B47/31F	1996	Dublin Bus, 2008
99	M659VRR	Volvo Olympian	Alexander RH	B47/27D	1996	Dublin Bus, 2008
58	HXI733	Mercedes-Benz 711	Wadham Stringer Vanguard III	BC25F	1996	Motorvation, Netherfield, 2008
	N129GAG	Mercedes-Benz 711	Mercedes-Benz	B18F	1996	Motorvation, Netherfield, 2008
	N130GAG	Mercedes-Benz 711	Mercedes-Benz	B18F	1996	Motorvation, Netherfield, 2008
	N306NTG	Iveco Daily 49-10		BC19F	1996	Motorvation, Netherfield, 2008
	BIG8385	Optare Excel L1150	Optare	N44F	1997	City of Nottingham, 2008
52	SIL7944	Volvo B10M-62	Plaxton Première 350	C48FT	1998	Motorvation, Netherfield, 2008
	S649RKW	Ford Euro Cargo 36	G C Smith	BC36C	1998	St John's Ambulance, 2009
	S456ATV	Volvo Olympian	East Lancs	B49/35F	1999	City of Nottingham, 2008
	S457ATV	Volvo Olympian	East Lancs	B49/35F	1999	City of Nottingham, 2008
80	T304JJF	Volvo Olympian	East Lancs	BC47/33F	1999	Circle Line, Naas, 2008
	T437JJF	Volvo Olympian	Alexander RH	B47/27D	1996	Dublin Bus, 2009
	T438JJF	Volvo Olympian	Alexander RH	B47/27D	1996	Dublin Bus, 2009
	T439JJF	Volvo Olympian	Alexander RH	B47/27D	1996	Dublin Bus, 2009
	T450JJF	Volvo Olympian	Alexander RH	B47/27D	1996	Dublin Bus, 2009
	T477JJF	Volvo Olympian	Alexander RH	B47/27D	1996	Dublin Bus, 2009

Volvo's re-entry into the integral coach market came with the 9700 which won the Coach of the Year award in 2008. The body is built in Poland and uses the B12B chassis with more recent arrivals using the B13R. Showing Skill's Signature livery as it passes through Trafalgar Square is N1SMC. *Dave Heath*

Recently departed from the fleet is PUJ925 a Mercedes-Benz Vario with the popular Plaxton Cheetah body. It was pictured while taking a break in Stratford. *Mark Doggett*

	V304EAK	Scania K113 DRB	East Lancs	B47/31F	1999	Veolia, 2011
	W301MKY	Scania K113 DRB	East Lancs	B47/31F	2000	Veolia, 2011
	W302MKY	Scania K113 DRB	East Lancs	B47/31F	2000	Veolia, 2011
	W303MKY	Scania K113 DRB	East Lancs	B47/31F	2000	Veolia, 2011
81	W752DOE	Volvo Olympian	East Lancs	BC47/33F	2000	Circle Line, Naas, 2008
79	PWJ925	Mercedes-Benz Vario O814	Plaxton Beaver 2	BC29F	2000	Spencer, Boughton, 2005
60	YT51FMC	Mercedes-Benz Vario O814	Frank Guy	B15F	2001	Clowne Community, 2007
	YR02UNJ	MAN 18.350	Noge Catalan 370	C49FT	2002	Robinson, Blackburn, 2011
	YR02UNK	MAN 18.350	Noge Catalan 370	C49FT	2002	Robinson, Blackburn, 2011
	YR02UNL	MAN 18.350	Noge Catalan 370	C49FT	2002	Robinson, Blackburn, 2011
74	FN53AKV	Mercedes-Benz Sprinter 411	Mercedes-Benz	M8	2003	
78	YN03LRY	Mercedes-Benz Sprinter 614D	Excel	C24F	2003	
	NY03KWR	Irisbus Daily 50C13	Onyx	M16	2003	
29	SIL7029	Setra S315 GT-HD	Setra	C49FT	2004	
30	BU53ZXB	Setra S315 GT-HD	Setra	C49FT	2004	
31	BU53ZXC	Setra S315 GT-HD	Setra	C49FT	2004	
32	MP53SKD	Setra S315 GT-HD	Setra	C49FT	2004	
34	BU53ZXD	Setra S315 GT-HD	Setra	C49FT	2004	
66	VCZ9811	Mercedes-Benz Vario O814	TransBus Cheetah	C33F	2004	Moore, Belfast, 2008
73	YC54EKO	Ford Transit	Frank Guy	M7	2004	
39	SIL9540	Volvo B7R	VDL Jonckheere Mistral	C53FT	2004	
42	SIL6436	Volvo B12B	Jonckheere Mistral 50	C53FT	2004	Callinan, Claregalway, 2007
45	SIL6438	Volvo B12B	Jonckheere Mistral 50	C53FT	2004	Callinan, Claregalway, 2007
46	SIL6437	Volvo B12B	Jonckheere Mistral 50	C53FT	2004	Callinan, Claregalway, 2007
	KN55KWR	Iveco EuroRider 397E.12.35	Beulas Stergo e	C49FT	2005	Redwing, London, 2010
	KN55KWT	Iveco EuroRider 397E.12.35	Beulas Stergo e	C49FT	2005	Redwing, London, 2010
	LX55CFD	Mercedes-Benz Sprinter 413 cdi	Frank Guy	M8	2005	van, 2007
70	AD55DDZ	Ford Transit	Ford	M16	2005	Motorvation, Netherfield, 2008
77	BL06JVM	Ford Transit	Frank Guy	M7	2006	van, 2007
	GX55NHY	Volvo B7TL	East Lancs	N49/32F	2006	Little. Ilkeston, 2011
	SIL9543	Scania K114 EB4	VDI Berkhof Axial 50	C55FT	2006	Leons, Stafford, 2009
	SIL9548	Scania K114 EB4	VDI Berkhof Axial 50	C53FT	2006	Radley, Barton-on-Humber, 2009
20	SIL6434	Neoplan Tourliner N2216/3 SHD	Neoplan	C61F	2008	
21	SIL6435	Neoplan Tourliner N2216/3 SHD	Neoplan	C61F	2008	
36	SIL7565	VDL Bova Futura FHD127.365	VDL Bova	C40FT	2008	
38	N1SMC	Volvo B12B	Volvo 9700	C53F	2008	
67	YN58CFM	Mercedes-Benz Vario O815	Plaxton Cheetah	C33F	2008	

Recent arrivals include five Neoplan Tourliners. Illustrating the type is MF11LVJ, seen in London's Park Lane.
Dave Heath

FJ08BZM	Volvo B12B	VDL Jonckheere SHV	C53FT	2008	Hamilton, Uxbridge, 2011
YT11LPJ	Scania K400 EB6	Scania OmniExpress	C63F	2011	
YT11LPK	Scania K400 EB6	Scania OmniExpress	C63F	2011	
MF11LVJ	Neoplan Tourliner N2216/3 SHD	Neoplan	C60F	2011	
MF11LVK	Neoplan Tourliner N2216/3 SHD	Neoplan	C60F	2011	
MF11LVL	Neoplan Tourliner N2216/3 SHD	Neoplan	C60F	2011	
MF11LVM	Neoplan Tourliner N2216/3 SHD	Neoplan	C60F	2011	
MF11LVN	Neoplan Tourliner N2216/3 SHD	Neoplan	C60F	2011	
PO12YLA	Neoplan Tourliner N2216/3 SHD	Neoplan	C60F	2012	
PO12YLB	Neoplan Tourliner N2216/3 SHD	Neoplan	C60F	2012	
PO12YLD	Neoplan Tourliner N2216/3 SHD	Neoplan	C60F	2012	

Previous registrations:

BIG8385	P543GAU	SIL6437	04G5402, FC04LDA
BU53ZXC	BU53ZXC, SIL3431	SIL6438	04G5403, FC04LDU
BU53ZXD	BU53ZXD, SIL6434	SIL7024	-
BU53ZXB	BU53ZXB, SIL7030	SIL7029	BU53ZXA
KJZ4397	K100SLT, SEL133, SEL36, K525OFM	SIL7030	-
KJZ8508	L816SAE	SIL7032	-
KJZ8509	H8BCH, KUI5365, H135FRP, HXI733	SIL7565	FJ08VOV
M418UKN	95D222	SIL7947	KSK983, N501PYS
M419UKN	95D225	SIL7948	YN06NZT
M420UKN	95D224	SIL9540	-
M421UKN	95D10235	SIL9541	ET06LCT
M658VRR	95D226	SIL9543	FT06LCT
M659VRR	95D228	T304JJF	99D58289
MP53SKD	SIL7032	T450JJF	99D536
PWJ925	W638MKY, 5611FH, N1SMC	T477JJF	99D509
N1SMC	FY08FYZ	T437JJF	99D525
N438BRR	96D274	T438JJF	99D524
OUH269X	OAF985X, UNJ408, 1836PG	T439JJF	99D10523
SIL3431	-	UJI6312	H814AHS
SIL6434	YN57AEB	VCZ9811	From new
SIL6435	YN57AEC	W752DOE	W752DOE, 00D64065
SIL6436	04G5401, FC04UBL		

Web: www.skillsholidays.co.uk

SOAMES

Soames - Forget-Me-Not

Forget-me-not (Travel) Ltd, The Garage, Chapel Road, Otley, IP6 9NT

M513MFX	Volvo B10M-60	Plaxton Première 350	C53F	1994	Excelsior, Bournemouth
P78OEW	Volvo B10M-62	Plaxton Première 350	C53F	1998	Kenzies, Shepreth
11PKN	Volvo B10M-62	Plaxton Première 350	C53F	1998	Berkeleys, Bristol
R17BUS	Volvo B10M-62	Van Hool T9 Alizée	C53F	1998	Whitelaw, Stonehouse
S4GET	Volvo B10M-62	Jonckheere Mistral	C57F	1999	Barratts, Nantwich
V57KWO	Volvo B10M-62	Plaxton Première 350	C53F	2000	Bebbs, Llantwit Fardre
X627AKW	Volvo B10M-62	Plaxton Paragon	C53F	2000	Logan, Dunloy
W6AMS	Volvo B10M-62	Van Hool T9 Alizée	C53F	2000	Dereham Coaches,
YS02YXZ	Volvo B12M	Plaxton Paragon	C53F	2002	Logan, Dunloy
WJ02VRT	Volvo B12M	Van Hool T9 Alizée	C49FT	2002	DAC
N303HLP	Volvo B7R	Transbus Profile	C57F	2003	Hunter, Sauchie, 2008
T4GET	Volvo B12M	Plaxton Paragon	C49FT	2004	Steel, Skipton, 2008
YN05HVH	Volvo B12B	Plaxton Panther	C57F	2005	Snowdon, Easington Colliery, '09
YN07WUO	Volvo B12B	Plaxton Panther	C57F	2007	Anderson, London, 2011
YX07AYD	Mercedes-Benz Vario O814	Optare Toro	C29F	2007	Stacey, Carlisle, 2011
KX09GMO	Volvo B12M	Plaxton Panther	C49FT	2009	
FJ59CBU	Volvo B9R	Plaxton Panther	C49FT	2010	Volvo demonstrator, 2011

Previous registrations:

11PKN	P616FTV	T4GET	YN04WTK
N303HLP	GO03WMS	YN05HVH	YN05HVH, P6SNO
S4GET	S72UBO, B4BCL		

Swans Travel fleet has seen major changes in recent years. Plaxton-bodied Volvo YN09HRZ is seen just prior to its withdrawal. Similar vehicles are operated by Soames of Otley. *Dave Heath*

SWANS TRAVEL

Swans Travel Ltd, The Travel Centre, Cobden Street, Chadderton, Oldham, OL9 9XA

MX55WDA	Enterprise Plasma EB01	Plaxton Primo	N28F	2005	
YN05HFV	Scania K114 EB4	VDI Berkhof Axial 50	C55FT	2005	Weardale, Stanhope, 2010
YN58CFX	ADL Javelin 12m	Plaxton Profile 70	S70F	2008	
YN58CFY	ADL Javelin 12m	Plaxton Profile 70	S70F	2008	
MX59AWC	ADL Dart 4	ADL Enviro 200	N29F	2009	
BK09WSZ	Mercedes-Benz Tourismo OC500	Mercedes-Benz	C49FT	2009	
BF60OFM	Mercedes-Benz Tourismo OC500	Mercedes-Benz	C49FT	2011	
BF60OFN	Mercedes-Benz Tourismo OC500	Mercedes-Benz	C49FT	2011	
BF60OFO	Mercedes-Benz Tourismo OC500	Mercedes-Benz	C49FT	2011	
BF60OFP	Mercedes-Benz Tourismo OC500	Mercedes-Benz	C49FT	2011	
BF60OFR	Mercedes-Benz Tourismo OC500	Mercedes-Benz	C53F	2011	
BF60OFS	Mercedes-Benz Tourismo OC500	Mercedes-Benz	C53F	2011	
BF60OFT	Mercedes-Benz Tourismo OC500	Mercedes-Benz	C53F	2011	
BF60OFU	Mercedes-Benz Tourismo OC500	Mercedes-Benz	C53F	2011	
BF60OFV	Mercedes-Benz Tourismo OC500	Mercedes-Benz	C53F	2011	
BF60OFW	Mercedes-Benz Tourismo OC500	Mercedes-Benz	C53F	2011	
BF60OFX	Mercedes-Benz Tourismo OC500	Mercedes-Benz	C49FT	2011	
BF61HBY	Mercedes-Benz Tourismo OC500	Mercedes-Benz	C53F	2012	
BF61HBZ	Mercedes-Benz Tourismo OC500	Mercedes-Benz	C53F	2012	

Previoius registrations:

R887SDT	98D10336, R887SDT, A18HLC	YN05HFV	YN05HFV, Y6WMS, GIB976

Depots: Broadway Business Park, Chadderton and Wincham Lane, Northwich.

Swans Travel operated a 30-seat Mercedes-Benz Tourino, BV08ZWS, which is seen working on a private hire in London. This coach has now been sold to BM Coaches and is listed on page 33 *Colin Lloyd*

TALISMAN

Talisman Coach Lines Ltd; Talisman Logistics Ltd, The Coach Station, Harwich Road, Great Bromley, CO7 7UL

NFX136P	Daimler Fleetline CRL6	MCW	CO43/31F	1976	Young, Faversham, 2008
YJN455S	DAF MB200DKL600	Plaxton Supreme IV	C50F	1978	Crusader Holidays, Clacton, 2003
RVW90W	Leyland Atlantean AN68A/1R	Eastern Coach Works	B43/31F	1980	Boon's, Boreham, 2003
EWF453V	MCW Metrobus DR102/13	MCW	PO46/27D	1980	Young, Faversham, 2008
SIJ8661	Van Hool T815	Van Hool	C49FT	1990	Essex Dog Display Team, 2012
H47MJN	Leyland Olympian ON2R50C13Z4	Leyland	BC43/29F	1991	Tellings-Golden Miller, 2008
H48MJN	Leyland Olympian ON2R50C13Z4	Leyland	B43/29F	1991	Tellings-Golden Miller, 2008
NSU668	Setra S250	Setra Special	C48FT	1998	Staines Crusader, Clacton, 2003
S268BTL	Setra S250	Setra Special	C48FT	1998	Boon's, Boreham, 1999
WSU225	Setra S315 GT-HD	Setra	C48FT	1999	Dereham Coachways, 2004
VSU803	Setra S315 GT-HD	Setra	C44FT	1999	The King's Ferry, Gillingham, 2006
LSU788	Setra S315 GT-HD	Setra	C49FT	2000	Dereham Coachways, 2006
LSU113	Setra S315 GT-HD	Setra	C49FT	2000	Tellings-Golden Miller, 2003
MY53TRA	Setra S415 HD	Setra	C48FT	2004	
EU08NEU	Setra S416 GT-HD	Setra	C53FT	2008	
OK08ULM	Setra S416 GT-HD	Setra	C49FT	2008	
BJ08KNM	Setra S415 HD	Setra	C48FT	2008	Evobus demonstrator, 2010
YR10BEO	Scania K360 EB4	Irizar Century	C49FT	2010	
YT10WLH	Scania K360 EB4	Irizar Century	C49FT	2010	On-a-Mission, Milton Keynes, '10
UL11ULM	Setra S416 GT-HD	Setra	C53FT	2011	

Special event vehicles:

WNO480	Bristol KSW5G	Eastern Coach Works	O33/29R	1953	Larking, Leigh-on-Sea, 2009
JJD535D	AEC Routemaster R2RH1	Park Royal	B40/32R	1966	Amberlee, Rochester, 2006
SGF483L	Bristol RELH6L	Plaxton Panorama Elite III	C51F	1971	The Running Footman, 2008

Previous registrations:

EWF453V	EWF453V, WLT753	SIJ8661	G103CJN
LSU113	W10TGM	TSU182	T250GON
LSU788	W2SET	VSU803	V35HAX, A6TKF
NSU668	S6TRA, S613AKP	WSU225	S268BTL
SGF483L	40WMN		

Web: www.talismancoachlines.co.uk

Talisman operates from a base in Essex close to the A120 road. Among the Setra coaches operated are two 'Top-Class' models including MY53TRA, seen in service at Stratford-upon-Avon. *Mark Doggett*

TATES

Tates Coaches Ltd, 44 High Street, Markyate, AL3 8PA

YIL8759	DAF SB220	Hispano	B47D	1990	Capital, West Drayton, 1999
YIL8758	Dennis Javelin 12m	Wadham Stringer Vanguard III	S70F	1992	APT Coaches, Rayleigh, 2005
WIJ297	DAF SB3000	Caetano Algarve 2	C49FT	1993	Heaton, Mayford, 2002
EIB502	Scania K124 IB4	Irizar Century 12.35	C49FT	1999	Leons, Stafford, 2000
T55ATE	Scania L94 IB4	Van Hool T9 Alizée	C49FT	1999	APT Coaches, Rayleigh, 2007
133MBJ	EOS E180Z	EOS	C49FT	2000	Williams, Brecon, 2007
T88ATE	Mercedes-Benz O414	Hispano Vita	C49FT	2001	
T888TES	Neoplan Euroliner N316 SHD	Neoplan	C53F	2002	Stolzenberg, Maesteg, 2008
T2TES	Bova Futura FHD12.340	Bova	C49FT	2003	Reay's Wigton, 2005
YN07LEF	Scania K340 EB4	Irizar Century 12.35	C49FT	2007	
YT59NZX	Scania K480 EB6	Irizar PB	C57FT	2009	Plan-it, Chesterfield, 2012

Previous registrations:

133MBJ	W4HWT	T88ATE	Y599TOV
EIB502	T100LCT, VLV815	WIJ297	K538CWN
KBG520	P977HWF	YIL8758	74KK94, K453CHU, ACH69A
T2TES	PX03EKN, 133MBJ	YIL8759	TIB400L(Singapore), G136CLF, CAP10
T55ATE	V77CCH, CNZ3818, Y20YAL		

Depot: Water End Road, Potten End

Epsom Downs provides the backdrop to this view of Irizar Century EIB502 from Tates' fleet. *Dave Heath*

TERRAVISION

Terravision Transport Ltd, Airways House, First Avenue, Stansted Airport, CM24 1RY

YN06NZA	Scania K114 EB6 13.7m	Irizar Century Capacity	C65F	2006	
YN06NZC	Scania K114 EB6 13.7m	Irizar Century Capacity	C65F	2006	
YN06NZD	Scania K114 EB6 13.7m	Irizar Century Capacity	C65F	2006	
YN06CFY	Scania K114 EB6 13.7m	Irizar Century Capacity	C65F	2006	
YN06NYM	Scania K114 EB6 13.7m	Irizar Century Capacity	C65F	2006	
YN08MLZ	Scania K114 EB6	Irizar Century Style	C63FT	2008	Scania demonstrator, 2008
YT10WLA	Scania K360 EB6 13.7m	Irizar Century Style	C63FT	2010	
YT10WLB	Scania K360 EB6 13.7m	Irizar Century Style	C63FT	2010	
YT10WLC	Scania K360 EB6 13.7m	Irizar Century Style	C63FT	2010	
YT10WLD	Scania K360 EB6 13.7m	Irizar Century Style	C63FT	2010	

Depots: First Avenue, Stansted Airport (S) and Trafford Park, Manchester (M)
Web: www.terravision.eu

Terravision operates the link between London and Stansted Airport for which many of the Scania coaches are lettered for the service. Illustrating the Century Capacity model is YN06NZC. *Colin Lloyd*

Recent arrivals have included further VDL Jonckheere coaches, some of which are in contract liveries. Showing corporate colours as is passes along Park Lane in the capital is PO11KFL. *Dave Heath*

PO12GWG	Volvo B9R	12.8m	Caetano Levanté	C48FT	2012
PO12GWJ	Volvo B9R	12.8m	Caetano Levanté	C48FT	2012
PO12GWL	Volvo B9R	12.8m	Caetano Levanté	C48FT	2012
PO12GWM	Volvo B9R	12.8m	VDL Jonckheere SHV	C53FT	2012
PO12GWP	Volvo B9R	12.8m	VDL Jonckheere SHV	C53FT	2012
PO12GWU	Volvo B9R	12.8m	VDL Jonckheere SHV	C53FT	2012
PO12GWW	Volvo B9R	12.8m	VDL Jonckheere SHV	C53FT	2012
PO12JMX	Volvo B9R	12.8m	VDL Jonckheere SHV	C53FT	2012
PO12JNF	Volvo B9R	12.8m	VDL Jonckheere SHV	C53FT	2012
PO12JNJ	Volvo B9R	12.8m	VDL Jonckheere SHV	C53FT	2012
PO12JNK	Volvo B9R	12.8m	VDL Jonckheere SHV	C53FT	2012

Previous registrations:

3TXO	PN08LAE	5146RU	PN02TJV
4JXX	PN08LAO	6137RU	PN05AZW
4ORX	PN08KWX	6267UA	PN09HGU
5HDX	PN08KWW	6682WY	PE55WLJ
6SVK	PO59OEE	7132ET	PN05AZX
8YTX	PN08KWV	7351RU	PN09HGL
10JWX	PN08KWU	7606UR	PE55WLH
18CU	PN08LBJ	7962IL	Y724HEC
37HE	PN07LML	8338RU	PN04NNT
38NE	PN07LME	8447WX	PN04NNU
48NR	PN08LBK	8468WX	PN09HGO
52RE	PN07LMM	8527RU	PN09HGP
100WXD	PO59OEC	9201FH	Y693HEC
509EBL	PN06KJU	BYP985	YN53ENJ
824HAO	PE55WLG	LSU939	PN07LHZ
899CAN	PN07LLZ	OET309	PN07LJA
2396VU	PN03UCH	OW5371	PO55OWY
2594XI	YC02DGF	UA5013	PN03UCP
3770RU	YN54XSP	UD1100	PN09HGM
3886UR	PN03UCM	UWR294	PN07LNK
4122YG	PN05AZU	WX7622	PN04NNR
4150RU	PN04NNV	XJF386	PN07LMO
479GTA	YN06NYS	XDO32	YX05AVG
5129UA	PN05AZV	XDL521	PN06KJK

TRUEMANS

Truemans Coaches (Fleet) Ltd; R C Trueman, Lynchford Road, Ash Vale, GU12 5PQ

J20TRU	Irisbus EuroRider 391E.12.35	Beulas El Mundo	C49FT	2003
J30TRU	Irisbus EuroRider 391E.12.35	Beulas Stergo e	C53F	2003
J33TRU	Irisbus EuroRider 391E.12.35	Beulas Stergo e	C53F	2003
J600TRU	Irisbus EuroRider 391E.12.35	Beulas El Mundo	C49FT	2003
J700TRU	Irisbus EuroRider 391E.12.35	Beulas Stergo e	C49FT	2003
J13TRU	MAN 18.360	Plaxton Panther	C53F	2007
J14TRU	MAN 18.360	Plaxton Panther	C53F	2007
J16TRU	MAN 18.360	Plaxton Panther	C49FT	2007
J17TRU	MAN 18.360	Plaxton Panther	C53F	2007
J200TRU	Neoplan Tourliner N2216 SHD	Neoplan	C44FT	2008
J300TRU	Neoplan Tourliner N2216 SHD	Neoplan	C49FT	2008
J400TRU	Neoplan Tourliner N2216 SHD	Neoplan	C44FT	2008
J500TRU	Neoplan Tourliner N2216 SHD	Neoplan	C53FT	2008
J18TRU	Neoplan Tourliner N2216 SHD	Neoplan	C53FT	2008
J19TRU	Neoplan Tourliner N2216 SHD	Neoplan	C44FT	2008

Previous registrations:

J13TRU	YN07EAF		J33TRU	FG03JBY
J14TRU	YN07EAG		J200TRU	RX58FNK, 1116RU
J16TRU	YN07EAC		J300TRU	YN58KSJ
J17TRU	YN07EAE		J400TRU	YN58KSF, 4227RU
J18TRU	from new		J500TRU	TH58HYR
J19TRU	from new		J600TRU	2003RU
J20TRU	FG03JBZ		J700TRU	2439RU
J30TRU	FG03JBX			

Trueman's Coaches colours are shown on Neoplan Tourliner J18TRU, one of six of the type in the fleet. An example of the 2-axle Tourliner is shown on page 134. *Dave Heath*

TURNERS

Turners Coachways (Bristol) Ltd, 59 Days Road, St Phillips, Bristol, BS2 0QS

L8CJT	Volvo B10M-60	Van Hool Alizée	S70F	1994	
M20CJT	Dennis Javelin 12m	Wadham Stringer Vanguard III	S70F	1995	MoD (CX73AA), 2003
M40CJT	Dennis Javelin 12m	Wadham Stringer Vanguard III	S70F	1995	MoD (CX65AA), 2003
M44CJT	Dennis Javelin 12m	Wadham Stringer Vanguard III	BC57F	1995	MoD (CX70AA), 2003
N599OAE	Dennis Javelin 8.5m	Wadham Stringer Vanguard III	BC35F	1996	MoD (ER46AA), 2003
N813OAE	Dennis Javelin 8.5m	Wadham Stringer Vanguard III	BC35F	1996	MoD (GE53AA), 2003
N829OAE	Dennis Javelin 8.5m	Wadham Stringer Vanguard III	BC35F	1996	MoD (GE54AA), 2003
N14CJT	Dennis Javelin 12m	Wadham Stringer Vanguard III	BC57F	1996	MoD (EC54AA), 2003
N966OAE	Dennis Javelin 12m	Wadham Stringer Vanguard III	BC54F	1996	MoD (EC55AA), 2003
R33CJT	Dennis Javelin 12m	UVG S320	BC57F	1998	MoD (LL06AA), 2006
R18CJT	Volvo B10M-62	Plaxton Première 320	S70F	1998	
R19CJT	Volvo B10M-62	Plaxton Première 320	S70F	1998	
L9CJT	Volvo B10M-60	Van Hool Alizée	C57F	1994	
P16CJT	Volvo B10M-62	Plaxton Première 320	S70F	1997	
R2CJT	Volvo B10M-62	Jonckheere Mistral 50	C49FT	1997	
R3CJT	Volvo B10M-62	Jonckheere Mistral 50	C49FT	1997	
R30CJT	Mercedes-Benz Atego 1120L	Optare/Ferqui Solera	C35F	1998	
S60CJT	Volvo B10M-62	Berkhof Axial 50	C49FT	1998	
X70CJT	Volvo B10M-62	Jonckheere Mistral 50	C49FT	2000	
X80CJT	Volvo B10M-62	Jonckheere Mistral 50	C49FT	2000	
W17CJT	Volvo B7R	Plaxton Prima	C53F	2000	Ulsterbus, 2001
GT02CJT	Toyota Coaster BB50R	Caetano Optimo V	C21F	2002	Z Cars, Bristol, 2004
DT04CJT	Scania K114 EB4	Irizar Century 12.35	C49FT	2004	
ET04CJT	Scania K114 EB4	Irizar Century 12.35	C49FT	2004	
FT04CJT	Scania K114 EB4	Irizar InterCentury 12.32	C57F	2004	
73WAE	Scania K114 IB4	Irizar Century 12.35	C49FT	2004	Chambers, Moneymore, 2008
HT04CJT	Mercedes-Benz Sprinter 413cdi	Onyx	M16	2004	
KT54CJT	Scania K114 EB4	Irizar Century 12.35	C53FT	2004	

The Temsa Safari has been available to British operators since 2006, although Temsa has been building coaches in Turkey since 1984. Illustrating the model is VT09CJT. *Dave Heath*

A feature of Turners' fleet is the CJT index mark collection with VDL Mistral RT05CJT shown at Aston Cross.
Colin Martin

PT05CJT	Volvo B12B	VDL Jonckheere Mistral 50	C53F	2005	Park's of Hamilton, 2007
RT05CJT	Volvo B12B	VDL Jonckheere Mistral 50	C53F	2005	Park's of Hamilton, 2007
NT05CJT	Scania K114 IB4	Irizar Century Capacity	C55F	2005	
OT55CJT	Scania K114 IB4	Irizar Century Capacity	C57F	2005	
110LHW	Scania K94 IB4	Irizar PB	C49FT	2005	Aherne, Tallaght, 2010
6486LJ	Scania K94 IB4	Irizar S-kool	S70F	2005	Weavaway, Newbury, 2007
7153MC	Scania K94 IB4	Irizar S-kool	S70F	2005	Weavaway, Newbury, 2007
3138DP	Scania K94 IB4	Irizar S-kool	S70F	2005	Weavaway, Newbury, 2007
AT55CJT	Volvo B12B	VDL Jonckheere Mistral 50	C49FT	2005	
BT55CJT	Volvo B12B	VDL Jonckheere Mistral 50	C49FT	2005	
LT06CJT	Ford Transit	Ford	M8	2006	
WT06CJT	Scania K114 IB4	Irizar Century Capacity	C53F	2006	Swan's, Chadderton, 2009
XT06CJT	Scania K114 IB4	Irizar Century Capacity	C53F	2006	Swan's, Chadderton, 2009
YT06CJT	Scania K114 IB4	Irizar Century Capacity	C53F	2006	Swan's, Chadderton, 2009
ST06CJT	Setra S415 GT-HD	Setra	C49FT	2006	
TT06CJT	Setra S415 GT-HD	Setra	C49FT	2006	
CT56CJT	Scania K310 EB4	Irizar Century Capacity	C53F	2007	Swan's, Chadderton, 2009
JT56CJT	Scania K310 EB4	Irizar Century Capacity	C53F	2007	Swan's, Chadderton, 2009
FJ08KOD	Toyota Coaster BB50R	Caetano Optimo V	C26F	2008	BM Coaches, Hayes, 2010
UT09CJT	Temsa Safari H	Temsa	C57F	2009	
VT09CJT	Temsa Safari H	Temsa	C57F	2009	
OYY3	Mercedes-Benz Tourino	Mercedes-Benz	C32FT	2009	
PO10CJT	Scania K124 IB4	Irizar Century	C49FT	2010	
SO10CJT	Scania K124 IB4	Irizar Century	C49FT	2010	

Previous registrations:

73WAE	YN04GGE		M20CJT	M250XWS
6486LJ	YN55PYZ		M44CJT	M463SMO
3138DP	YN55PYY, NDZ70		N14CJT	EC54AA, N823OAE
110LHW	05CN476		N829OAE	N989TOK
7153MC	YN55PYX, NBZ70		OYY3	-
CT56CJT	YN56NTK		PT05CJT	LSK839, SF05XDA
JT56CJT	YN56NTL		RT05CJT	LSK835, SF05XDB
GT02CJT	WJ02UVV		W17CJT	W58DOE
LT06CJT	WG06LNW		WT06CJT	YN06NZE
			XT06CJT	YN06NZF
			YT06CJT	YN06NZG

Web: www.turnerscoachways.co.uk

WELSH'S TOURS

Welsh's Coaches Ltd, Field Lane, Upton, Pontefract, WF9 1BH

X846HEE	Mercedes-Benz 412D	Autobus	M16	2000
YN05CPZ	Mercedes-Benz Sprinter 311 cdi	Mercedes-Benz	M16	2005
W7HOL	Setra S415 HD	Setra	C48FT	2004
W10HOL	Setra S415 GT-HD	Setra	C48FT	2005
W25HOL	Setra S416 GT-HD	Setra	C48FT	2006
W26HOL	Setra S416 GT-HD	Setra	C48FT	2007
W6HOL	Setra S416 GT-HD	Setra	C48FT	2007
NT08BGU	Mercedes-Benz Vito 111cdi	Mercedes-Benz	M8	2008

Previous registration:
NT08BGU   1308RW

Web: www.welshscoaches.com

Another operator who has selected the Setra GT-HD as the standard vehicle is Welsh's of Pontefract having started in 1967 and progressed from being a taxi and minicoach operation to providing continental tours. Seen in London is W26HOL. *Mark Doggett*

WESTWAY

Westway Coach Services, 7a Rainbow Ind Est, Station Approach, Raynes Park, London, SW20 0JY

Reg	Chassis	Body	Seats	Year	History
17EJU	Volvo B10M-61	Van Hool T8 Astral	C47/10DT	1984	Shorey, Flitwick, 2001
45CG	Volvo B10M-50	Van Hool T8 Astral	C8/7FT	1989	Wright, Watford, 2004
715ATV	Volvo B12T	Van Hool T8 Asrobel	C57/14CT	1993	Berry, Taunton, 1998
39WT	Volvo B10M-60	Van Hool Alizée HE	C53F	1993	Maynes of Buckie, 2010
90RXT	Volvo B10M-62	Van Hool T8 Alizée	C46FT	1996	
45DG	Volvo B12T	Jonckheere Monoaco	C57/14CT	1997	Clarkes of London, 2004
B19WSC	Volvo B12T	Jonckheere Monoaco	C57/14CT	1997	Clarkes of London, 2004
37WT	EOS E230Z	EOS	C28FT	1998	Go-Goodwins, Eccles, 2004
67MTV	Volvo B10M-48	Van Hool Alizée	C34FT	1998	Hilton, Newton-le-Willows, 2007
T9MCL	Volvo B10M-62	Van Hool T9 Alizée	C49FT	1999	Owens, Oswestry, 2012
74WT	Volvo B10M-55	Van Hool T9 Alizée	C46FT	1999	
32WT	Volvo B10M-55	Van Hool T9 Alizée	C28FT	2000	Barratts, Nantwich, 2005
W6STS	Volvo B10M-62	Van Hool T9 Alizée	C55FT	2000	
53WT	DAF SB3000	Van Hool T9 Alizée	C53FT	2000	Westbus, 2010
WE51WAY	Volvo B12M	Van Hool T9 Alizée	C49FT	2003	
27WT	Van Hool T917 Astron	Van Hool	C38FT	2005	Go-Goodwins, Eccles, 2007
300GRX	Mercedes-Benz Vario 0815	Sitcar Beluga 2	C29F	2006	London Mini, Isleworth, 2012

Seen approaching Hyde Park is Westway's 29WT, a Van Hool T917 Astron, and one of three currently operated.
Colin Lloyd

RV06RUY	Volkswagen Traveller	Volkswagen	M8	2006	
VSC16	Volvo B12B	Van Hool T9 Astrobel	C61/18DT	2006	
449GTU	Volvo B12B	Van Hool T9 Astrobel	C61/18DT	2006	
60VV	Volvo B12B	Van Hool T9 Alizée	C53FT	2006	Redden, Coldingham, 2008
BL56GKJ	Mercedes-Benz Sprinter	Mercedes-Benz	B12	2007	
KUB1C	Volvo B12B	Van Hool T9 Astrobel	C61/18DT	2008	
28WT	Van Hool T917 Astron	Van Hool	C36FT	2008	Parry, Cheslyn Hay, 2011
29WT	Van Hool T917 Astron	Van Hool	C36FT	2008	Parry, Cheslyn Hay, 2012
BSK853	Van Hool T916 Acron	Van Hool	C57FT	2009	BM Coaches, Hayes, 2011
WA10CFM	Volvo B12B	Van Hool T9 Astrobel	C61/18DT	2010	
WA11AED	Mercedes-Benz Vario O815	Sitcar Beluga 3	C29F	2011	
WA12AWF	Mercedes-Benz Vario O815	Sitcar Beluga 3	C29F	2012	

WOODS

Woods Coaches Ltd, 211 Gloucester Crescent, Wigston, Leicester, LE18 4YH

CHZ4744	Volvo B10M-62	Plaxton Première 350	C49FT	1995	Charlton & Martin, Maidstone, '02
CHZ4745	Volvo B10M-62	Plaxton Première 350	C51FT	1996	Minsterley Motors, 2002
WDZ6259	Volvo B10M-62	Plaxton Première 350	C53F	1996	Battersby, Morecambe, 2004
WDZ6570	Volvo B10M-62	Plaxton Première 350	C53F	1996	Options, Castleton, 2003
CHZ7466	Volvo B10M-62	Plaxton Première 350	C51FT	1998	Wallace Arnold, Leeds, 2003
WDZ1232	Volvo B10M-62	Plaxton Première 350	C46FT	1999	TM, Old Tupton, 2006
WDZ7683	Volvo B10M-62	Plaxton Première 350	C49FT	2000	Wallace Arnold, Leeds, 2005
WDZ2826	Volvo B10M-62	Plaxton Première 350	C49FT	2000	Wallace Arnold, Leeds, 2005
WDZ1733	Volvo B10M-62	Plaxton Paragon	C53F	2000	Fleetwing Travel, Aldershot, 2006
WDZ1666	Volvo B10M-62	Plaxton Paragon	C53F	2000	Fleetwing Travel, Aldershot, 2006
6844WF	Neoplan Starliner N516 SHD	Neoplan	C44FT	2003	Ellison, St Helens, 2007
WDZ565	Neoplan Starliner N516 SHD	Neoplan	C48FT	2005	Parry, Cheslyn Hay, 2008
WDZ595	Neoplan Starliner N516 SHD	Neoplan	C48FT	2005	Parry, Cheslyn Hay, 2008
WDZ727	Neoplan Starliner N516 SHD	Neoplan	C48FT	2005	Parry, Cheslyn Hay, 2008
WDZ1691	Mercedes-Benz Vario O814	Mercedes-Benz Medio	C29F	2005	Evobus demonstrator, 2007

Previous registrations:

782EUL	R419FWT	WDZ1232	T501EUB
CHZ4744	M291SBT	WDZ1666	HSK656, W488ASB
CHZ4745	N206HWX, 8980WA, N574ACP	WDZ1691	BX54EDJ
CHZ7466	R421FWT	WDZ1733	HSK655, W487ASB
6544WF	YN03AWW, GFF405	WDZ2826	W658FUM
WDZ565	YN05BWB	WDZ6259	N891AEO, 4360WF
WDZ595	YN05BWD	WDZ6570	N285OYE
WDZ727	YN05BWC	WDZ7683	W654FUM

Depot: Bedford Road, Wigston

Woods operates four Neoplan Starliner coaches one of which is the 44-seat 6844WF. It also carries VIP lettering. *Colin Martin*

Recent changes at York Pullman have seen the bus services transferred to Transdev leaving York Pullman with contracts and coaching work. Seen at the British Coach Rally is Duple Laser-bodied Volvo EFD923Y.
John Marsh

294	G35OCK	Leyland Olympian ONCL10/2RZ	Leyland	BC43/31F	1990	Stagecoach, 2011
295	BV57MPU	BMC Falcon 225	BMC	B56F	2007	BMC demonstrator, 2011
296	YX10FDZ	Mercedes-Benz Vario O816	Plaxton Cheetah	C33F	2010	
297	B18KJT	Volvo B10M-62	Van Hool Alizée H	C46FT	1997	Johnson Bros, Hodthorpe, 2011
298	G35OCK	Leyland Olympian ONCL10/2RZ	Leyland	B47/31F	1990	Stagecoach, 2011
306	F297DRJ	Leyland Olympian ONLXB/1RZ	Northern Counties	B43/30F	1989	Stagecoach, 2011
309	C543HCA	Ford R1115	Plaxton Paramount 3200 II	C53F	1985	Alexander
311	J3YPB	Volvo B12M	Plaxton Paragon	C53FT	2006	
312	YN06MXS	Volvo B12B	Plaxton Panther	C49FT	2006	Woottens, Chesham, 2011
313	A8YPB	Volvo B12B	Plaxton Panther	C49FT	2006	Woottens, Chesham, 2011
314	CE52TZY	Mercedes-Benz Sprinter	UVG	M16	2002	
315	K5YPB	DAF SB3000	Plaxton Première 320	C53F	1999	Fourway, Guisley, 2012
316	SF05XDE	Volvo B12B	Jonckheere Mistral 50	C53F	2005	Geoff Amos, Daventry, 2012
317	YN61AWX	Mercedes-Benz Vario O816	Plaxton Cheetah	C33F	2011	
318	FFK312	Volvo B10M-62	Plaxton Première 350	C48FT	1997	Geoff Amos, Daventry, 2012
319	MUI4784	Volvo B10M-62	Van Hool T8 Alizée HE	C49FT	1994	Grahams, 2012
320	E330MSG	Leyland Olympian ONCL10/1RZ	Alexander RH	B51/34F	1985	Rotala, 2012
321	E331MSG	Leyland Olympian ONCL10/1RZ	Alexander RH	B51/34F	1985	Rotala, 2012
322	E332MSG	Leyland Olympian ONCL10/1RZ	Alexander RH	B51/34F	1985	Rotala, 2012
323	MX55HSX	Mercedes-Benz Sprinter	Mercedes-Benz	M16	2005	
324	V582NRH	Mercedes-Benz Sprinter	Mercedes-Benz	M16	1999	
325	J4CRC	DAF MB230	Van Hool T8 Alizée	C49FT	1992	Robinson, Great Harwood, 2012
328	LKZ7691	Leyland Olympian ONLXB/1R	Eastern Coach Works	B45/32F	1983	Holmeswood Coaches, 2012
329	FD03YNN	Irisbus EuroMidi CC80E	Indcar Maxim 2	C29F	2003	
330	R5YPB	Volvo B9M	Van Hool T8 Alizée	C38FT	1997	Thirlwell, Newcastle, 2012
331	BX56VSG	Mercedes-Benz 1836RL Touro	Mercedes-Benz	C49FT	2006	MCH, Uxbridge, 2012
332	YN07EDX	VDL SB4000	Hispano Diva	V57F	2007	Stewart, Glazeley Green, 2012
333	AB07TPB	Mercedes-Benz Tourismo	Mercedes-Benz	C49FT	2007	Stewart, Glazeley Green, 2012
335	R625GFS	Mercedes-Benz Vario O814	Mellor	BC24F	1997	Glover, Ashbourne, 2012

A more recent vehicle with York Pullman is K1YPB, a Volvo B12M with Plaxton Paragon bodywork. *John Marsh*

Special event vehicles:

71	ODN348	AEC Regent V MD3RV	Roe	B33/28R	1957	York Pullman
	OEY324J	Bedford SB3	Duple Vega	C41FT	1971	Robinson, Halifax, 2012
235	HHK369B	Bedford VAS1	Duple Bella Vista	C29F	1964	Girt, Tilbury

Previous registrations:

792UXA	WLT787	K1YPB	R72VVP, C11ECB
A8YPB	YN06MXX	K5YPB	T162AUA
A10YBP	R783WSB, LGV34, R798WSB	K100BLU	L109TCP
AB07YPB	BX07NLJ	LKZ7691	CWR526Y
AEZ7248	N902ABL	MFF578	WLT329
B2YPB	J836HHE	MIW5785	N958DWJ, N2SFC
B10YPS	M128UWY	MIW5791	P396MDT
B12KJT	AT52LCT	MIW5792	L321JUJ, 3572NT
B13KJT	BT52LCT	MIW5794	M102UWY, 8665WA, M170EYG
B18KJT	P311VWR	NJZ9182	R361DJN
B19KJT	T894HBF, PRN909	OJZ1836	G608YMD, G406JMK, JIL3964, 255CYA
J2YPB	J47UFL	R5YPB	R429JTN
J3YPB	YN06RWL	R421SER	R2CAV
J4CRC	J247LFR	SF05XDE	LSK830
JJZ6563	E899KYW, HIL4211	XJI2605	F261RJX

Vehicle index

1KOV	Harry Shaw	96RT	Johnson Bros
2SXV	Sharpes	100WXD	The Traveller' Choice
3KOV	Harry Shaw	108GYC	Redwoods
3TXO	The Traveller' Choice	110LHW	Turners
3TYX	Sharpes	112AXN	Bowens
3WSM	Ellison's	112FYA	Woods Travel
4JBT	Johnson Bros	123RT	Johnson Bros
4JXX	The Traveller' Choice	133MBJ	Tates
4ORX	The Traveller' Choice	147VKN	Bowens
5AAX	Holmeswood	149CYY	Compass Royston
5HDX	The Traveller' Choice	152ENM	Holmeswood
5JBT	Johnson Bros	152JUP	Ellison's
6JBT	Johnson Bros	153WAR	Richmond's
6SVK	The Traveller' Choice	171CLC	Crawley Luxury
7JXO	Sharpes	184XNO	Holmeswood
7OWX	Sharpes	188TAE	Titterington
8JBT	Johnson Bros	194WHT	Bakers Dolphin
8XNE	Sharpes	195JOH	Bowens
8YTX	The Traveller' Choice	198FYB	Woods Travel
9JBT	Johnson Bros	212VPF	Titterington
10GJD	Lakeside	224ASV	Barfordian
10JWX	The Traveller' Choice	230WYA	Barfordian
11PKN	Soames	237AJB	Roselyn
17EJU	Westway	239AJB	Roselyn
18CU	The Traveller' Choice	239LYC	Richmond's
18XWC	Leons	240FRH	Ambassador
22CDX	Sharpes	244AJB	Roselyn
27WT	Westway	253FYW	Woods Travel
28WT	Westway	274FYP	Woods Travel
29WT	Westway	275FUM	Richmond's
32WT	Westway	279JJO	Bowens
37HE	The Traveller' Choice	289BUA	Maynes
37WT	Westway	296HFM	Holmeswood
38NE	The Traveller' Choice	300GRX	Westway
39WT	Westway	307FYG	Woods Travel
43RT	Johnson Bros	315MWL	Bakers Dolphin
45CG	Westway	316UVX	Richmond's
45DG	Westway	340MYA	Bakers Dolphin
46AEW	Lodge's	345BLA	Andrews
48NR	The Traveller' Choice	348FYY	Woods Travel
52CLC	Crawley Luxury	352BWB	Abbotts
52RE	The Traveller' Choice	352STG	Selwyns
53WT	Westway	368SHX	Titterington
55XY	Sharpes	403BGO	Maynes
60VV	Westway	403NMM	Richmond's
60XYT	Sharpes	405MDV	Bowens
60YWX	Sharpes	406AOT	Princess
63RT	Johnson Bros	424KPP	Richmond's
67MTV	Westway	426YRA	Richmond's
71RT	Johnson Bros	438XYA	Richmond's
73WAE	Turners	449GTU	Westway
74WT	Westway	461XPB	Heyfordian
74YKP	Ellison's	464HYB	Holmeswood
76RT	Johnson Bros	466YMG	Holmeswood
77RT	Johnson Bros	478FHW	Reay's
79RT	Johnson Bros	479COT	Princess
84KOV	Harry Shaw	479GTA	The Traveller' Choice
86JBF	Castleways	481HYE	Heyfordian
90RXT	Westway	487VYA	Bowens
90WFC	Motts	489AOU	Princess
94RT	Johnson Bros	489SYB	Barfordian
94SHU	Eagle	498FYN	Woods Travel

503FYC	Woods Travel		
509EBL	The Traveller' Choice		
513SRL	Roselyn		
526VVK	Henry Cooper		
539DTE	Holmeswood		
549KYA	Princess		
5516PP	Galloway		
551ALW	Eddie Brown		
577HTX	Richmond's		
587FYF	Woods Travel		
593FGF	Richmond's		
593UXJ	Bowens		
613WHT	Eagle		
622HFJ	Bowens		
629LFM	Holmeswood		
647PJO	Bowens		
647PYC	Roselyn		
648EAU	Richmond's		
649ETF	Richmond's		
653GBU	Heyfordian		
654JHU	Bluebird		
666VMX	Lucketts		
668PTM	Richmond's		
671MBB	Henry Cooper		
675PBM	Barfordian		
685CLC	Crawley Luxury		
687CLC	Crawley Luxury		
695CWR	Reay's		
701UDE	Roselyn		
712GRM	Reay's		
715ATV	Westway		
716GRM	Holmeswood		
728FDV	Roselyn		
729KTO	Richmond's		
750DCD	Kenzies		
753LNU	Richmond's		
754GHO	Henry Cooper		
7740KO	Bakers Dolphin		
774FUO	Abbotts		
778XYA	Abbotts		
779UXU	Bluebird		
784CLC	Crawley Luxury		
789CLC	Crawley Luxury		
790CVD	Ambassador		
791WHT	Bakers Dolphin		
792UXA	York Pullman		
800XPC	Peter Carol		
802AOJ	Bowens		
824HAO	The Traveller' Choice		
846FHA	Bowens		
848AFM	Holmeswood		
848KMX	Compass Royston		
851FYD	Richmond's		
863EXX	Eagle		
872KMY	Bowens		
890TTE	Titterington		
892LTV	Richmond's		
899CAN	The Traveller' Choice		
906GAU	Maynes		
916VBH	Gee-Vee		
917DBO	Leons		
931DHT	Eagle		

938HNM	Bowens	5146RU	The Traveller' Choice	9958PH	Hodge's
943YKN	Heyfordian	5188RU	Johnson Bros	99D455	Compass Royston
947JWD	Leons	5226PH	Hodge's	99D458	Compass Royston
958VKM	Bakers Dolphin	5611PP	Galloway	A2EXC	Elcock Reisen
978UYD	Crawley Luxury	5615RO	Bowens	A2WOH	Eddie Brown
987FOU	Princess	5705MT	Motts	A2XEL	Excelsior
1210PH	Hodge's	5812MT	Motts	A3EBT	Eddie Brown
1359UP	Battersby-Silver Grey	5814MT	Motts	A3XEL	Excelsior
1389NT	Elcock Reisen	5881PH	Hodge's	A4HWD	Holmeswood
1398NT	Elcock Reisen	5946PP	Galloway	A5WOH	Eddie Brown
1435VZ	Heyfordian	6037PP	Galloway	A5XEL	Excelsior
1440PP	Galloway	6130EL	Eagle	A7BKE	Eddie Brown
1482PP	Galloway	6137RU	The Traveller' Choice	A7XEL	Excelsior
1516KM	K M	6247MT	Motts	A8CLN	Country Lyon
1577NT	Elcock Reisen	6267UA	The Traveller' Choice	A8YPB	York Pullman
1598PH	Hodge's	6399PP	Galloway	A9CLN	Country Lyon
1624WY	Compass Royston	6486LJ	Turners	A9EBT	Eddie Brown
1725LJ	Crawley Luxury	6595KV	Heyfordian	A10CLC	Country Lyon
1754PP	Galloway	6601MT	Motts	A10SFC	Holmeswood
1842PP	Galloway	6682WY	The Traveller' Choice	A10XEL	Excelsior
1932NT	Elcock Reisen	6691PH	Hodge's	A10YPB	York Pullman
2086PP	Galloway	6787MT	Motts	A11XEL	Excelsior
2185NU	Heyfordian	6791RU	Ausden Clark	A12CLN	Country Lyon
2396VU	The Traveller' Choice	6844WF	Woods	A12HLC	Lucketts
2480PH	Hodge's	6957MT	Motts	A12WTN	Bowens
2482NX	Heyfordian	6967PH	Hodge's	A12XEL	Excelsior
2508EL	Chenery	7017UN	Battersby-Silver Grey	A13EBT	Eddie Brown
2513PP	Galloway	7107PH	Hodge's	A13HLC	Lucketts
2568PH	Hodge's	7132ET	The Traveller' Choice	A13XEL	Excelsior
2594XI	The Traveller' Choice	7153MC	Turners	A14CLC	Country Lyon
2622NU	Heyfordian	7179TW	Travel Wright	A14EBT	Eddie Brown
2779UE	Heyfordian	7209RU	Heyfordian	A14XEL	Excelsior
3138DP	Turners	7298RU	Heyfordian	A15CLC	Country Lyon
3182NF	Battersby-Silver Grey	7351RUL	The Traveller' Choice	A15CLN	Country Lyon
3367PP	Galloway	7396LJ	Heyfordian	A15EBT	Eddie Brown
3379PP	Galloway	7529UK	Andrews	A15NFC	Country Lyon
3408NT	Elcock Reisen	7606UR	The Traveller' Choice	A15XEL	Excelsior
3419NT	Elcock Reisen	7622UK	Battersby-Silver Grey	A16CLC	Country Lyon
3493CD	Bowens	7845LJ	Heyfordian	A16EBT	Eddie Brown
3556PH	Hodge's	7845UG	Battersby-Silver Grey	A16HLC	Lucketts
3572NT	Elcock Reisen	7958NU	Heyfordian	A16TVL	Durham City
3770RU	The Traveller' Choice	7962IL	The Traveller' Choice	A16XEL	Excelsior
3860PP	Galloway	8194WF	Eagle	A17CLN	Country Lyon
3886UR	The Traveller' Choice	8216FN	Heyfordian	A17EBT	Eddie Brown
3900PH	Hodge's	8338RU	The Traveller' Choice	A17HLC	Lucketts
4078NU	Heyfordian	8447WX	The Traveller' Choice	A17XEL	Excelsior
4092PP	Galloway	8466PH	Hodge's	A18CLN	Country Lyon
4122YG	The Traveller' Choice	8468WX	The Traveller' Choice	A18HLC	Lucketts
4148VX	Battersby-Silver Grey	8488NU	Johnson Bros	A18XEL	Excelsior
4150RU	The Traveller' Choice	8527RU	The Traveller' Choice	A19CLN	Country Lyon
4360WF	Battersby-Silver Grey	8548VF	Heyfordian	A19HLC	Lucketts
4402PH	Hodge's	868AVO	Heyfordian	A19HWD	Holmeswood
4426BY	Reay's	8732PG	Andrews	A19LTG	Lucketts
4442MT	Motts	8850WU	Battersby-Silver Grey	A19XEL	Excelsior
4465KM	K M	8874PH	Hodge's	A20CLC	Country Lyon
4631PH	Hodge's	8896PH	Hodge's	A20EFA	Holmeswood
4827WD	Heyfordian	8990PH	Hodge's	A20HWD	Holmeswood
5038NT	Elcock Reisen	9201FH	The Traveller' Choice	A20XEL	Excelsior
5048PP	Galloway	9346PL	Leons	A50WVL	Kettlewells
5049PH	Hodge's	9467MU	Heyfordian	A133SMA	Johnson Bros
5092EL	Chenery	9489PH	Hodge's	A182XCA	Irving's
5096WF	Battersby-Silver Grey	9649PH	Hodge's	A283HAY	Johnson Bros
5108VX	Battersby-Silver Grey	9682FH	Heyfordian	A288ANT	Anthony's Travel
5129UA	The Traveller' Choice	9775MT	Motts	A295FDL	Johnson Bros
5134PH	Hodge's	9920MT	Motts	A530OKH	Johnson Bros

L1CLN	Country Lyon	LIW4291	Compass Royston	M659VRR	Skills
L1HDC	Leons	LJ03WBG	PC Coaches	M660VJB	Compass Royston
L1OND	Country Lyon	LKZ7691	York Pullman	M661MVV	Country Lyon
L1ONU	Country Lyon	LLZ5719	Bowens	M661VJB	Compass Royston
L2POW	Berkeley	LOT7E	Ellison's	M687HPF	Roselyn
L3JBT	Johnson Bros	LP12BUS	Pulham's	M687TDB	Greys of Ely
L4HWD	Holmeswood	LR07RAM	Rambler	M741RCP	Bluebird
L5BNM	Compass Royston	LRU822	Prospect	M743KJU	Ambassador
L5HWD	Holmeswood	LSU113	Talisman	M805RCP	Eagle
L7JSF	Country Lyon	LSU788	Talisman	M833HNS	Heyfordian
L8TCC	Compass Royston	LSU939	The Traveller' Choice	M849LFP	Bowens
L9CJT	Turners	LSU954	Compass Royston	M850LFP	Bowens
L10NBB	Country Lyon	LT06CJT	Turners	M884WAK	Compass Royston
L10NCC	Country Lyon	LTA752	Lodge's	M939JJU	Silverdale
L10NHH	Country Lyon	LUI1508	Ausden Clark	M945SUX	Leons
L10NKK	Country Lyon	LUI1522	Bowens	M948TSX	Marshalls
L29CAY	Travel Wright	LUI3166	Heyfordian	M955HRY	Godson
L30CAP	York Pullman	LUI7869	Abbotts	M964RKJ	Compass Royston
L50ULS	Barfordian	LUI7871	Bowens	M993HHS	Heyfordian
L100CLA	Hills	LUI8400	Heyfordian	MA07BUS	Motts
L157LBW	Roselyn	LUI9301	Heyfordian	MA11NYV	Hamilton
L170PDO	Compass Royston	LUO391	Crawley Luxury	MA11NYW	Hamilton
L238OYC	Berrys	LV02LKC	Holmeswood	MA61KLP	Ellison's
L268ULX	Heyfordian	LV02LKE	Holmeswood	MAZ6771	Abbotts
L400CLA	Hills	LVL804V	Johnson Bros	MB04DVJ	Reay's
L408GDC	Bowens	LVL807V	Johnson Bros	MB07ANT	Anthony's Travel
L409GPY	Heyfordian	LW52AKK	Clarkes of London	MB07BUS	Motts
L445FHD	Ambassador	LW52AKN	Clarkes of London	MB56MAT	Princess
L579JSA	Heyfordian	LX06FFA	Epsom Coaches	MB61FWB	Bibby's of Ingleton
L584JSA	Heyfordian	LX06FFB	Epsom Coaches	MC07DCC	Durham City
L585JSA	Heyfordian	LX10CUY	Reay's	MCT612	Silverdale
L587JSA	Heyfordian	LX55CFD	Skills	MCZ4304	Marchants
L70CLN	Country Lyon	LXH869	Compass Royston	MCZ4305	Marchants
L743YGE	Heyfordian	M1JBT	Johnson Bros	MCZ4306	Marchants
LAZ130	Sharpes	M2BNM	Compass Royston	MCZ4326	Marchants
LB52UYK	Selwyns	M4YNC	Maynes	MCZ4413	Marchants
LC11PCC	PC Coaches	M4YNF	Maynes	MCZ4426	Marchants
LCZ4009	Prospect	M20CJT	Turners	MCZ4431	Marchants
LD10BEL	Belle	M21GAT	Compass Royston	MCZ4437	Marchants
LDD488	Pulham's	M33CRT	Compass Royston	MCZ5995	Marchants
LDY173	Rambler	M35KAX	Ambassador	MCZ7087	Marchants
LDZ2502	Heyfordian	M40CJT	Turners	MF09ZLN	Shearings
LDZ2503	Heyfordian	M40CRT	Compass Royston	MF09ZMO	Shearings
LEW16W	Kenzies	M44CJT	Turners	MF11LUJ	Johnson Bros
LF05DPV	Compass Royston	M50ULS	Barfordian	MF11LUL	Johnson Bros
LHE601W	Johnson Bros	M70CLN	Country Lyon	MF11LUO	Johnson Bros
LIB226	Roselyn	M73WYG	Lodge's	MF11LVD	Sea View
LIB6437	Maynes	M99PCC	PC Coaches	MF11LVE	Sea View
LIB6440	Holmeswood	M300MFC	Pearces	MF11LVG	Sea View
LIB6445	Berkeley	M339UKN	Silverdale	MF11LVJ	Skills
LIL2174	Ausden Clark	M343UKN	Silverdale	MF11LVK	Skills
LIL9452	Belle	M378FMW	Compass Royston	MF11LVL	Skills
LIL9454	Belle	M418UKN	Skills	MF11LVM	Skills
LIL9455	Belle	M419UKN	Skills	MF11LVN	Skills
LIL9456	Belle	M420UKN	Skills	MF12HGK	Sea View
LIL9457	Belle	M420VYD	Scotland & Bates	MF52UKD	Kettlewells
LIL9458	Belle	M421UKN	Skills	MFF578	York Pullman
LIL9713	Belle	M438BRR	Skills	MFF580	Henry Cooper
LIL9714	Belle	M455TCH	Motts	MH02NGG	Reay's
LIL9715	Belle	M472ACA	Travel Wright	MH02NGN	Reay's
LIL9716	Belle	M513MFX	Soames	MH08BAN	Banstead Coaches
LIL9717	Belle	M525WHF	Rambler	MH10BAN	Banstead Coaches
LIL9718	Belle	M537WHF	Roselyn	MHZ1473	Roselyn
LIL9815	Compass Royston	M611APN	Roselyn	MHZ9321	Selwyns
LIL9816	Compass Royston	M658VRR	Skills	MHZ9322	Selwyns

Escourting a party from Japan, 438XYA is a Van Hool T916 Astron operated by Richmond's. At 3.7 metres the Astron comapres with the Acron at 3.6 metres and the Alicron at 3.47 metres. *Mark Doggett*

MIB580	Leons	MT03MTT	Motts	MW52PYY	Compass Royston
MIB658	Sharpes	MT04MTT	Motts	MW52PYZ	Compass Royston
MIB6571	Sharpes	MT05MTT	Motts	MW52PZB	Compass Royston
MIL3503	Belle	MT06MTT	Motts	MW52UCS	Grayway
MIL8340	Marshalls	MT07MTT	Motts	MWG940X	Johnson Bros
MIL9576	Holmeswood	MT08MTT	Motts	MX03AAV	Shearings
MIL9746	Abbotts	MT09MTT	Motts	MX03AAY	Shearings
MIW2422	Johnson Bros	MT11MTT	Motts	MX03AAZ	Shearings
MIW5785	York Pullman	MT12MTT	Motts	MX03ABK	Shearings
MIW5794	York Pullman	MT51MTT	Motts	MX03ACJ	Shearings
MIW9046	Compass Royston	MT56MTT	Motts	MX03ACY	Shearings
MJ11DHG	City Circle	MT60MTT	Motts	MX03ACZ	Shearings
MJ11LVP	City Circle	MT61HUP	Leons	MX03AED	Shearings
MJ11LVR	City Circle	MT61HVE	Ellison's	MX03AEE	Shearings
MJ11WKU	City Circle	MT61HVF	Ellison's	MX03AEF	Shearings
MJ11WKV	City Circle	MT61HVG	Ellison's	MX03AEG	Shearings
MJ61AVT	Hamilton	MT61HVU	Ellison's	MX03AET	Shearings
MJB481	Lodge's	MT61HVW	Ellison's	MX03AEU	Shearings
MK59LXP	Shearings	MU51HHM	The Traveller' Choice	MX03AEV	Shearings
MK59LXR	Shearings	MU53BOY	Golden Boy	MX03AEW	Shearings
MK59LXU	Shearings	MUI4784	York Pullman	MX04AEA	Shearings
MK59LXV	Shearings	MUI7799	Ausden Clark	MX04AEB	Shearings
MK59LXW	Shearings	MUI7939	Ausden Clark	MX04AEC	Shearings
MKZ7186	Marshalls	MV12ODS	Silverdale	MX04AED	Shearings
MKZ7190	Marshalls	MV12ODT	Silverdale	MX04AEE	Shearings
ML61CXE	Hamilton	MV12ODU	Silverdale	MX04AEF	Shearings
ML61CXF	Hamilton	MV12ODW	Silverdale	MX04AEG	Shearings
MLZ3922	Compass Royston	MV12ODX	Silverdale	MX04AEJ	Shearings
MM02DBO	Harry Shaw	MV12ODY	Silverdale	MX04AEK	Shearings
MP03CYF	Reay's	MV12OEA	Ellison's	MX04AEL	Shearings
MP03FZJ	K M	MV12OEB	Ellison's	MX04AEM	Shearings
MS03MER	Bibby's of Ingleton	MV12OEC	Ellison's	MX04AEP	Shearings
MSU462	Compass Royston	MV12OED	Hamilton	MX04AEU	Shearings
MT02MTT	Motts	MW52PYX	Compass Royston	MX04AEV	Shearings

Pictured in London is PR08PET operated by prospect of Lye. This ADL Javelin carries Plaxton Profile bodywork intended for school duties with this example fitted with seventy seats. *Dave Heath*

MX04AEW	Shearings	MX05ENE	Compass Royston	MX10DXY	Compass Royston
MX04AEY	Shearings	MX05OSZ	The Traveller' Choice	MX10OFD	Sea View
MX04AEZ	Shearings	MX05OUC	Holmeswood	MX10OFE	Sea View
MX04AFA	Shearings	MX06AKN	Shearings	MX10OFF	Sea View
MX04AFE	Shearings	MX06AKO	Shearings	MX10OFG	Sea View
MX04AFF	Shearings	MX06AKP	Shearings	MX12DYS	Bakers Dolphin
MX04AFJ	Shearings	MX06AKU	Shearings	MX12DYT	Bakers Dolphin
MX04AFK	Shearings	MX06AKV	Shearings	MX53FDN	Galloway
MX04AFN	Shearings	MX06AKY	Shearings	MX54KYA	Ambassador
MX04AFU	Shearings	MX06AKZ	Shearings	MX54KYB	Ambassador
MX05AFU	Shearings	MX06ALO	Shearings	MX54KYC	Ambassador
MX05AFV	Shearings	MX06ALU	Shearings	MX54WME	Ambassador
MX05AFY	Shearings	MX06AMK	Shearings	MX55BXR	Compass Royston
MX05AFZ	Shearings	MX06BSU	Johnsons	MX55BXS	Compass Royston
MX05AGO	Shearings	MX06ULP	Compass Royston	MX55HSX	York Pullman
MX05AGU	Shearings	MX06XMM	Castleways	MX55WDA	Swans
MX05AGV	Shearings	MX07BBN	Castleways	MX55WDZ	Holmeswood
MX05AGY	Shearings	MX07JOA	Holmeswood	MX55WUY	Compass Royston
MX05AGZ	Shearings	MX07JOH	Compass Royston	MX55WVA	Compass Royston
MX05AHA	Shearings	MX07JOJ	Compass Royston	MX55WVC	Compass Royston
MX05AHC	Shearings	MX07JOU	Compass Royston	MX56AAY	Holmeswood
MX05AHD	Shearings	MX07LBG	Holmeswood	MX56LNR	Johnsons
MX05AHE	Shearings	MX07NTO	Compass Royston	MX56NHB	Holmeswood
MX05AHF	Shearings	MX09AON	Richmond's	MX56NHC	Holmeswood
MX05AHG	Shearings	MX09MJE	Bakers Dolphin	MX57CCD	Compass Royston
MX05AHJ	Shearings	MX10DDA	Silverdale	MX57CCE	Compass Royston
MX05AHK	Shearings	MX10DDF	Robinsons	MX57CCF	Compass Royston
MX05AHL	Shearings	MX10DDJ	Robinsons	MX59AWC	Swans
MX05AHN	Shearings	MX10DDL	Silverdale	MX59BYK	Redwing
MX05AHO	Shearings	MX10DFJ	City Circle	MX59BYM	Redwing
MX05AHP	Shearings	MX10DFK	City Circle	MX59BYN	Redwing
MX05AHU	Shearings	MX10DFL	Silverdale	MX59BYO	Redwing
MX05AHV	Shearings	MX10DFN	Silverdale	MX59BYP	Redwing
MX05EMV	Compass Royston	MX10DXM	Compass Royston	MX59BYR	Redwing

MX59BYS	Redwing	N758CYA	Berrys	NH09KRH	Shearings
MX59KTL	Robinsons	N776WEF	Compass Royston	NH09LRH	Shearings
MX59KTU	Robinsons	N795PDS	Travel Wright	NH09MRH	Shearings
MX59XJT	Abbotts	N803TPK	Heyfordian	NH09NRH	Shearings
MX60EGK	Selwyns	N807KRL	Sea View	NH09ORH	Shearings
MX60EKH	Selwyns	N813OAE	Turners	NH09PRH	Shearings
MY02AOL	Abbotts	N822DKU	Ambassador	NH09RRH	Shearings
MY02BAN	Banstead Coaches	N824DKU	Ambassador	NH09SRH	Shearings
MY52BAN	Banstead Coaches	N829OAE	Turners	NH10BSH	Shearings
MY53TRA	Talisman	N896KFA	Holmeswood	NH10CSH	Shearings
N1JBT	Johnson Bros	N899KFA	Prospect	NH10DSH	Shearings
N1SMC	Skills	N912DWJ	Prospect	NH10FSH	Shearings
N2DCC	Durham City	N950RBC	Excalibur	NH10GSH	Shearings
N2GVT	Gee-Vee	N966OAE	Turners	NH10HSH	Shearings
N2RED	Redwoods	N999RWC	Chenery	NH10JSH	Shearings
N5AOL	Abbotts	NBN922	Chenery	NH10KSH	Shearings
N6AOL	Abbotts	NBU707	Chenery	NH10LSH	Shearings
N7CLC	Crawley Luxury	NBZ2248	Buzzlines	NH10MSH	Shearings
N10JRJ	Johnsons	NBZ301	Sharpes	NH10NSH	Shearings
N10PCC	PC Coaches	NC06CLC	Crawley Luxury	NH10OSH	Shearings
N10TGM	Berrys	NC06PCC	PC Coaches	NH10PSH	Shearings
N12CLC	Crawley Luxury	NC56FXU	Durham City	NH10RSH	Shearings
N14CJT	Turners	ND54WKE	Abbotts	NH10SSH	Shearings
N30BAN	Banstead Coaches	NDD672	Pulham's	NH11BTH	Shearings
N30CRT	Compass Royston	NDO609	Bowens	NH11CTH	Shearings
N33CRT	Compass Royston	NDO619	Bowens	NH11DTH	Shearings
N37EUG	Godson	NDY962	Rambler	NH11FTH	Shearings
N60CLC	Crawley Luxury	NEC237K	Johnson Bros	NH11GTH	Shearings
N101HGO	Marchants	NFX136P	Talisman	NH11HTH	Shearings
N117YHH	Reay's	NG2414	Rambler	NH11JTH	Shearings
N127RJF	Silverdale	NGM168G	Johnson Bros	NH11KTH	Shearings
N129GAG	Skills	NH04BCH	Shearings	NH11LTH	Shearings
N130GAG	Skills	NH04CCH	Shearings	NH11MTH	Shearings
N167ONH	Gee-Vee	NH04DCH	Shearings	NH11NTH	Shearings
N172LHU	Heyfordian	NH04ECH	Shearings	NH11OTH	Shearings
N175LHU	Heyfordian	NH04FCH	Shearings	NH11PTH	Shearings
N177LHU	Heyfordian	NH04GCH	Shearings	NH11RTH	Shearings
N179LHU	Heyfordian	NH04HCH	Shearings	NH11STH	Shearings
N180LHU	Heyfordian	NH04JCH	Shearings	NIB4162	Maynes
N191LPN	Rambler	NH04KCH	Shearings	NIB6064	Andrews
N199DYB	Berrys	NH04LCH	Shearings	NIB6179	Ausden Clark
N222ASH	Barfordian	NH05BDH	Shearings	NIL4981	Bakers Dolphin
N256THO	Durham City	NH05CDH	Shearings	NIL4982	Bakers Dolphin
N301XRP	Rambler	NH05DDH	Shearings	NIL4983	Bakers Dolphin
N303HLP	Soames	NH05EDH	Shearings	NIL5381	Bakers Dolphin
N306NTG	Skills	NH05FDH	Shearings	NIL5382	Bakers Dolphin
N367TJT	Holmeswood	NH05GDH	Shearings	NIL5905	Compass Royston
N375EAK	Ambassador	NH05HDH	Shearings	NIL7250	Country Lyon
N388OTY	Roselyn	NH06BEH	Shearings	NIL8258	Maynes
N395LPN	Roselyn	NH06CEH	Shearings	NIL9774	Maynes
N399LPN	Roselyn	NH06DEH	Shearings	NIL9886	Crawley Luxury
N446XVA	Marshalls	NH06EEH	Shearings	NJI5510	Eddie Brown
N590BRH	Motts	NH06FEH	Shearings	NJI9241	Belle
N592BRH	Lodge's	NH06GEH	Shearings	NJI9243	Belle
N593BRH	Lodge's	NH06HEH	Shearings	NJI9244	Belle
N599OAE	Turners	NH06JEH	Shearings	NJI9245	Belle
N605JGP	Heyfordian	NH06KEH	Shearings	NJZ9182	York Pullman
N623RAP	Buzzlines	NH06LEH	Shearings	NK51ORN	Atkinson's
N660BRH	Motts	NH09BRH	Shearings	NKZ2490	Bowens
N713AHP	Prospect	NH09CRH	Shearings	NLE145	Ellison's
N726UVR	Heyfordian	NH09DRH	Shearings	NLZ116	Sharpes
N728UVR	Heyfordian	NH09FRH	Shearings	NLZ708	Sharpes
N732UVR	Heyfordian	NH09GRH	Shearings	NM07EDE	Roselyn
N755OAP	PC Coaches	NH09HRH	Shearings	NSU611	Compass Royston
N756CYA	Scotland & Bates	NH09JRH	Shearings	NSU668	Talisman

Reg	Operator	Reg	Operator	Reg	Operator
NT05CJT	Turners	OO09PSW	Paul S Winson	P78OEW	Soames
NT06GKA	Compass Royston	OO10BOY	Golden Boy	P88TCC	Prospect
NT08BGU	Welsh's	OO11PSW	Paul S Winson	P061KAA	Holmeswood
NUF276	Roselyn	OO12BOY	Golden Boy	P061KAE	Holmeswood
NUI1575	Abbotts	OO51BOY	Golden Boy	P061KAK	Holmeswood
NUI1585	Abbotts	OO57BOY	Golden Boy	P101HNC	PC Coaches
NUI1589	Bowens	OSF305G	Johnson Bros	P137CVN	Abbotts
NUI2424	Ausden Clark	OSU386	Compass Royston	P144GHE	Holmeswood
NUI4181	Bowens	OT55CJT	Turners	P169SGT	Abbotts
NUI7645	Compass Royston	OU04BZR	BM Coaches	P170SGT	Abbotts
NUI7726	Bowens	OU05AVY	Barns	P174HBC	Country Lyon
NV51YFJ	Compass Royston	OU07FKA	Pearces	P179ANR	Travel Wright
NV51YFU	Compass Royston	OU07FKB	Pearces	P200GTA	Worth's
NV53YVC	Compass Royston	OU07FKD	Pearces	P224LKK	Redwoods
NV53YVE	Compass Royston	OU07FKE	Pearces	P274NRH	Johnson Bros
NX03ANF	Compass Royston	OU07HFR	Pearces	P312VWR	Grayway
NX07BOU	Compass Royston	OU07JWD	Heyfordian	P318KTW	Paul S Winson
NX10AAF	Compass Royston	OU08AYF	Heyfordian	P411MDT	Ambassador
NX10AAJ	Compass Royston	OU08AYG	Heyfordian	P412MDT	Ambassador
NX10CCA	Compass Royston	OU08EKJ	Pearces	P414HRB	Heyfordian
NX54CHR	Abbotts	OU08EKK	Pearces	P415HRB	Heyfordian
NX59BYC	Compass Royston	OU09BZD	Pearces	P417KSX	Heyfordian
NXI4241	York Pullman	OU59BVO	Pearces	P425JDT	Prospect
NY03KWR	Skills	OU59BVP	Pearces	P440JDT	Prospect
OB07ANT	Anthony's Travel	OUH269X	Skills	P474FJF	Travel Wright
OBR297	Henry Cooper	OUI3914	Bowens	P519SDM	Crawley Luxury
OC51CLC	Crawley Luxury	OUI3918	Bowens	P568SWC	Heyfordian
OCZ8001	Eddie Brown	OUI3920	Bowens	P604HRM	Holmeswood
ODF561	Pulham's	OUI6364	Compass Royston	P700AOL	Abbotts
ODL661R	Johnson Bros	OV51OOC	Marchants	P728JYA	Scotland & Bates
ODL662R	Johnson Bros	OVS822	Bowens	P792AHR	Marshalls
ODL663R	Johnson Bros	OWE854R	Johnson Bros	P802BTA	Roselyn
ODL664R	Johnson Bros	OWE857R	Johnson Bros	P803BLJ	Ambassador
ODL770V	Roselyn	OWE858R	Johnson Bros	P814GBA	Berrys
ODN348	York Pullman	OX05HOD	Hodsons	P821GBA	Berrys
ODR29	Ellison's	OYY3	Turners	P865VFG	PC Coaches
ODY395	Rambler	OZJ1836	York Pullman	P866VFG	PC Coaches
ODY607	Rambler	P1GVT	Gee-Vee	P868VFG	PC Coaches
OED201	Maynes	P1JBT	Johnson Bros	P869VFG	PC Coaches
OET309	The Traveller' Choice	P1RWL	Pearces	P870VFG	PC Coaches
OEY324J	York Pullman	P2CAP	Crawley Luxury	P871VFG	PC Coaches
OHH977G	Irving's	P2HWD	Holmeswood	P872VFG	PC Coaches
OIL3046	Compass Royston	P3CAP	Crawley Luxury	P878HCD	PC Coaches
OIW7026	Elcock Reisen	P3JBT	Johnson Bros	P879HCD	PC Coaches
OJB53	Ellison's	P3JBT	Johnson Bros	P888RWC	Chenery
OJI4627	Belle	P4BAN	Banstead Coaches	P914SUM	Johnsons
OJI4754	Belle	P4CLN	Country Lyon	P918HNA	Travel Wright
OJI4755	Belle	P5CLN	Country Lyon	P996JBC	Compass Royston
OJI4756	Belle	P6WRS	Marchants	PAZ3878	Andrews
OJI4758	Belle	P7AOL	Abbotts	PAZ3882	Andrews
OJZ3499	Compass Royston	P11JWH	Andrews	PB04DAF	Bibby's of Ingleton
OK02AOL	Abbotts	P14CLC	Crawley Luxury	PB07DAF	Bibby's of Ingleton
OK06AOL	Abbotts	P15CLC	Crawley Luxury	PB09DEN	Princess
OK08ULM	Talisman	P15PCC	PC Coaches	PB10DAF	Bibby's of Ingleton
OK53AOL	Abbotts	P16CJT		PB55LFC	Bibby's of Ingleton
OK54AOL	Abbotts	P20GRT	Abbotts	PBV779	Holmeswood
OKZ7928	Sharpes	P22TCC	Prospect	PBZ3656	Abbotts
ONU77	Ellison's	P24FTA	Berrys	PBZ3658	Abbotts
ONZ1167	Ausden Clark	P26RFG	Anthony's Travel	PBZ8301	Abbotts
ONZ1168	Ausden Clark	P30ANT	Anthony's Travel	PBZ8343	Compass Royston
OO03BOY	Golden Boy	P50ANT	Anthony's Travel	PBZ9153	Ambassador
OO04BOY	Golden Boy	P50HWD	Holmeswood	PC02PCC	PC Coaches
OO05BOY	Golden Boy	P66TCC	Prospect	PC05PCC	PC Coaches
OO06BAN	Banstead Coaches	P70AOL	Abbotts	PC05SFC	Princess
OO08BOY	Golden Boy	P77TCC	Prospect	PC06PCC	PC Coaches

PC08PCC	PC Coaches	PN04NTX	Holmeswood	PN09ELJ	Johnsons
PC09MOM	Prospect	PN04PFX	Holmeswood	PN09EMJ	Johnsons
PC09PCC	PC Coaches	PN04PFZ	Holmeswood	PN09ENJ	Johnsons
PC09SFC	Princess	PN04PLF	The Traveller' Choice	PN09HMH	Alfa
PC10BOS	Prospect	PN05AEZ	Alfa	PN09HMJ	Alfa
PC10BOS	Prospect	PN05AFE	Alfa	PN09XCX	Robinsons
PC11PCC	PC Coaches	PN05AMV	Alfa	PN10AFE	Holmeswood
PC58NEC	Prospect	PN05BHL	The Traveller' Choice	PN10AFF	Holmeswood
PC58PCC	PC Coaches	PN05CNA	Holmeswood	PN10AFJ	Holmeswood
PC59PCC	PC Coaches	PN05CNC	Holmeswood	PN10AFK	Holmeswood
PD11TRD	Prospect	PN05CVB	Holmeswood	PN10AFV	Holmeswood
PDF567	Pulham's	PN05CVB	Holmeswood	PN10AFY	Silverdale
PDY272	Rambler	PN05CVC	Holmeswood	PN10AFZ	Silverdale
PE11KGZ	Buzzlines	PN06KJO	The Traveller' Choice	PN10AGO	Holmeswood
PE11KHA	Compass Royston	PN06KJV	Alfa	PN10AHD	Johnson Bros
PE11KHB	Compass Royston	PN06KJX	Alfa	PN10FOA	Barns
PE11KHC	Compass Royston	PN06KJY	Alfa	PN10GJU	The Traveller' Choice
PE11XBK	Robinsons	PN06KJZ	Alfa	PN10GJV	The Traveller' Choice
PE12OXF	City Circle	PN06KKA	Alfa	PN10GJX	The Traveller' Choice
PE12OXG	City Circle	PN06KLJ	The Traveller' Choice	PN11EYP	Robinsons
PE12OXH	City Circle	PN06TVF	Holmeswood	PN11EYR	Robinsons
PE12OXJ	City Circle	PN06TVJ	Holmeswood	PN55NXF	Holmeswood
PE12OXK	City Circle	PN06TVL	Holmeswood	PN56PCU	Holmeswood
PE12OXL	City Circle	PN06TVT	Holmeswood	PN57CCU	The Traveller' Choice
PE56UJX	The Traveller' Choice	PN06TVZ	Holmeswood	PN57CUW	Holmeswood
PE56XMJ	Rambler	PN07EHB	Holmeswood	PN57CUX	Holmeswood
PEB2R	Kenzies	PN07EHC	Holmeswood	PN57CVB	Holmeswood
PF51KHC	Battersby-Silver Grey	PN07EHD	Holmeswood	PN57CVD	Holmeswood
PF57XHS	Robinsons	PN07EHE	Holmeswood	PN57CVE	Holmeswood
PF57XHT	Robinsons	PN07EHF	Holmeswood	PN57CVF	Holmeswood
PG04XUA	The Traveller' Choice	PN07EHG	Holmeswood	PN57CVS	Sea View
PHL454R	York Pullman	PN07EHH	Holmeswood	PN57CVT	Sea View
PIB3360	Berrys	PN07EHJ	Holmeswood	PN57CVU	Sea View
PIB4019	Berrys	PN07EHO	Holmeswood	PN57RVT	The Traveller' Choice
PIJ3379	Ambassador	PN07EHU	Holmeswood	PN61UOE	Ellison's
PIL6648	Andrews	PN07EHW	Holmeswood	PNZ4424	Ausden Clark
PIL6833	Gee-Vee	PN07LLE	Alfa	PO10CJT	Turners
PIL9376	Irving's	PN07LLF	Alfa	PO11HVZ	Godson
PJ02PZK	Heyfordian	PN07LLG	Alfa	PO11HWC	Holmeswood
PJ54EHV	The Traveller' Choice	PN07LLJ	Alfa	PO11HWG	Holmeswood
PJ54VAE	Holmeswood	PN07LLK	Alfa	PO11KFK	The Traveller' Choice
PJ56SVY	Holmeswood	PN07XDY	Holmeswood	PO11KFL	The Traveller' Choice
PJE999J	Kenzies	PN07XEB	Holmeswood	PO11MDU	The Traveller' Choice
PJT267R	Ambassador	PN08CMO	Holmeswood	PO11MGX	The Traveller' Choice
PK09XDB	Robinsons	PN08CMU	Holmeswood	PO12CZV	P & J Ellis
PK54VNY	The Traveller' Choice	PN08CMV	Holmeswood	PO12EOA	Holmeswood
PKE810M	Johnson Bros	PN08CMX	Holmeswood	PO12EOC	Holmeswood
PL03BBZ	Holmeswood	PN08CNE	Holmeswood	PO12GWG	The Traveller' Choice
PL03BCE	Holmeswood	PN08CNF	Holmeswood	PO12GWJ	The Traveller' Choice
PL05PUL	Pulham's	PN08CNJ	Holmeswood	PO12GWL	The Traveller' Choice
PLZ3055	Irving's	PN08CNK	Holmeswood	PO12GWM	The Traveller' Choice
PLZ6542	Ausden Clark	PN08KXH	Alfa	PO12GWP	The Traveller' Choice
PLZ6542	Ausden Clark	PN08KXJ	Alfa	PO12GWU	The Traveller' Choice
PN03OSF	Prospect	PN08KXK	Alfa	PO12GWW	The Traveller' Choice
PN03OVM	Alfa	PN08KXL	Alfa	PO12JMX	The Traveller' Choice
PN03OVP	Alfa	PN08KXM	Alfa	PO12JNF	The Traveller' Choice
PN03PFV	Alfa	PN08KXO	Alfa	PO12JNJ	The Traveller' Choice
PN03PFX	Alfa	PN09CWP	Holmeswood	PO12JNK	The Traveller' Choice
PN03POA	Alfa	PN09CWT	Sea View	PO12XLA	Skills
PN04NMM	Alfa	PN09CWU	Sea View	PO12XLB	Skills
PN04NMU	Alfa	PN09CWV	Sea View	PO53KZZ	Battersby-Silver Grey
PN04NMV	Alfa	PN09CXA	Holmeswood	PO54NAA	Holmeswood
PN04NMX	Alfa	PN09CXB	Holmeswood	PO54NAE	Holmeswood
PN04NMY	Alfa	PN09CXC	Holmeswood	PO54NHA	Holmeswood
PN04NPA	Holmeswood	PN09CXJ	Holmeswood	PO54NHB	Holmeswood

PO54NLA	Holmeswood	R2CJT	Turners	R922LAA	Elcock Reisen
PO55NXG	Holmeswood	R2POW	Berkeley	R922YBA	Abbotts
PO55OWY	The Traveller' Choice	R3CJT	Turners	R923YBA	Abbotts
PO56PBY	Holmeswood	R3HWD	Holmeswood	R997PEO	Grayway
PO56PBZ	Holmeswood	R3YPD	York Pullman	R998PEO	Grayway
PO56PCF	Selwyns	R4HLC	Lucketts	RB53ANT	Anthony's Travel
PO58ACU	Holmeswood	R4HWD	Holmeswood	RDY155	Rambler
PO58LLV	Bibby's of Ingleton	R4POW	Berkeley	RE05ANN	Holmeswood
PO59FHX	Alfa	R4SCC	Siesta	RE06JAK	Royal
PO59FHY	Alfa	R5PSW	Paul S Winson	RE08PSV	Royal
PO60DBV	Anderson	R5YPB	York Pullman	RE12JAC	Royal
PO60HYP	Holmeswood	R6HWD	Holmeswood	RE12JAK	Royal
PO60HYR	Holmeswood	R7DCC	Durham City	RE54JAK	Royal
PO60MMX	Anderson	R8BUS	Irving's	RE56JAK	Royal
PO61CHX	Redwing	R8PSV	Redwoods	RE57JAK	Royal
PO61LVA	Redwing	R8WMS	Worth's	REZ5237	Ausden Clark
PO61MYW	Robinsons	R14SCC	Siesta	RFO361	Roselyn
PPY238	Chenery	R17BUS	Soames	RIB7856	Grayway
PR05TER	Compass Royston	R18CJT	Turners	RIB8747	Holmeswood
PR08BET	Prospect	R19CJT	Turners	RIL516	Sharpes
PR08ECT	Prospect	R20CLC	Crawley Luxury	RIL3619	Dodsworth
PR08PET	Prospect	R30CJT	Turners	RIL5261	Heyfordian
PR11JES	Prospect	R33CJT	Turners	RIL7163	Heyfordian
PR57LYE	Prospect	R47LNU	Compass Royston	RJ10VYO	Ellison's
PR57PSV	Prospect	R50MTT	Motts	RJI5721	Ambassador
PR57TCC	Prospect	R54YDT	Johnson Bros	RJI5723	Ambassador
PR58BEC	Prospect	R55EBT	Eddie Brown	RLZ1176	Compass Royston
PR58WYN	Prospect	R70DCC	Durham City	RM05GSM	York Pullman
PR61ROS	Prospect	R70PUL	Pulham's	RO08PZM	Bluebird
PRP3V	Country Lyon	R80PSW	Galloway	RO51UWD	Redwoods
PSU572	Compass Royston	R102HEV	Chenery	RO61PJY	Reay's
PSU970	Ellison's	R131LNR	Leons	ROI1229	Peter Carol
PT05CJT	Turners	R134CUX	Prospect	ROI1417	Peter Carol
PT2053	Henry Cooper	R147OYS	Grayway	ROI1913	Peter Carol
PTT98R	Johnson Bros	R160GNW	Atkinson's	ROI2929	Peter Carol
PU10HAM	Pulham's	R174VBM	Abbotts	ROI8235	Peter Carol
PU12HAM	Pulham's	R177TKU	Prospect	ROX634Y	Sharpes
PUA917	Andrews	R204STF	Horseman	RSU429	Compass Royston
PUI6623	PC Coaches	R278RAU	Compass Royston	RT05CJT	Turners
PUI6625	PC Coaches	R340RCJ	Travel Wright	RTV438X	Johnson Bros
PUI6626	Bowens	R418AKJ	Heyfordian	RUI2125	Roselyn
PUI6629	Bowens	R43GNW	Lodge's	RUI8266	Silverdale
PUI6684	PC Coaches	R454YDT	Holmeswood	RV06RUY	Westway
PUI8031	Roselyn	R459BAY	Compass Royston	RV60DMZ	Ellison's
PWJ925	Skills	R471RRA	Silverdale	RVW90W	Talisman
PX09AAF	Titterington	R474RRA	Silverdale	RWT544R	Johnson Bros
PX10ABZ	Holmeswood	R507YWC	Heyfordian	RX06WVA	Horseman
PX10ACE	Holmeswood	R509YWC	Heyfordian	RX06WVB	Horseman
PX10ACF	Holmeswood	R512KNJ	Marchants	RX06WVC	Horseman
PX10BHK	Reay's	R619BAY	Compass Royston	RX06WVD	Horseman
PX10BHL	Reay's	R625GFS	York Pullman	RX06WVE	Horseman
PX10BHN	Reay's	R634VYB	Scotland & Bates	RX06WVL	Horseman
PX10BHO	Reay's	R710SLU	Lodge's	RX06WVM	Horseman
PX12BSY	Reay's	R710YWC	Rambler	RX06WVN	Horseman
PX12BSZ	Reay's	R714FLG	Prospect	RX07KDF	Horseman
PX12RJU	Reay's	R832CCK	Grayway	RX07KDJ	Horseman
PX12RRV	Reay's	R841FWW	Silverdale	RX07KDK	Horseman
PX51DVJ	Compass Royston	R869SDT	PC Coaches	RX07KDN	Horseman
PX51DVL	Compass Royston	R870SDT	Holmeswood	RX07KDO	Horseman
PX56AAF	Hodsons	R871SDT	Lucketts	RX07KDV	Horseman
PX61AXZ	Reay's	R872MDY	Heyfordian	RX07KDZ	Horseman
PX61AYA	Reay's	R874MDY	Heyfordian	RX07KEJ	Horseman
PXI1319	York Pullman	R887SDT	Swans	RX12HNP	Horseman
R1GVT	Gee-Vee	R917YBA	Abbotts	RX12HNU	Horseman
R2BAN	Banstead Coaches	R920SBV	Redwoods	RX12HNV	Horseman

RX51EXM	Horseman	S707JJH	Ambassador	SIL7949	Silverdale
RX51EXN	Horseman	S804LRM	Compass Royston	SIL9043	Belle
RX51EXO	Horseman	S823AFG	Marshalls	SIL9044	Belle
RX51EXP	Horseman	S874OHN	Compass Royston	SIL9540	Skills
RX53AWF	Barfordian	S929RNP	Abbotts	SIL9543	Skills
RX57GXL	Horseman	S961YOO	Maynes	SIL9548	Skills
RX57GXM	Horseman	SA02CCU	Marchants	SIW1931	Barfordian
RX57GXN	Horseman	SA02CDE	Marchants	SIW1932	Barfordian
RX57GXO	Horseman	SA52AXV	Grayway	SIW1936	Barfordian
RX57GXP	Horseman	SAZ4077	Abbotts	SJ04KBF	Grayway
RX57GXR	Horseman	SB04BUZ	Buzzlines	SJI4428	Heyfordian
RX57GXS	Horseman	SBV703	Holmeswood	SJI5861	Abbotts
RX57GXT	Horseman	SC04XOW	Galloway	SJI8100	Marshalls
RX57GXU	Horseman	SC51HOD	Hodsons	SJI8103	Marshalls
RX57GXV	Horseman	SC52AHC	Redwoods	SJI8106	Marshalls
RX57GXW	Horseman	SC54PCC	PC Coaches	SJI9076	Belle
RX61GDY	Horseman	SCK225X	Bowens	SK02VSY	Durham City
RX61GDZ	Horseman	SDY788	Rambler	SK07FVA	Berkeley
RXI3337	York Pullman	SE02RUV	Durham City	SL02MVR	Durham City
RXI3338	York Pullman	SEL23	Selwyns	SL08HOD	Hodsons
RYG684	Chenery	SEL36	Selwyns	SL52CPX	Heyfordian
RYY544	Crawley Luxury	SEL73	Selwyns	SL60PUL	Pulham's
S1CLN	Country Lyon	SEL133	Selwyns	SM9562	Marshalls
S2AOL	Abbotts	SEL392	Selwyns	SN03TKF	Barfordian
S4GET	Soames	SEL702	Selwyns	SN05FLP	Berkeley
S6WMS	Worth's	SEL853	Selwyns	SN05MFY	Ausden Clark
S9BOS	Holmeswood	SF04HXU	Ambassador	SN06AAE	Elcock Reisen
S20ACL	Ausden Clark	SF05XDE	York Pullman	SN06BRV	Compass Royston
S20YAL	Royal	SF06VYV	Grayway	SN06BRX	Compass Royston
S45KSM	Silverdale	SF06VYX	Grayway	SN08CNF	Compass Royston
S60CJT	Turners	SF06WDX	The Traveller' Choice	SN08EHL	Ambassador
S100CBK	Kenzies	SF06WMG	Grayway	SN08HUH	Elcock Reisen
S126RLE	Roselyn	SF06WNB	Grayway	SN09FFD	PC Coaches
S128RLE	Roselyn	SF07DLY	Lakeside	SN09FFE	PC Coaches
S130NRB	Abbotts	SF07KCE	Heyfordian	SN11CTV	Elcock Reisen
S131NRB	Abbotts	SF07OSC	Royal	SN51SZZ	Compass Royston
S132RLE	Roselyn	SF07WBL	The Traveller' Choice	SN52PXH	Reay's
S136RLE	Rambler	SF07YTP	The Traveller' Choice	SN54KYK	Elcock Reisen
S138RLE	Roselyn	SF07YTU	Andrews	SN56ENP	Ambassador
S151NKE	Abbotts	SF09FXP	Harry Shaw	SN56ENR	Ambassador
S166UAL	Travel Wright	SF53KUV	Ambassador	SN56EOA	Ambassador
S192WAN	Horseman	SF57JRO	Elcock Reisen	SN58CCU	Ambassador
S193WAN	Horseman	SF57JSX	Reay's	SN58CCV	Ambassador
S252EGK	Leons	SG02ONA	Leons	SO05HOD	Hodsons
S258JFR	Robinsons	SGF483L	Talisman	SO10CJT	Turners
S259JFR	Robinsons	SH51MHO	Selwyns	SPV555	Chenery
S260JFR	Robinsons	SH51MHU	Selwyns	SSV269	Maynes
S268BTL	Talisman	SH51MKO	Selwyns	ST06CJT	Turners
S276LGA	Bluebird	SIB6719	Leons	SUI1478	Roselyn
S282LGA	Redwoods	SIB8398	Berrys	SUI3159	Roselyn
S295UAL	Compass Royston	SIB9309	Berrys	SUI7802	Marshalls
S299JRM	Grayway	SIJ8661	Talisman	SUI7803	Marshalls
S300MTT	Motts	SIL706	Sharpes	SUI7804	Marshalls
S350SET	Ambassador	SIL2732	Holmeswood	SUI7805	Marshalls
S373SET	Lucketts	SIL3431	Skills	SUI8190	Daish's Coaches
S376TMB	Ambassador	SIL3924	Bowens	SUI8191	Daish's Coaches
S456ATV	Skills	SIL6434	Skills	SUI8192	Daish's Coaches
S457ATV	Skills	SIL6436	Skills	SUI8193	Daish's Coaches
S474MTF	K M	SIL6437	Skills	SUI8194	Daish's Coaches
S482ETV	Ambassador	SIL6438	Skills	SUI8195	Daish's Coaches
S484KJT	Horseman	SIL7029	Skills	SUI8196	Daish's Coaches
S550ETV	Ambassador	SIL7030	Skills	SUI8197	Daish's Coaches
S555HOD	Hodsons	SIL7032	Skills	SUI8198	Daish's Coaches
S592RGA	Compass Royston	SIL7944	Skills	SUI8199	Daish's Coaches
S649RKW	Skills	SIL7947	Skills	SVL177W	Johnson Bros

English Bus Handbook: Coaches

Registration	Operator	Registration	Operator	Registration	Operator
SVL178W	Johnson Bros	TAA744	Country Lyon	UD1100	The Traveller' Choice
SVL179W	Johnson Bros	TAZ4517	Ambassador	UDF936	Pulham's
SVL180W	Johnson Bros	TAZ4518	Ambassador	UDL668S	Johnson Bros
SYK910	Bowens	TC02PCC	PC Coaches	UDY512	Rambler
T1CLN	Country Lyon	TDR725	Leons	UDY910	Rambler
T2AOL	Abbotts	TDT864S	Johnson Bros	UDZ3004	Ausden Clark
T2TES	Tates	TDY946	Rambler	UFC221	Bowens
T3AOL	Abbotts	TFO532	Reay's	UFH277	Roselyn
T3HLC	Lucketts	TFX663	Barfordian	UIA29	Roselyn
T3JBT	Johnson Bros	TGY698	Bowens	UIL5952	Berkeley
T3RED	Redwoods	TH04HOL	Titterington	UIL7825	Abbotts
T4FEG	Andrews	TIA5599	Chenery	UIL7826	Abbotts
T4GET	Soames	TIB2574	Holmeswood	UIL7829	Abbotts
T4GLF	Heyfordian	TIL1184	Heyfordian	UJI3791	Bakers Dolphin
T4JBT	Johnson Bros	TIL3338	Ambassador	UJI6312	Skills
T4POW	Berkeley	TIL3714	Ausden Clark	UJT366	Johnson Bros
T7HLC	Lucketts	TIL4508	Leons	UK06BUZ	Buzzlines
T7PCC	PC Coaches	TIL5084	Gee-Vee	UK06MTT	Motts
T7PSW	Paul S Winson	TIL5637	Roselyn	UK53AOL	Abbotts
T8PSW	Paul S Winson	TIL5704	Roselyn	UKZ2873	Bakers Dolphin
T9MCL	Westway	TIL5973	Heyfordian	UKZ2874	Bakers Dolphin
T9MTT	Motts	TIL5974	Heyfordian	UKZ2875	Bakers Dolphin
T10DMB	Horseman	TIL5975	Heyfordian	UKZ2915	Bakers Dolphin
T14CRT	Compass Royston	TIL6878	Roselyn	UKZ2916	Bakers Dolphin
T16CLC	Crawley Luxury	TIL7165	Heyfordian	UKZ2917	Bakers Dolphin
T17CLC	Crawley Luxury	TIL7509	Heyfordian	UKZ2923	Bakers Dolphin
T19CLC	Crawley Luxury	TIL8195	Durham City	UKZ2926	Bakers Dolphin
T20DMB	Horseman	TIL8251	Ausden Clark	UKZ2932	Bakers Dolphin
T27PCC	PC Coaches	TIL8252	Ausden Clark	UKZ2934	Peter Carol
T32JBA	Travel Wright	TIL9216	Ambassador	UKZ2935	Peter Carol
T44BOY	Golden Boy	TIL9217	Ambassador	UKZ5476	Bakers Dolphin
T50BAN	Banstead Coaches	TIL9262	Heyfordian	UKZ5478	Bakers Dolphin
T54AUA	Eagle	TIL9653	Ausden Clark	UKZ6724	Bakers Dolphin
T55ATE	Tates	TIW113	Sharpes	UL11ULM	Talisman
T88ATE	Tates	TIW2554	Andrews	UNJ408	Crawley Luxury
T99BOY	Golden Boy	TIW5645	Travel Wright	UOL387	Bowens
T100MTT	Motts	TJF757	Castleways	UPV337	Chenery
T200MTT	Motts	TJI4929	Godson	UPV487	Bakers Dolphin
T206AUA	Holmeswood	TJI5402	Ambassador	USU345	Compass Royston
T208AUA	Holmeswood	TJI6925	Selwyns	USU365	Compass Royston
T222ADY	Rambler	TKU540	Maynes	USU641	Reay's
T300MTT	Motts	TL07DGE	Lodge's	USV330	Redwoods
T304JJF	Skills	TMY700	Lodge's	USV331	Redwoods
T322UCH	Silverdale	TN07ECD	Silverdale	USV462	Redwoods
T376JWA	Holmeswood	TPD118X	Bowens	USV511	Redwoods
T379PAJ	Compass Royston	TRX615	Bowens	USV556	Redwoods
T400MTT	Motts	TSO30X	Country Lyon	USV562	Redwoods
T437JJF	Skills	TSU324	Bowens	USV577	Redwoods
T438JJF	Skills	TSU646	Compass Royston	USV620	Redwoods
T439JJF	Skills	TT06CJT	Turners	USV625	Redwoods
T439KPP	Bibby's of Ingleton	TT06PSW	Paul S Winson	USV628	Redwoods
T442KPP	Compass Royston	TUT888H	Roselyn	USV630	Redwoods
T450JJF	Skills	TVY659	Bowens	USV676	Redwoods
T477JJF	Skills	TW08FDW	Travel Wright	USV859	Redwoods
T500MTT	Motts	TW09TDW	Travel Wright	UT09CJT	Turners
T544CDM	Marshalls	TW53WMS	Worth's	UTF119	Holmeswood
T578MAW	Dodsworth	TXI1348	Godson	UU07BOY	Golden Boy
T600MTT	Motts	TXI1356	York Pullman	UU53BOY	Berkeley
T637JWB	Prospect	TXI1357	Godson	UU54BOY	Golden Boy
T638JWB	Prospect	TXI1358	York Pullman	UU55BOY	Golden Boy
T645XNP	Prospect	TXI1359	York Pullman	UU57BOY	Golden Boy
T675ASN	Dodsworth	TYT653	Titterington	UU59BOY	Golden Boy
T760JYB	Scotland & Bates	UA5013	The Traveller' Choice	UUD12	Rambler
T777RWC	Chenery	UCE665	Maynes	UVO530	Reay's
T888TES	Tates	UCT838	Bluebird	UWR294	The Traveller' Choice

UXI1372	Bowens	VUB396H	Dodsworth	W391JOG	Castleways
UXI1375	Bowens	VV57BOY	Golden Boy	W409UGM	Travel Wright
UXI1376	Bowens	VV58BOY	Golden Boy	W413UGM	Travel Wright
UXI1377	Bowens	VVE885	Kenzies	W478KSG	Galloway
UXI476	Sharpes	VVV66S	Bowens	W561WKH	Prospect
UXI551	Eddie Brown	VWF328	Eagle	W567RYC	Scotland & Bates
V2RED	Redwoods	VX51AWO	Marchants	W608FUM	Crawley Luxury
V4HWD	Holmeswood	VX53AVF	Buzzlines	W609FUM	Crawley Luxury
V9WMS	Worth's	VXT571	Bowens	W618CHJ	Gee-Vee
V10PSW	Paul S Winson	W1AOL	Abbotts	W645MKY	Prospect
V11BUS	Irving's	W1CLN	Country Lyon	W647SNN	Paul S Winson
V22CLC	Crawley Luxury	W2AOL	Abbotts	W648RCG	Travel Wright
V30BUS	Irving's	W2HLC	Lucketts	W657FRN	Grayway
V40DGE	Lodge's	W3AOL	Abbotts	W682FRN	Grayway
V54HAX	Marchants	W3HLC	Lucketts	W682MVV	Crawley Luxury
V56KWO	Lakeside	W4HWD	Holmeswood	W716UJH	Titterington
V57KWO	Soames	W5HLC	Lucketts	W751AAY	Bowens
V118LVH	Lodge's	W5WMS	Worth's	W752DOE	Skills
V145LGC	Johnsons	W6AMS	Soames	W799KVL	Bowens
V186OOE	Marchants	W6HOL	Welsh's	W822BOM	Bowens
V199ERA	Travel Wright	W6PCC	PC Coaches	W898YNK	Richmond's
V200OCC	Castleways	W6STS	Westway	W995JNF	Compass Royston
V200OER	Elcock Reisen	W7BAN	Banstead Coaches	WA03EYL	Chalfont
V200RAD	Lucketts	W7BOY	Golden Boy	WA03HPY	Scotland & Bates
V222PDY	Rambler	W7HOL	Welsh's	WA03HPZ	Barns
V264DTE	Prospect	W7PCC	PC Coaches	WA04EHS	PC Coaches
V265HEC	Holmeswood	W8EDE	Roselyn	WA04EWL	Barns
V287DBR	Compass Royston	W9BOY	Golden Boy	WA04EWR	Scotland & Bates
V304EAK	Skills	W9PSW	Paul S Winson	WA04MHF	Berrys
V334EAK	Kettlewells	W10ANT	Anthony's Travel	WA04ZNR	Daish's Coaches
V359POB	Bowens	W10HOL	Welsh's	WA05DFF	Barns
V430DRA	Holmeswood	W17CJT	Turners	WA05DFG	Marshalls
V433DRA	Holmeswood	W25HOL	Welsh's	WA05JWM	Marshalls
V465ESL	Prospect	W26HOL	Welsh's	WA05JWU	Berrys
V582NRH	York Pullman	W30CLC	Crawley Luxury	WA06CDK	Barns
V936VUB	Lodge's	W40CLC	Crawley Luxury	WA06CDO	Scotland & Bates
VA02NTK	Compass Royston	W44CLC	Crawley Luxury	WA06GSU	Bluebird
VA53WHL	Hodsons	W55CLC	Crawley Luxury	WA06JGO	Barns
VAD141	Pulham's	W56SJH	Horseman	WA07BGV	Berrys
VAO141	Pulham's	W57SJH	Horseman	WA07BGX	Barns
VBW846	Bowens	W59SJH	Horseman	WA07BGY	Anderson
VC51CLC	Crawley Luxury	W66CLC	Crawley Luxury	WA07BGY	Bowens
VCZ155	Sharpes	W77CLC	Crawley Luxury	WA07BHD	Anderson
VCZ9811	Skills	W83JBN	Maynes	WA07BHE	Anderson
VDF365	Pulham's	W87NDW	Compass Royston	WA07BHK	Scotland & Bates
VDY468	Rambler	W100TEN	Bowens	WA07BHK	Barns
VE05ZTR	Pulham's	W104CEO	Hodsons	WA07KYC	Berrys
VEX301X	Country Lyon	W107RTC	Berkeley	WA08AOZ	Berrys
VFJ627	Bowens	W148EEC	Holmeswood	WA08APF	Berrys
VHM847	Bowens	W151EEC	Holmeswood	WA08APO	Selwyns
VIL5317	Prospect	W152EEC	Holmeswood	WA08GPE	Anderson
VIL6771	Andrews	W161RYB	Berrys	WA08GPF	Anderson
VJO204X	Bowens	W201CDN	Eagle	WA08GPJ	Anderson
VK54LBE	Parrys International	W201EAG	Selwyns	WA08GPK	Anderson
VKX510	Bowens	W214CDN	Bibby's of Ingleton	WA08GPX	Anderson
VNP893	Bowens	W221UGX	Travel Wright	WA08GPY	Anderson
VO10BOY	Golden Boy	W222LAY	Travel Wright	WA08GPZ	Anderson
VRE150	Leons	W286NAE	Abbotts	WA08GRU	Barns
VSC16	Westway	W301MKY	Skills	WA08GSO	Scotland & Bates
VSF438	Heyfordian	W302MKY	Skills	WA08JVO	Barns
VSU803	Talisman	W303MKY	Skills	WA09AYY	Berrys
VT09CJT	Turners	W309WRE	Crawley Luxury	WA09AZC	Chalfont
VU02TPX	Compass Royston	W317SBC	Hills	WA09AZG	Scotland & Bates
VU03ZPS	Travel Wright	W322SBC	Travel Wright	WA09AZL	Barns
VU06KFL	Motts	W354EOL	Chenery	WA09AZN	Barns

Reg	Operator	Reg	Operator	Reg	Operator
WA09DZS	Anderson	WDZ727	Woods	WYR562	Holmeswood
WA09DZT	Anderson	WDZ1232	Woods	X4GVT	Gee-Vee
WA09DZV	Anderson	WDZ1666	Woods	X4HWD	Holmeswood
WA09DZW	Anderson	WDZ1691	Woods	X50CLC	Crawley Luxury
WA09KZO	Barns	WDZ1733	Woods	X70CJT	Turners
WA10CFM	Westway	WDZ2826	Woods	X80CJT	Turners
WA10CFU	Barns	WDZ6259	Woods	X93EEF	Abbotts
WA10CFV	Scotland & Bates	WDZ6570	Woods	X117BUJ	Lakeside
WA10CFX	Barns	WDZ7683	Woods	X218HCD	Compass Royston
WA10CFY	Barns	WE51WAY	Westway	X498AHE	Lucketts
WA10CFZ	Barns	WEZ5969	Ausden Clark	X500GDY	Rambler
WA10ENE	BM Coaches	WF10ZRU	Bakers Dolphin	X627AKW	Soames
WA10ENJ	Chalfont	WF10ZRV	Bakers Dolphin	X642AKW	Marshalls
WA10ENK	Chalfont	WF10ZRX	Bakers Dolphin	X663WCH	Paul S Winson
WA10ENL	Chalfont	WF10ZRY	Bakers Dolphin	X719WPR	Sea View
WA10ENM	Chalfont	WGR565	Greys of Ely	X787HFE	Dodsworth
WA10KNC	BM Coaches	WH05HOD	Hodsons	X846HEE	Welsh's
WA10KND	BM Coaches	WHA325	Leons	X962KUT	Travel Wright
WA10KNL	Royal	WIB1444	Barns	XAP956	Titterington
WA11AED	Westway	WIJ297	Tates	XBL333	Chenery
WA11AEJ	Anderson	WIJ551	Eddie Brown	XCT550	Heyfordian
WA11AEK	Anderson	WIL3608	Abbotts	XDG614	Pulham's
WA11AEL	Anderson	WIL3610	Abbotts	XDL521	The Traveller' Choice
WA11AEM	Anderson	WJ02KDN	Scotland & Bates	XDO32	The Traveller' Choice
WA11HXM	Hamilton	WJ02VRO	Barns	XDZ9422	Abbotts
WA11HXO	Barns	WJ02VRT	Soames	XDZ9423	Abbotts
WA11HXP	Anderson	WJ02YYK	Bluebird	XEA745	Bowens
WA12AWF	Westway	WJ52MTO	Barns	XEL158	Excelsior
WA12AWN	Barns	WJ55TVP	Daish's Coaches	XEL254	Excelsior
WA12AWO	Barns	WJI3491	Bakers Dolphin	XHO856	Bowens
WA54KTP	Scotland & Bates	WJI3493	Bakers Dolphin	XIB3421	Barns
WA56ENM	Chalfont	WJI3496	Bakers Dolphin	XIL3674	Grayway
WA57CYT	Bluebird	WJI3497	Bakers Dolphin	XIL5932	Ausden Clark
WA57CYU	Bluebird	WJI6879	Bakers Dolphin	XIL8422	Bakers Dolphin
WA57CYW	Berkeley	WJI6880	Bakers Dolphin	XIL8423	Bakers Dolphin
WA57CZB	Compass Royston	WJI9363	Marshalls	XIL8425	Bakers Dolphin
WA57JZR	Chalfont	WL06AOL	Abbotts	XJA386	The Traveller' Choice
WA57JZT	Chalfont	WM55BUS	Worth's	XJI2605	York Pullman
WA57JZU	Chalfont	WM57DGY	The Traveller' Choice	XJI3831	Ausden Clark
WA57JZV	Chalfont	WNO480	Talisman	XJI5457	Bakers Dolphin
WA57JZW	Barns	WP11BCK	Buzzlines	XJI5458	Bakers Dolphin
WA58EOK	BM Coaches	WP11LWW	Buzzlines	XJI5459	Bakers Dolphin
WA58JNN	Barns	WP11LWX	Buzzlines	XJI6330	Bakers Dolphin
WA59EAP	Berkeley	WP12BUS	Pulham's	XJI6331	Bakers Dolphin
WA59EAW	Berrys	WPX582	Bowens	XJI6332	Bakers Dolphin
WA59EBC	Chalfont	WPX852	Bowens	XJI6333	Bakers Dolphin
WA60DWP	Scotland & Bates	WR02RVX	Berkeley	XK06AOL	Abbotts
WA60DZG	Chalfont	WRC419	Silverdale	XL03AOL	Abbotts
WA60DZO	Barns	WRCAOL	Silverdale	XL06AOL	Abbotts
WA61AKF	Chalfont	WSM3	Ellison's	XL08AOL	Abbotts
WA61AKP	Chalfont	WSU225	Talisman	XL53AOL	Abbotts
WA61AKU	Chalfont	WSU484	Greys of Ely	XL59BCL	Princess
WA61GPO	Berrys	WSU485	Greys of Ely	XLH570	Bakers Dolphin
WA61GRU	Scotland & Bates	WSU873	Compass Royston	XO02BOY	Golden Boy
WA61GRX	Berrys	WT06CJT	Turners	XO08BOY	Golden Boy
WB03EDE	Roselyn	WT54JAC	Eagle	XO10BOY	Golden Boy
WBN106	Bowens	WU55OAB	Berrys	XO11BOY	Golden Boy
WC02CLC	Crawley Luxury	WVJ539	Richmond's	XO12BOY	Golden Boy
WCZ9954	Ausden Clark	WWW883	Bowens	XO59BOY	Golden Boy
WCZ9955	Ausden Clark	WX05YTT	Berkeley	XSK144	Worth's
WDD194	Pulham's	WX06SLV	Heyfordian	XT06CJT	Turners
WDF946	Pulham's	WX51YXN	Eagle	XTJ802	Bowens
WDL694Y	Johnson Bros	WX57DXY	Chalfont	XVE8T	Kenzies
WDZ565	Woods	WX7622	The Traveller' Choice	XVY392	Bowens
WDZ595	Woods	WXI4384	Bowens	XWC18	Leons

XWG254	Bowens	YER469	Richmond's	YJ05FXL	Johnsons
XX06PSW	Paul S Winson	YEZ5553	Ausden Clark	YJ05FXR	Barfordian
XX07PSW	Paul S Winson	YEZ6670	Roselyn	YJ05PVX	Eavesway
XX09PSW	Paul S Winson	YG52CKE	Eagle	YJ05PWE	Selwyns
XX11PSW	Paul S Winson	YG57FVW	Redwoods	YJ05PWF	Selwyns
XX12PSW	Paul S Winson	YIB827	Sharpes	YJ05PWK	Eagle
XX56PSW	Paul S Winson	YIL1223	Compass Royston	YJ05PXF	Selwyns
XX57BOY	Golden Boy	YIL1224	Compass Royston	YJ05PXT	Galloway
XX57PSW	Paul S Winson	YIL1225	Compass Royston	YJ05XMX	Holmeswood
XX58AOL	Abbotts	YIL1226	Compass Royston	YJ05XMY	Richmond's
Y2HLC	Lucketts	YIL1227	Compass Royston	YJ05XNX	Holmeswood
Y2HOD	Hodsons	YIL1229	Compass Royston	YJ05XWO	Birmingham International
Y2JBT	Johnson Bros	YIL1230	Compass Royston	YJ05XXB	Daish's Coaches
Y2POB	Compass Royston	YIL1842	Abbotts	YJ06GKV	Birmingham International
Y3HLC	Lucketts	YIL7713	Bowens	YJ06GKZ	Anderson
Y3JBT	Johnson Bros	YIL8758	Tates	YJ06LCN	Eagle
Y4HLC	Lucketts	YIL8759	Tates	YJ06LFM	Eavesway
Y4REP	Elcock Reisen	YJ03GYB	Johnsons	YJ06LFN	Eavesway
Y4WMS	Worth's	YJ03GYC	Johnsons	YJ06LFV	Selwyns
Y6BAN	Banstead Coaches	YJ03GYD	Johnsons	YJ06LGC	Eavesway
Y8LAG	Laguna	YJ03GYE	Johnsons	YJ06LGD	Eavesway
Y27OXF	Crawley Luxury	YJ03VMH	Shearings	YJ06YRA	Johnson Bros
Y92HHG	Grayway	YJ03VMK	Shearings	YJ06YRM	Holmeswood
Y177JSH	Excalibur	YJ03VML	Shearings	YJ06YRN	Holmeswood
Y224NYA	Scotland & Bates	YJ03VMM	Shearings	YJ06YST	Pulham's
Y257LRN	Grayway	YJ03VMP	Shearings	YJ06YSU	Pulham's
Y289RSO	Berkeley	YJ03VMR	Shearings	YJ07DVT	Bluebird
Y335HWT	Compass Royston	YJ03VMT	Shearings	YJ07DVY	Durham City
Y605JSH	Atkinson's	YJ03VMW	Shearings	YJ07DVZ	Castleways
Y656HWY	Johnsons	YJ03VMX	Shearings	YJ07DWF	Johnsons
Y657HWY	Johnsons	YJ03VMY	Shearings	YJ07DWG	Johnsons
Y706NVW	Holmeswood	YJ03VMZ	Shearings	YJ07DWP	Lakeside
Y709HWT	Grayway	YJ03VNA	Shearings	YJ07EHG	Johnsons
Y711HWT	Grayway	YJ03VNB	Shearings	YJ07EHH	Johnsons
Y738BPR	Eagle	YJ03VNC	Shearings	YJ07JHE	Eavesway
Y739BPR	Eagle	YJ03VND	Shearings	YJ07JHF	Eavesway
Y744HWY	Holmeswood	YJ03VNE	Shearings	YJ07JJV	Eavesway
Y744NAY	Silverdale	YJ03VNF	Shearings	YJ08DGY	Selwyns
Y751OBE	Hills	YJ03VNG	Shearings	YJ08DHF	Selwyns
YAF872	Roselyn	YJ03VNS	Shearings	YJ08DLD	BM Coaches
YAY537	Heyfordian	YJ03VOB	Shearings	YJ08DXC	City Circle
YAZ4111	Ausden Clark	YJ03VOC	Shearings	YJ08DXD	City Circle
YB06JON	Princess	YJ03VOD	Shearings	YJ08DXE	City Circle
YB06VOK	Holmeswood	YJ03VOF	Shearings	YJ08DXF	City Circle
YBZ3260	Heyfordian	YJ03VOG	Shearings	YJ08EAA	Eavesway
YC02DHM	Worth's	YJ03VOH	Shearings	YJ08EAC	Eavesway
YC02DJX	Daish's Coaches	YJ03VOK	Shearings	YJ08EAE	Eavesway
YC54EKO	Skills	YJ03VOM	Shearings	YJ08EAF	Eavesway
YD02FDZ	Dodsworth	YJ03VOP	Shearings	YJ08EAG	Eavesway
YD02PXA	Johnsons	YJ04BJF	Selwyns	YJ08EAK	Eavesway
YD02PXB	Johnsons	YJ04BNL	Grayway	YJ08EAM	Eavesway
YD02PXG	Gee-Vee	YJ04BNN	Grayway	YJ08EAO	Eavesway
YD02PXM	K M	YJ04BOV	Selwyns	YJ08EAP	Eavesway
YD02PXP	Johnsons	YJ04BYH	Selwyns	YJ08EBP	Compass Royston
YD02PXV	Gee-Vee	YJ04DEF	Compass Royston	YJ08ECX	BM Coaches
YD02RHZ	Johnsons	YJ04DEK	Compass Royston	YJ08EGC	Eagle
YD02RJX	Godson	YJ04DEM	Compass Royston	YJ08NRY	Godson
YD58GAU	Lakeside	YJ04GYA	Johnsons	YJ08NSF	Birmingham International
YDK795	Johnson Bros	YJ04GYB	Johnsons	YJ08NSO	Reay's
YDL435	Crawley Luxury	YJ04GYC	Johnsons	YJ08NTE	Leons
YDL676T	Johnson Bros	YJ04GYD	Johnsons	YJ08NTK	Silverdale
YE03VSK	Bowens	YJ04HHY	Selwyns	YJ08PGX	Johnsons
YE52FGX	The Traveller' Choice	YJ04HHZ	Selwyns	YJ08PGY	Johnsons
YE52KPK	Travel Wright	YJ04ZVG	Compass Royston	YJ09CUU	BM Coaches
YE52KPP	Travel Wright	YJ05FXK	Johnsons	YJ09CVV	BM Coaches

YJ09CWW	Eavesway	YJ12CHN	Reay's	YJ60GKK	BM Coaches
YJ09CWY	Bibby's of Ingleton	YJ12CHO	Reay's	YJ60KHH	Country Lyon
YJ09CXA	BM Coaches	YJ12CHV	Reay's	YJ60KHK	Country Lyon
YJ09CXA	Grayway	YJ12CHX	Reay's	YJ60LBX	Excalibur
YJ09CXX	Eavesway	YJ12CHY	Reay's	YJ60LCW	Parrys International
YJ09CYY	Eavesway	YJ12CKA	Eavesway	YJ61FFS	Johnson Bros
YJ09CZZ	Grayway	YJ12CKC	Eavesway	YJB717	Bowens
YJ09FHM	Birmingham International	YJ12CKD	Eavesway	YJE3T	Kenzies
YJ09FHP	K M	YJ12CKE	Eavesway	YJI6038	Bowens
YJ09FHX	Reay's	YJ12KFC	Parrys International	YJI7372	Ausden Clark
YJ09FHY	Reay's	YJ12KFO	Birmingham International	YJI8595	Bluebird
YJ09FJF	Parrys International	YJ12KFX	Siesta	YJI8597	Bowens
YJ10DCV	BM Coaches	YJ12KFY	Siesta	YJN455S	Talisman
YJ10DCX	BM Coaches	YJ12KFZ	Siesta	YK04FVU	Reay's
YJ10DCY	BM Coaches	YJ12KG	Johnsons	YK04FVZ	Durham City
YJ10DCZ	BM Coaches	YJ12KGE	Johnsons	YK07YFD	Eddie Brown
YJ10DFD	Eavesway	YJ54CFD	Selwyns	YK51KOW	Gee-Vee
YJ10DFE	Eavesway	YJ54CHG	Dodsworth	YL57PUU	Leons
YJ10DFF	Eavesway	YJ54EXL	Johnsons	YM03EOP	Johnsons
YJ10DFG	Eavesway	YJ54UBX	Johnsons	YM03EOR	Johnsons
YJ10DJY	City Circle	YJ55BMO	Johnsons	YM52TOU	Compass Royston
YJ10DLF	Eagle	YJ55BMU	Johnsons	YM52TSO	Johnsons
YJ10JYC	Johnsons	YJ55EYY	Barfordian	YM52TSU	Johnsons
YJ10JYD	Johnsons	YJ55KZO	Silverdale	YMJ555S	Lodge's
YJ10JYE	Johnsons	YJ56APZ	Pulham's	YN03AVE	Johnson Bros
YJ10JYF	Johnsons	YJ56AUE	Holmeswood	YN03LRY	Skills
YJ10JYN	Parrys International	YJ56AUF	Holmeswood	YN03NCZ	PC Coaches
YJ10JYO	Parrys International	YJ56AUM	Holmeswood	YN03NDV	PC Coaches
YJ10JYP	Parrys International	YJ57EGU	Johnsons	YN03NJE	Castleways
YJ10JYR	Parrys International	YJ57EGV	Pulham's	YN03WPV	Redwoods
YJ10JYS	Parrys International	YJ57EYT	Birmingham International	YN03WRW	Maynes
YJ10JYT	K M	YJ57YCL	Johnsons	YN04AHZ	Siesta
YJ10JYU	Excalibur	YJ58FDM	BM Coaches	YN04AJY	Ausden Clark
YJ10JYV	Excalibur	YJ58FGO	Castleways	YN04AKU	Redwoods
YJ10JYW	Reay's	YJ58FHV	Grayway	YN04AKY	Ausden Clark
YJ10JYX	Reay's	YJ59AYZ	Compass Royston	YN04AVL	Lucketts
YJ10JYZ	Harry Shaw	YJ59BAA	BM Coaches	YN04AVM	Reay's
YJ10JZA	Compass Royston	YJ59BBE	BM Coaches	YN04AWR	Redwoods
YJ10JZC	Elcock Reisen	YJ59BBF	BM Coaches	YN04GOC	Lucketts
YJ10MBG	Heyfordian	YJ59BBK	BM Coaches	YN04GOH	Lucketts
YJ10MBO	Heyfordian	YJ59BBV	BM Coaches	YN04GOJ	Lucketts
YJ10MHA	Johnsons	YJ59BBX	BM Coaches	YN04GOK	Lucketts
YJ11AMO	Johnsons	YJ59BBZ	BM Coaches	YN04GOP	Hills
YJ11AMU	Johnsons	YJ59BZO	Reay's	YN04HJJ	Johnson Bros
YJ11AMX	Harry Shaw	YJ59GEU	Johnsons	YN04UKB	Excalibur
YJ11ANR	Johnsons	YJ59GEY	Johnsons	YN04UKC	Excalibur
YJ11ANX	Harry Shaw	YJ59GFA	Johnsons	YN05BJS	Ausden Clark
YJ11AOA	Parrys International	YJ59GFE	Johnsons	YN05CPZ	Welsh's
YJ11AOC	Parrys International	YJ59GFV	Heyfordian	YN05GXA	Eddie Brown
YJ11AOD	Parrys International	YJ59NMO	Abbotts	YN05GXB	Eddie Brown
YJ11AOE	Parrys International	YJ59NMU	Abbotts	YN05GXC	Eddie Brown
YJ11AOK	Birmingham International	YJ59NMX	Heyfordian	YN05GXD	Eddie Brown
YJ11AOO	Reay's	YJ59NNG	Heyfordian	YN05GXE	Eddie Brown
YJ11AOP	Reay's	YJ59NNH	Heyfordian	YN05GXY	Ausden Clark
YJ11EJE	Johnsons	YJ59NNL	Heyfordian	YN05GYX	PC Coaches
YJ11EJF	Johnsons	YJ59NNM	Heyfordian	YN05HFK	Lucketts
YJ11EJG	Johnsons	YJ59NNO	Heyfordian	YN05HFL	Lucketts
YJ11EJK	Johnsons	YJ59NNP	Heyfordian	YN05HFM	Bowens
YJ11EJL	Johnsons	YJ59NNR	Castleways	YN05HFR	Laguna
YJ11GGV	Galloway	YJ60GBY	Bibby's of Ingleton	YN05HFS	Ausden Clark
YJ11GKA	Eavesway	YJ60GDO	Reay's	YN05HFV	Swans
YJ11GKC	Eavesway	YJ60GFA	Reay's	YN05HUZ	Holmeswood
YJ11GKD	Eavesway	YJ60GGF	Reay's	YN05HVB	Barfordian
YJ11GKE	Eavesway	YJ60GGO	Reay's	YN05HVH	Soames
YJ12CGG	Barns	YJ60GGY	Reay's	YN05HVR	Amport & District

YN06CFL	Grayway	YN08AVU	Redwing	YN10AAV	Anderson
YN06CFM	Grayway	YN08AVV	Redwing	YN10ABU	Anderson
YN06CFV	Bibby's of Ingleton	YN08AVW	Redwing	YN10ACJ	Anderson
YN06CFY	Terravision	YN08AVY	Redwing	YN10ADO	Anderson
YN06CFZ	Excalibur	YN08AWA	Redwing	YN10ADZ	Andrews
YN06CHL	Excalibur	YN08AWC	Redwing	YN10BWZ	Anderson
YN06CHV	Bowens	YN08AWF	Redwing	YN10EOC	Alfa
YN06CHX	Excalibur	YN08AWG	Redwing	YN10EOF	Alfa
YN06CJF	Excalibur	YN08BKG	Eddie Brown	YN10EOG	Alfa
YN06CKE	Excalibur	YN08CCM	Princess	YN10EOK	Alfa
YN06CKG	Excalibur	YN08DFC	Lucketts	YN10EOL	Eddie Brown
YN06CYA	Eddie Brown	YN08DFD	Lucketts	YN10EOP	Lucketts
YN06JFJ	The Traveller' Choice	YN08DFE	Lucketts	YN10FKM	Selwyns
YN06JXA	Excalibur	YN08DFF	Lucketts	YN10FKO	Selwyns
YN06JXF	Maynes	YN08DFG	Excalibur	YN10FKP	Selwyns
YN06JXG	Maynes	YN08DGE	PC Coaches	YN10FKR	Selwyns
YN06JXH	Maynes	YN08DMV	Epsom Coaches	YN10FKS	Selwyns
YN06MXE	Elcock Reisen	YN08DMX	Epsom Coaches	YN10FKT	Selwyns
YN06MXH	Elcock Reisen	YN08FYE	Robinsons	YN10FKV	Selwyns
YN06MXS	York Pullman	YN08FYF	Robinsons	YN10FLA	City Circle
YN06MXW	Bowens	YN08HZA	Clarkes of London	YN10FLB	City Circle
YN06NYM	Terravision	YN08HZB	Clarkes of London	YN10FNV	Compass Royston
YN06NYO	Excalibur	YN08HZC	Clarkes of London	YN10FZF	Reay's
YN06NYP	Excalibur	YN08HZD	Clarkes of London	YN10FZG	Reay's
YN06NYT	Amport & District	YN08HZE	Clarkes of London	YN10FZK	Compass Royston
YN06NYU	Clarkes of London	YN08HZF	Clarkes of London	YN10FZL	Compass Royston
YN06NYV	Clarkes of London	YN08HZG	Clarkes of London	YN10FZT	Battersby-Silver Grey
YN06NYW	Clarkes of London	YN08JAO	Johnsons	YN10FZV	Battersby-Silver Grey
YN06NZA	Terravision	YN08JBE	Amport & District	YN10HHU	Compass Royston
YN06NZC	Terravision	YN08MLZ	Terravision	YN10JYG	Battersby-Silver Grey
YN06NZD	Terravision	YN08MOV	Amport & District	YN10JYH	Battersby-Silver Grey
YN06OPG	Johnson Bros	YN08NKK	Excelsior	YN11AWU	Irving's
YN06TFY	Selwyns	YN08NKL	Excelsior	YN11AXD	Andrews
YN07DUA	Bibby's of Ingleton	YN08NKM	Excelsior	YN11AXX	Andrews
YN07DVA	Compass Royston	YN08NNC	Eddie Brown	YN11AYA	Selwyns
YN07DVG	Eddie Brown	YN08NNE	Eddie Brown	YN11AYB	Selwyns
YN07DZU	Bowens	YN08NWV	Bowens	YN11AYC	Selwyns
YN07DZV	Bowens	YN08OBW	Bowens	YN11AYD	Selwyns
YN07DZW	Bowens	YN08OCS	Hills	YN11AYH	Battersby-Silver Grey
YN07EBV	Sea View	YN08OWC	Bowens	YN11EOL	Anderson
YN07EBX	Sea View	YN08OWD	Bowens	YN11FTT	Abbotts
YN07EBZ	Sea View	YN08OWF	Bowens	YN11FTU	Selwyns
YN07EDX	York Pullman	YN08OWG	Bowens	YN11FTV	Selwyns
YN07EXR	Reay's	YN08OWH	Bowens	YN11FTX	Compass Royston
YN07EYG	Leons	YN08OWM	Durham City	YN11FTY	Compass Royston
YN07KHH	Battersby-Silver Grey	YN09AOT	Andrews	YN11FTZ	Compass Royston
YN07LDJ	Clarkes of London	YN09AOU	Compass Royston	YN11FUB	Berkeley
YN07LDK	Clarkes of London	YN09AOW	Anderson	YN11FVA	Compass Royston
YN07LDL	Clarkes of London	YN09AOX	Anderson	YN11FVB	Compass Royston
YN07LDO	Clarkes of London	YN09APF	Anderson	YN11FVC	City Circle
YN07LDU	Clarkes of London	YN09APK	Redwoods	YN11FVD	City Circle
YN07LEF	Tates	YN09DYA	Prospect	YN11FVE	City Circle
YN07LGF	Siesta	YN09DYB	Prospect	YN11FVF	Compass Royston
YN07LJA	Lucketts	YN09HRG	Horseman	YN11FVG	Compass Royston
YN07LJV	Bowens	YN09HRJ	Battersby-Silver Grey	YN11FWP	Abbotts
YN07NUP	Anderson	YN09HRX	Prospect	YN11HXC	Horseman
YN07NWD	Reay's	YN09HRZ	Prospect	YN12BVR	Lucketts
YN07OPE	Battersby-Silver Grey	YN09HZA	BM Coaches	YN12BVS	Lucketts
YN07OPL	Battersby-Silver Grey	YN09HZB	BM Coaches	YN51MFZ	PC Coaches
YN07OPS	P & J Ellis	YN09KHO	Selwyns	YN51XMH	Barfordian
YN07OZX	Anderson	YN09KHP	Selwyns	YN53CSY	Barfordian
YN07WUO	Soames	YN10AAE	Johnson Bros	YN53EHY	Heyfordian
YN08ATO	Silverdale	YN10AAF	Johnson Bros	YN53GDX	Siesta
YN08AVF	Redwing	YN10AAJ	Lakeside	YN53GHH	Heyfordian
YN08AVG	Redwing	YN10AAK	Lakeside	YN53PBX	Siesta

Reg	Operator	Reg	Operator	Reg	Operator
YN53SVX	Johnsons	YN58OKT	City Circle	YR02ZZD	Lucketts
YN53SVY	Holmeswood	YN58OKU	City Circle	YR10BAA	Laguna
YN53SVZ	Holmeswood	YN58OKV	City Circle	YR10BBV	Laguna
YN53YHA	Johnsons	YN58OKW	City Circle	YR10BEO	Talisman
YN53YHB	Johnsons	YN59BKF	Hills	YR52MDV	Lucketts
YN54OAY	PC Coaches	YN59CXR	BM Coaches	YR52ZKC	Travel Wright
YN55KLV	Grayway	YN59GPE	Reay's	YR58RUA	Heyfordian
YN55KME	Elcock Reisen	YN59GPF	Reay's	YR58RUJ	Heyfordian
YN55KWV	Bowens	YN60BYY	Leons	YR58RVA	Laguna
YN55KWW	Bowens	YN60BZK	Anderson	YR59YND	Barns
YN55KWX	Bowens	YN60BZM	Hills	YR60AAZ	Buzzlines
YN55NMM	Marchants	YN60EOL	Anderson	YR60AGZ	Buzzlines
YN55WSO	Selwyns	YN60FML	Amport & District	YR60AKU	Buzzlines
YN55WSX	Marshalls	YN60FMO	Selwyns	YR60AUJ	Buzzlines
YN56BKK	Travel Wright	YN60FMP	Amport & District	YR60AUM	Buzzlines
YN56FFX	Excalibur	YN60FMV	Bowens	YS02XDW	Maynes
YN56FGG	Lucketts	YN60FMX	Bowens	YS02XED	Johnson Bros
YN56FGJ	Lucketts	YN61AWX	York Pullman	YS02YXZ	Soames
YN56FGK	Lucketts	YN61AXW	Buzzlines	YS02YYB	Crawley Luxury
YN56FGM	Lucketts	YN61AXX	Buzzlines	YS03ZLK	Lucketts
YN56FGO	Lucketts	YN61EOU	Anderson	YSU871	Reay's
YN56NDC	Bibby's of Ingleton	YN61EOW	Anderson	YSU912	Compass Royston
YN56NNE	Johnsons	YNH19W	Country Lyon	YSU991	Holmeswood
YN56NNF	Johnsons	YNR778	Paul S Winson	YSV604	Johnson Bros
YN56NNG	Johnsons	YOI7757	Compass Royston	YSV815	Bowens
YN56NRX	Laguna	YOR456	Roselyn	YT06CEK	Andrews
YN56NTE	Lucketts	YP07WFJ	Sharpes	YT06CJT	Turners
YN56NTF	Lucketts	YP09NPK	Abbotts	YT09FLP	Johnsons
YN56NTG	Lucketts	YP10BUS	York Pullman	YT09FLR	Johnsons
YN56ORY	Lakeside	YP10VZA	Bowens	YT09FLW	Lucketts
YN56ORZ	Lakeside	YP10VZB	Bowens	YT09FLX	Bowens
YN56OSG	Selwyns	YP10VZC	Bowens	YT09FLZ	Lucketts
YN56OSJ	Selwyns	YP10VZD	Bowens	YT09FMA	Maynes
YN57AEB	Skills	YP10VZE	Bowens	YT09FMC	Maynes
YN57AEC	Skills	YP10VZF	Bowens	YT09FMD	Maynes
YN57AEZ	City Circle	YP10VZG	Bowens	YT10ASO	Buzzlines
YN57BVS	Elcock Reisen	YP10VZH	Bowens	YT10OAX	Excalibur
YN57BVT	Elcock Reisen	YP10VZJ	Bowens	YT10OAY	Excalibur
YN57BWX	Maynes	YP10VZK	Bowens	YT10WLA	Terravision
YN57BWY	Maynes	YP12NUE	Redwing	YT10WLB	Terravision
YN57EOE	Sea View	YP12NUF	Redwing	YT10WLC	Terravision
YN57FWE	Excalibur	YP12NUH	Redwing	YT10WLD	Terravision
YN57FWF	Excalibur	YP12NUJ	Redwing	YT10WLH	Talisman
YN57FWV	Laguna	YP12NUK	Redwing	YT11AOF	Harry Shaw
YN57FYZ	Laguna	YP12NUM	Redwing	YT11LPA	Lucketts
YN57GBV	Ausden Clark	YP12NUO	Redwing	YT11LPC	Lucketts
YN57GBX	PC Coaches	YP12NUU	Redwing	YT11LPE	Lucketts
YN57MDU	Lakeside	YP12NUV	Redwing	YT11LPJ	Skills
YN57OTX	Excelsior	YP12NUW	Redwing	YT11LPK	Skills
YN57OTY	Excelsior	YP12NUX	Redwing	YT11LPU	Lucketts
YN57OTZ	Excelsior	YP12NUY	Redwing	YT11LPV	Lucketts
YN58AFU	BM Coaches	YP52KRZ	Selwyns	YT11LRE	Harry Shaw
YN58AFZ	BM Coaches	YPL764	Pulham's	YT11LRF	Maynes
YN58BHX	Hills	YR02PYV	Lakeside	YT11LRK	Excalibur
YN58CFM	Skills	YR02RDX	The Traveller' Choice	YT11LRN	Excalibur
YN58CFV	Johnson Bros	YR02UNJ	Skills	YT12RNJ	Laguna
YN58CFX	Swans	YR02UNK	Skills	YT12YUA	Excalibur
YN58CFY	Swans	YR02UNL	Skills	YT12YUB	Excalibur
YN58CGE	Bowens	YR02UOA	Sea View	YT12YUC	Excalibur
YN58CGF	Bowens	YR02UOB	Barfordian	YT12YUD	Excalibur
YN58CGV	Johnson Bros	YR02ZLZ	Marshalls	YT12YUE	Excalibur
YN58CHC	Andrews	YR02ZYL	Galloway	YT12YUS	Princess
YN58FXO	Reay's	YR02ZZA	Lucketts	YT51FMC	Skills
YN58FXP	Bibby's of Ingleton	YR02ZZB	Lucketts	YT59NZJ	Maynes
YN58NCY	Amport & District	YR02ZZC	Lucketts	YT59NZK	Maynes

YT59NZP	Redwoods	YX07AYE	Lakeside	YX60DXA	Reay's
YT59NZX	Tates	YX07GVD	Holmeswood	YX60DXB	Reay's
YT60OSM	Maynes	YX07HPA	Reay's	YX60DXC	Reay's
YT60OSN	Maynes	YX07HPC	Compass Royston	YX60DXD	Reay's
YT60OTD	Leons	YX07HPF	Reay's	YX60DXE	Reay's
YT60OTH	Laguna	YX08AOK	Johnsons	YX60DXF	Reay's
YT61FDU	Ausden Clark	YX08AOV	Johnsons	YX60DXG	Reay's
YT61FEF	Harry Shaw	YX08AOW	Johnsons	YX60DXH	Reay's
YTY867	Holmeswood	YX08HWR	Redwing	YX60DXJ	Reay's
YU04XJG	Godson	YX10ECY	Reay's	YXI2730	Bakers Dolphin
YU05VRY	Godson	YX10FDZ	York Pullman	YXI7923	Holmeswood
YUE338	Heyfordian	YX10FFP	Bowens	YY51BNB	Eddie Brown
YUI338	Heyfordian	YX10FFR	Bowens		
YUU556	Roselyn	YX10FFS	Bowens		
YV03TZN	Marchants	YX10FFT	Bowens		
YX05DHZ	Anderson	YX10FFU	Bowens		
YX06AXN	Dodsworth	YX54BGO	Lakeside		
YX07AYD	Soames	YX56AFZ	Anderson		

ISBN 9781904875 68 0   © Published by British Bus Publishing Ltd, August 2012

British Bus Publishing Ltd, 16 St Margaret's Drive, Telford, TF1 3PH

Telephone: 01952 255669

web; www.britishbuspublishing.co.uk
e-mail: sales@britishbuspublishing.co.uk